5.30

Books by MacKinlay Kantor

FICTION

BEAUTY BEAST (1968)
STORY TELLER (1967)
SPIRIT LAKE (1961)
IF THE SOUTH HAD WON THE
  CIVIL WAR (1961)
THE WORK OF SAINT FRANCIS
  (1958)
ANDERSONVILLE (1955)
  Pulitzer Prize Novel, 1956
GOD AND MY COUNTRY (1954)
THE DAUGHTER OF BUGLE ANN
  (1953)
WARWHOOP (1952)
DON'T TOUCH ME (1951)
SIGNAL THIRTY-TWO (1950)
ONE WILD OAT (1950)
THE GOOD FAMILY (1949)
WICKED WATER (1949)
MIDNIGHT LACE (1948)

GLORY FOR ME (1945)
  On which the motion picture
  The Best Years of Our Lives
  was based
AUTHOR'S CHOICE (1944)
HAPPY LAND (1943)
GENTLE ANNIE (1942)
CUBA LIBRE (1940)
VALEDICTORY (1939)
HERE LIES HOLLY SPRINGS (1938)
THE NOISE OF THEIR WINGS (1938)
THE ROMANCE OF ROSY RIDGE
  (1937)
AROUSE AND BEWARE (1936)
THE VOICE OF BUGLE ANN (1935)
LONG REMEMBER (1934)
THE JAYBIRD (1932)
EL GOES SOUTH (1930)
DIVERSEY (1928)

JUVENILE

GETTYSBURG (1952)
LEE AND GRANT AT APPOMATTOX (1950)
ANGLEWORMS ON TOAST (1942)

PERSONALIA

HAMILTON COUNTY (1970)
  (With Tim Kantor)
MISSOURI BITTERSWEET (1969)
THE DAY I MET A LION (1968)

MISSION WITH LEMAY (1965)
  (With General Curtis E. LeMay)
LOBO (1957)
BUT LOOK, THE MORN (1947)

VERSE

TURKEY IN THE STRAW (1935)

I Love You, Irene

MacKinlay Kantor

I Love You, Irene

1972

Doubleday & Company, Inc., Garden City, New York

To Paul and Ruthie Reynolds

CONTENTS

I. *ARE YOU LOOKING FOR THE*
GRAEME PLAYERS?

1.

I hold myself to be a fortunate man, not only because I am here now, alive and able to tell a story, but because I have such a natural tale to tell. As in durable love ballads of the past, its texture is woven from lust and tenderness.

There can be identified a strain and rivalry, the ultimate capitulation, the winning through; but we had no wizard advising or guiding. We proceeded blindly, powered by the emotion of the moment (which I deem a good thing, and hope it will persist)—possessed by feeling rather than by a sum of thought, as the young must venture.

Initially appeared a classified advertisement—one which I had read and acted upon nearly a year before. It ran each Sunday in the Chicago *Tribune*.

> Wanted. Talented people to join
> drama group. Write Apartment O,
> 541 North Michigan Avenue.

If you wrote to Apartment O and received no reply, that was the end of it. Often palpably illiterate or bizarre letters appeared, to be cast aside. But if replies suggested any promise whatsoever, applicants were invited to appear at the apartment either on a Friday evening or a Sunday afternoon when rehearsals took place. Should the individuals stand up under scrutiny of the Graeme Players, they were invited to return.

Soon they would be cast in a play, and the Players found out whether the new people could act or not.

Actually they didn't have to act too well. I know of only one Graeme Player who went on to any eminence on the stage. She was Ruth Hunter, who played through years the part of Essie in *Tobacco Road* in New York. A few of the others drifted into radio or similar pursuits, and had good lives. Ruth was the only one who gave herself wholly to the theater.

I'd answered the advertisement in May of 1925, about the time I got a job as rodman with a Cook County surveying crew. After several weeks of semi-starvation in a grim room on Oak Street, and after beating my mauled head against newspaper office doors with no fortune, it was good to have any sort of job. This took me out into fields and the open air, and I was happy accordingly. Also delighted with the thirty-four dollars and eighty cents accruing for each week's work.

My letter to Apartment O made the grade and I was invited to appear. I went readily, and enjoyed the folks I met. They gathered under the banner of a former actress and dramatic instructor, a Swedish woman named Sigrid Graeme. She had lost her voice insofar as ordinary teaching was concerned. A few intimates, former students of hers, banded together and formed the group originally in order to support Miss Graeme. Thus she was the mistress at Apartment O. Occasionally one or two of the girls lived with her if they were out of work. Her perennial attendant was a handsome youth, Joe Driscoll, who married her a few years later. Joe played straight leads, and sometimes parts bordering on the juvenile.

The company filled engagements mainly in Chicago suburbs, going as far afield as Indiana or southern Wisconsin. For eleven memorable weeks we were at a west side movie house, the Apollo, and went through our entire repertoire there. The plays were the tried and true of that and previous periods, with heavy emphasis on Winchell Smith, George M. Cohan, Booth Tarkington.

Two of the Players were the rather effeminate sons of well-to-do families; there were a taxi driver, a seamstress, a photographer, clerks and waitresses, a girl who demonstrated pianos for Lyon and Healy. We had an office manager in an employment bureau, a bank teller, a fruit juice salesman: all sorts, with ages ranging from the late teens to the middle forties.

. . . Gaiety in between rehearsals: beach parties, picnics, Halloween and New Year's Eve frolics, a give-away-one-present-apiece Christmas ball. They promulgated a rule against what they termed "twosing" (Miss Graeme and Joe Driscoll were exempt) but there was no way to enforce it. There were girls to chase and men to chase them. I pursued one girl after another. One girl got pregnant and had a baby out of wedlock. I don't know who the father was—not me. I never had a date with that babe in my life.

One of the girls was named Mabel, she was the music store one. I wrote a poem about her, "To Mabel in a Music Store," and was joyed in disposing of it to *College Humor*. My talent for versification was greeted generally with approval—and, in a few cases, awe—by the crowd. They accepted me as a little-bit-published writer; and some degree of jealousy was expended because there were several would-be writers in the group who had never published anything. All read the "Line O' Type" column in the *Tribune* inverterately, and admired R.H.L., the columnist, from a distance. Excitement which I had caused with "Floyd Collins' Cave" and a few other poems of later date was appreciated. But after all I wasn't being paid for that stuff, and dollars were important to nearly all of us. Even dimes and nickels were important.

Money won from our presentation of shows went to pay the apartment rent, light and gas bills, and to maintain Miss Graeme herself, although she could not be said to have dwelt in luxury. You could come up and eat there before Friday night rehearsal, if you told them in advance that you were coming, at a cost of thirty-five cents. It was an onerous dishwashing job: a list was maintained, and people were put down for dishwashing in order. The kitchen was a closet with a wide sink at one end, and shall we say that the plumbing needed work done on it too. Tag ends of suds and grease went down most reluctantly. We did not dine on steaks or turkey. Spaghetti and baked beans were more in our line.

Clammy dishwater or no, we felt a maiden vitality. Even the in-his-middle-forties office manager, long a member, seemed often as young as the youngest of us; so did Miss Graeme, who was alleged to have reached the advanced age of thirty. The striplings, male and female, thrived on our high-pitched expenditure of energy and ambition. We sniffed the air of Chicago and its seasons with the verve of fabled fire horses.

You found Apartment O on the top floor of the rickety building after climbing five flights of stairs. From our dining room window next to the closet kitchen we had a gorgeous view of Michigan Avenue sloping north, downhill from the Tribune Tower and the Wrigley building. The latter structure seemed in its pristine glistening white youth a storied castle or a temple built to honor the struggle of the city, and to signify a yearning to the youths who were born there or who were drawn by its magnet. The air of Chicago itself was sour and oppressive, laden commonly with thick yellowish odor of the stockyards; yet we thought it a tonic. Evening traffic crushed by, tires hissed, the huge bus engines rumbled. Colored lights haunted on some of the distant buildings . . . holy echo of ship whistles on the river and out to the lake, across those once swampy lands where in wilderness the wild onions had grown, and had given the city its very name.

"Jennie's eyes are red, and she's kind of trembly. Don't say anything to her about it."

"What you mean? She's been crying?"

"Did you read about that fellow who got shot on a corner, out on West Willow last night?"

"Yes, but—"

"You see, Jennie's father was killed the same way. It's some kind of Italian Mafia or something. I guess this other guy was a friend of her father's, or maybe a distant relative or something. Anyhow it brought it all back to her. So I just thought I'd tip you folks off. Don't mention her eyes."

"We sure as hell won't."

Members got transferred and were compelled to move out of town, members lost their jobs, members fell ill. We felt forever the nervous uncertainty of those who exist in what is termed the economic fringe (the dwelling place of those so multitudinous and often so sad).

It was excruciating to cast a production, work the play into shape through rehearsals, then be able to put on a performance and be certain that the cast would be there and working. The Graeme Players could never be a financial success. That eleven-week engagement at the Apollo was the only one of such duration.

"Look out for Miss Graeme. Boy, she's in a mean mood tonight!"

"What happened?"

"Myron's company closed his department, and he's going to be out of a job unless he goes to St. Louis."

"Gosh. And he's playing—"

"The old magnate. That's a very important character job, and we've got a date coming up a week from Monday, and who the hell will step into it if Myron has to go? Better steer clear of Miss Graeme. Is she touchy!"

Still the responses to our advertisement flocked in, and after I had been a member for a few months I got to see some of these. Usually Miss Graeme and Joe Driscoll looked them over, sometimes helped by a few of the others. The notes came with persistence. We needed to have them come that way.

Dear Sir or Madam:
    What does your ad mean? I consider myself much more than a talented amateur, but there is something suspicious in the sound. Do you have to pay to get into your club? How much?

Dear Friends,
    I notice you wish talented amateurs. Well, how about a talented professional instead? I have worked in the carnival business for three years, but am resting right now. Maybe

you know my act, "Viola the Virgin from Venus," if you are
interested in the carnie business.

Dear Sirs—
   I enclose two newspaper clippings from my home town,
Pelican Bay, Michigan. As you can see from reading these,
I made quite a hit in the Elks Lodge production of
"Charley's Aunt" last year. You don't say what you are
paying talented people, but I would consider a minimum
of one hundred dollars per week.

Dear Apartment O:
   Are you some kind of free-love Bohemian colony or what?
You do not say. I should like to know, because my mother
would not consider having me join anything like that. Let
me know if you are on the up and up.

Gentlemen,
   I specialize in acrobatic dancing, not necessarily in the
nude, although I have posed for some artists etc. Please
inform me as to your rates etc. I have great ambitions both
as a dancer and choreographer, and would be glad to show
you a sample of my skills when I perform a ballet which I
do to the melody of Swan Lake with veils etc.

Even as these silly people hunted some sort of fulfillment,
so were we all searching; also some of us were silly, and some
were not. The city moaned its challenge in front of us. If you
were responsive you thought that it was representative of all
cities and all times. Chicago was by turns a bandit, a prostitute,
a priest, a doctoring lover, a demon provoked and dashing.
   I recalled the first night I had spent in its toils. That was in
1911. Our mother had fetched my sister and myself to Chicago
from Iowa at the behest of our father . . . the first time I ever
saw him. The recollection is keen, parading and hateful, still in
this minute. We were installed at the old Saratoga Hotel on
Dearborn Street . . . long gone, oh long gone. Clamor of the
Loop and its color and its life might be a wonder to any seven-
year-old. We were on the fourth floor of the hotel, not too high
above the parade of clashing streetcars. I hung half out of the

window, watching the gush of electricity which snapped from trolley cables and fell with a splash like fireworks. People, people hastening in their richness or their rags.

All those years afterward I could feel it, as I stared from the window at Apartment O.

On Friday, April 2nd, I'd invited my boyhood chum Herbert Arthur to come along to the club.

Herbert said, "You're always talking about the Graeme Players. What is it?"

He entertained no desire to be an actor, and was working in an architect's office in that same polished ivory Wrigley building up the slope. But Herbert was a good-natured soul—an expert clarinet player, who loved dates and dancing and contributed a merry masculine spark wherever he went.

He came with me. Like the few of the regulars who were there for dinner, he ate bologna and macaroni and cabbage salad with the rest of us, and sat and smoked affably while I did the dishwashing chore to which I had been posted.

Rehearsal hadn't yet begun. Various of the Players kept arriving, but by rule they never rang the bell when they came up. Only strangers rang the bell.

Now it sounded: bell and buzzer combined. Miss Graeme cried out and put her face in her hand. She had been working at wall painting in the bathroom that day, and was in no mood to greet newcomers.

"Oh, Lord, visitors! On a night like this! And George isn't here yet—"

George Butzen, a huge and jovial redhead, was our cheerful greeter.

"—Somebody please go down and tell the visitors to *go away!*"

Perhaps I was standing near the outer door . . . "I'll get rid of 'em."

There was laughter, some of the boys said not to get rid of any good-looking female visitors. I went clattering down the stairs.

Those five flights took a while, and our visitor was under-

standably impatient. She had pressed the bell of Apartment O
and, not receiving immediate response, was exploring the lower
hall when I got there. She was a trifle over five feet tall, dainty
on her high heels, and she wore a maroon winter coat with
gray squirrel trimmings, and a little aqua hat. Her face seemed
made mostly of eyes . . . great gray-green ones.

I asked, "Are you looking for the Graeme Players?"

"Yes, thank you."

I told her that it was halfway to heaven. "Five flights. Do you
mind the climb?"

"Not at all."

I gestured for her to precede me up the stairs, so that I could
have a chance to see whether I liked her legs.

I told that not long ago in a commencement address. "And I
did like them," was the last line.

2.

The play we were working on was a dismal little number by
Rachel Crothers, entitled *The Three of Us.*

(Thirty years later our daughter was to write a novel and have
it published by Houghton Mifflin under the title *The Four of
Them.* If her parents' Graeme activities had anything to do with
this selection of title, definitely it could not be called prenatal
influence . . . something less tangible: precourtship influence.)

I was cast in the role of Clem, younger brother of the heroine.
Clem was developing money troubles. He stole money, or was
suspected of stealing money or writing bad checks, or something
awful like that. I didn't fancy the part; but there I was, and
considering myself in no way set to form an appealing illusion to
a prospective bride or even a prospective girl friend.

We worked at the front of the apartment: an extended double
living room with a wide suggestion of doorway in the middle.
That doorway was our proscenium. Miss Graeme sat in darkling

silence in a nearby chair, a script spread before her. We actors came in and out, on and off, from the sides.

Whenever there was opportunity, I witnessed the newcomer with eagerness. She was surrounded by some of the non-actors of the moment, males mostly. She appeared to be giving a very good social account of herself. We had exchanged names when we met in the lower hallway. I said, "Mack Kantor," and she told me later that she had missed the Kantor completely and found no reason to associate me with the Chicago *Tribune* "Line O' Type" versifier.

I liked the sound of her name. Irene Layne. There was inherent an effortless gentility in the three syllables. During those periods when I was offstage, I moved as close to the group around her as I could do conveniently. I learned that, young as she was, she was a commercial artist who had worked for a time at the same company where one of our members was employed. She said that jobs didn't come in, and she had been dropped by the wayside along with several others. Now she had a momentary situation painting lamp-shades, and she chuckled with the rest about that.

Herbert seemed trying to claim the most of her attention, and for the first time since we were boys and had an army of which Herbert was general and I a lowly captain— I felt seeds of hostility toward Herbert breaking their skins and flowering within me. Why had I dragged him along with me on this particular night? Why hadn't it been a week or two previously, before the advent of Irene Layne with the pliant face, the shapely legs, the shimmering hair and becalming gray eyes?

An artist by profession? Possibly she had a studio apartment where she dwelt. My imagination leaped with fervor and spice. I imagined myself calling for Miss Layne at her studio, taking her out . . . the wine at La Boheme, a genial if tacky restaurant in a run-down mansion on Rush Street, cost a dollar and a half a bottle; the bread which came with it was free. If you wanted the regular dinner, an Italian dinner for two, it would cost—

Rapidly I reviewed my financial condition. There was another

check due from the Collegiate World Publishing Company. (I
needed to send money back home to Iowa, out of my regular
checks.) I never knew the amount of Editor H. N. Swanson's
payments until they arrived. This one might be for as much as
eleven dollars, might even be for fifteen. Would I be able to
invite Miss Layne to dinner? I saw us becoming cozy and nearly
affectionate in the restaurant, with a shambling Giovanni beaming as he plied us with wine. Then I'd take Irene home to her
studio, and she might invite me in. . . .

For her debut at the Players she wore a beige dress with an
iridescent gloss to it. How gratifying to observe the curve of
her legs under the gown! I liked her slippers. They were a bit
shabby, but— Truly there was much which might be written
with good effect about the shape of women's shoes. In vague
fashion I recalled references to shoe fetishism which I had
read in Krafft-Ebing and such . . . that wasn't exactly what I
meant. I'd always considered myself a leg boy or a leg man, pure
and simple, and was even a little confused by the idea of
breasts. But the shape of Miss Layne's black suede pumps—
That round part at the heel: it bulged out slightly and then
curved in just the right way, and went down into the heel, and
the heel was sharp and high.

Perhaps too high? She was a small girl and— Did she en-
danger her body in wearing such high heels?

And she walked on them with such prettiness.

At a seeming very long last, Clem, the cringing creation of
Playwright Crothers, exited from the stage. I would be free for
the rest of the time, except for sitting in on the general sum-
mation by Sigrid Graeme.

Other tardy Players had arrived, and I worked my way
cautiously into the circle gathered near our visitor.

With disgust I found Herbert Arthur, notebook in hand, taking
down her address.

That polished off the evening. If Herbert was going to date
her—O.K., O.K. Forget the whole thing.

I left in more or less of a huff. We were early birds, had to be.

Most of us must arise betimes, as ancient chroniclers put it, to get to our regular Saturday jobs. Six days constituted a working week for the majority. Rehearsals on Friday started at seven p.m., and usually we were out of there by ten-thirty. People went chattering down the stairs, and Irene joined several girls who also were seeking a northbound bus.

Slabs of crystallized snow piled along the curbs and Michigan Avenue sidewalks, relics of a heavy out-of-season storm which howled a few days before. We crossed Ohio Street to the front of the Lake Shore Trust & Savings Bank, and I watched Miss Layne as she skipped amid snowy cakes where an aisle was cut for pedestrians. Herbert and I climbed on the bus last; the rest were far up the aisle, and other passengers got in the way, so I spoke no more to Irene Layne on this evening. Herbert made his way forward at one point and reaffirmed something about the appointment they had arranged. When we came to Diversey Parkway, he and I got off. He talked a little on the way over to the rooming house where we both lived, on Cambridge Avenue, but I wasn't in a conversational mood.

A gloomy blank called Saturday lay in between, and then dazzled the magic of Sunday afternoon rehearsal. I reached the Graeme Players earlier than usual, about a quarter to two, and folks were surprised to see me there so soon. At least, I thought grimly, there wasn't any Herbert along.

He had made no move toward wishing to join the organization—just said with cheer that dramatic presentations weren't quite in his line.

"We used to do a lot together when we were kids." I spoke in reminiscence. "Remember how I tried to make a dramatic presentation out of those boys' Civil War books by Byron A. Dunn? About Fred Shackelford and Calhoun Pennington? One went with the North and the other with the South, and Fred's father became a general for the Confederacy. You were pretty good in the part when we gave the show out in our barn. You played the elder Shackelford, and you had a beard and mustache made out of white cotton which you grayed for the occasion. When Russell

Tweedie, playing Fred, announced his intention of going with the
Union, you put on a staggering act. You staggered across the
room with your hand clamped to your head, staggered to the
safe, opened it, drew out a package of money— Remember those
old fake Confederate ten-dollar bills that we used to play with?
You staggered back and pressed it into Fred's hand. Your lines
were, 'Take this money, Fred. It's the last I shall give you. Take
this thousand dollars, and your horse Prince, and go. *Go!*'"

"Maybe I wasn't so bad," said Herbert modestly. "But I still
don't think that I'd care to spend much time at the Graeme
Players." He didn't know until years later how relieved I felt
at his utterance.

3.

Irene Layne arrived on proper schedule. Miss Graeme informed
her that she had been cast for a bit part in *The Three of Us*.
She was to play an Irish maid who appeared infrequently with
some line like "Sure, and when am I goin' to get to be cleanin'
up this room?" I in particular felt that her talents were wasted
when applied in this direction. I had plans for her displaying
them in other ways.

There was favorable discussion about her before she reached
the apartment, with several of the members saying how much
they admired her *type*, as they called it. I didn't think she was
any type at all. I felt her to be unique, and scorned any notion
of typing her. The girls did say that she had had the lead in the
senior drama at Lake View High School, and Lake View High
School was a big place, with thousands of students; and held
to be the mothering-ground of Edgar Bergen and Janet Gaynor.
Irene Layne had to be pretty good as an actress, though I was
incensed at Miss Graeme's demeaning her into the role of slavey.

Unfortunately this notion of an Irish maid conjured up the
cartoon of an elderly frump in mobcap and dirty apron. Therefore one could not consider Miss Layne effective when she

glared her way on stage, and emitted her line, "Sure, and when am I goin' to get to be cleanin' up this room?" Her physical appearance outstripped even the most active imagination on the part of this beholder. Her dress was of liqueur gold, the skirt swung pleasantly as she walked inside it. Her hair reminded me of the sheer Virginia Dare wine which I had first drunk to excess when I was fifteen. There was nothing old Irish or maidish or cleanin'-uppish about her. It was best to assume that travesty could be wrought with makeup later on.

I wallowed through my own part and went up in my lines a couple of times, at which Miss Graeme voiced disapproval. Strangely, it might seem, she directed her plays with godly patience, and did not expect to find Sothern or Marlowe in her flock. She did expect us to have our lines. I realized that my own performance was fumbling, and apologized to our mentor afterward, but could not explain to her the real reason: my preoccupation with ardor for our latest-come Player.

On this Sunday, the 4th of April, we did not rehearse both afternoon and evening. A few social hours were in prospect. One of the girls had been ill but was now convalescent to the point of being able to entertain. Her mother, a Czech possessed of admirable cooking skills, had invited the Players to her apartment to welcome daughter June back into active circulation. It was my first hope that Irene Layne would be too diffident to go; then maybe we could proceed on a date that very evening. But she was in a jolly mood, and ready to accompany members up to the Woitek place.

By this time I was far past the point of reluctance because of Herbert or whatever other rivals there might be. I would perish in a puddle if an engagement could not be arranged immediately.

I managed to steer the lady into a corner and inform her of my desire to achieve social contact with her.

She said, "I think that would be very nice."

"Tomorrow night?"

She shook her head. "I'm sorry. I have a date for tomorrow evening."

Herbert had come into the picture again.

"Then Tuesday night?" I was prepared for Wednesday?—
Thursday?—Friday? and the rest.

She nodded. Tuesday would be agreeable.

The *College Humor* check had not yet arrived. Mail would be
coming, on Monday and on Tuesday. I faltered, but thought I'd
better not suggest dinner. "Tuesday evening, then. What time
shall I call for you?"

She asked if eight o'clock would be all right. All Chicagoans
dined early in those days, at least the Chicagoans within our
periphery.

"And the address?"

"It's 2200 Wilson Avenue. The name is on the second mailbox
inside the lobby."

2200 Wilson did not sound very studio-ish. After all, we had
ridden on the bus on Friday; I should have realized that she
lived out northwest somewhere. I tried to conjure up a picture
of a young lady artist's studio in the bland Ravenswood district,
but was not successful.

Permission to escort her home on this Sunday evening was
the next logical goal. She told me gently that Norma and
Leo—indicating two fellow Players—lived not far from her and
had already volunteered to take her home.

"Leo has his car. We drove up here to this apartment together."

Since I had no car and didn't expect to own one until my
first novel was published—whenever that merry year rang in—I
let the matter drop.

Tuesday had never seemed a particularly star-studded day in
the pattern of my own historic weeks. Now it gleamed with
radiance. On Tuesday I sought out Herbert Arthur.

"You had a date with Irene Layne last night?"

"Oh, yes."

"Well, tell me about it."

He laughed. "Why, there's nothing much to tell."

"Where did you go?"

"I took her to the Alamo."

"What's that?"

"Oh, a restaurant over near the lake, up there north of Wilson."

"What did you do?"

"Danced. They've got a good orchestra. Don't you know the place?"

"No, I don't know anything about dancing places." Momentarily I was miserable. She demanded dancing! I considered myself to be a horrid dancer; and so, I reckoned, did the rest of the world. I could barely shuffle across the floor in time to music . . . had never shared other young people's desire for this particular sport. With a girl I'd much rather go for walks in the woods, or walks anywhere; or, if there were a convenient blanket, or if her folks were gone away and there was a sofa handy— I considered dancing a waste of time, when we might be pursuing more intimate and active romance.

"Yes," Herbert said. "They've got a mirror on the floor there, and the girls think that's a lot of fun."

"Well, what did you do? Just dance?"

"Oh sure. And we had sandwiches and so on. Say, what is all this?"

I told him in desperation, "I've got a date with her tonight. I want to know just what to expect. Tell me everything about her."

"You're the damndest guy. Well, what do you want to know?"

"Everything!"

"Well—"

"Does she have a studio?"

"Studio? No, she lives with her folks. Her father and stepmother—"

Stepmother. I entertained a vision of a pinch-faced shrew as described in fairy stories. Gone were my dreams of faded gilt ceilings, fire on the hearth, a candle or two, and myself entertaining her by singing "Jesse James" or reciting Kipling and Whitman and Stephen Vincent Benét. "Oh, she lives with her folks? Anybody else around?"

"She's got a brother or two. I met one of her brothers. And

there was some kind of a country cousin. I guess he was just visiting that night or something."

Promptly I saw in phantasm a country cousin arrayed in vaudeville togs: straw hat, blue overalls, sprinkled with straw or hayseeds. I told Herbert in vexation, "Maybe I'm the damndest guy, as you say, but you're not very informative."

"Well, gosh. There just isn't much to tell."

I went away and counted the oversized money of the time which was thin in my wallet. How dared *College Humor* take so insufferably long in sending that check? I had hoped to arrive grandly in a taxicab, keep the taxi waiting, pick up the lady. Now that seemed unwise. Take her home in a taxicab? Yes; because it would be late . . . dago-red wine cost a dollar and a half a quart, the bread came with it. Nevertheless I would need to tip Giovanni. And then— The taxicab.

Maybe Miss Layne would crave more than mere bread and wine? She had not said anything about a book of verses, but I was more than willing to recite to her some of my own.

Since Herbert had bought her a sandwich—or maybe two?— I might have to go into the sandwich business.

It would cost me ten cents to ride into the western Wilson Avenue area by bus, and only five cents by streetcar. I ran to Clark Street, climbed on a car, asked for a transfer. Got off at Lawrence, took a Lawrence Avenue car over to a characterless cross street named Robey, and walked four blocks down to the corner where 2200 shone in gilt letters on the door of a brick apartment building.

I looked at my watch for the dozenth time. At one minute after eight I pressed the button beside the mailbox marked *Layne*.

. . . Pressure of the button, the buzzer sounding.

Pulling of the bell rope.

The knock on the door. *Knock—knock, knock, knock.*

(First bars of the Fifth Symphony, a future illusion of freedom materializing in an unhappy Europe where never has a nation or a people been able to agree on the delineation of freedom.)

Knock—knock, knock, knock.

Buzz. Ring.

Casual caller, salesman, mailman, the telegraph boy of olden pursuit.

Kate Bar-Lass, sliding her slim naked arm through the flanges. *Twill hold, she said, until they break the bone.*

"Good evening, George."

"*Melanie!* How wonderful to see you!"

"How do you do, ma'am? May I take a minute of your time? I'm with the National Kitchenware Association and—"

"Morning, Mrs. Murtog. I've got a registered letter for you to sign. Guess it must be from your boy Ralph—"

"Oh, doctor, thank God you came quickly! We're scared to death! He's just lying there, and he doesn't seem to know us—"

"*Will Arrive Ten Twenty Tonight Park Row Station Please Meet Me Love Ellen.*"

"*The Army Department Deeply Regrets to Inform you—*"

Finger on the bell, bell ringing inside, or a buzzer making its coarser sound.

Sometimes the bell doesn't work, sometimes you have to go upstairs and knock. If there isn't any locked inner lobby door, you can go on to the second floor. . . .

The bell worked, and Miss Layne was waiting. I didn't know about her diary, and she didn't tell me about her diary for a long time. She neglected to write in it any more, soon after we met. But she'd admired my work before I knew her.

Went to the Graeme Players, an amateur drama group, for the first time tonight. Met MacKinlay Kantor who writes for the Line O' Type column. I had already cut out "Floyd Collins' Cave" and "Leather Gods." But he ran down to answer my ring wearing an old khaki flannel shirt and a black vest. Ugh.

She had come and opened the door of the apartment while I was climbing half flights of stairs. She wore a pale green dress

with pleats, and she was one of the most gorgeous objects I had
ever set my eyes on. Her hair was woven by witches.

"Good evening," she said.

4.

Irene remembered herself as sitting in her swing which hung
from a tree in a wide side yard on Byron Street; and she had
learned how to twist herself up in ropes of the swing, turning
round and round, plying her way with feet on the ground until
both ropes were tightly wound from top to bottom, and she
could turn no more, and ducked her head under the inverted
V where ropes pulled together. Then, lifting her feet off the
ground, the ropes would start to unwind of their own accord,
and she would go round and round, faster and faster, until
she had to close her eyes at the dizziness. Then again the ropes
would try to turn back the other way; and finally at long last
the swing itself and the child in it would be motionless. Then
she'd push with her feet, to start swinging in normal fashion once
more . . . swinging slightly . . . and she would look at the big
gray house and think, "That's my house, our house, and that's
Mother's room up there, and Mother is sick-a-bed."

She could go back to winter, back to her birthday. In snowy
weather she sought to play with her sled—she'd be bundled in
leggings and mufflers—and first she'd use the slide her elder
brothers fashioned out of heaped-up frozen snow; but if there
was no one to join in sledding, she loved to sit and watch sunset fade to blue and then to pink . . . their house bulked so
dark beyond . . . she was warm as toast, she liked to crouch
on her sled and worship evening light . . . *Irene! Irene!*
voices from the porch would begin crying. *Come in now, you've
played out long enough.* She'd think dreamily, *Ah, but I
haven't been here long. Yes, I'm warm, warm as fresh hot toast
with butter melting on it, I wish I had some now, I'm growing
hungry, but still the shade of color spread across a western sky,*

it's pink as currant jelly on my toast, but oh the twilight makes a comfort . . . warm and lone amid the snow.

There came a somber afternoon when she danced all the long blocks home from school. *Now I am seven, seven on this day.* She'd prayed and prattled for a birthday treat. Downtown: they'd ride down in an elevated train, and her mother'd take her there, to Marshall Field's, the wonder place, a treasure trove of gleaming things to see, the crowds, the throngs of folk a-seeing things, they had a catalogue with millions millions, toys and things and dolls and toys and what a place to go and see. She yelled and heckled. *Mamma, hurry, hurry up, you're taking me to Marshall Field's—* Her elder sister Ruth was there upstairs (and why was it so quiet down below? Was that the outer door a-opening and closing? No, no, it couldn't be) and Ruth had helped her, as she danced around, to change her dress. *Oh, hurry hurry, Mamma, we're going down to Marshall Field's—*

Then Ruth looked out the window, and she saw another Ruth approaching. She was Ruth Synwolt from their church, an older girl, she liked to go to parties. "Best go down," they told Irene. "Explain to her," and she skipped down the stairs, and feeling all important, to tell Ruth Synwolt she was sorry but she couldn't stay. *We're going down to Marshall Field's—*

Parlor doors were opened up, the faces, all the ribbon bows on well-brushed hair, the little girls she knew, they'd hidden in the parlor there. Surprise, surprise! Oh Happy Birthday to Irene! Surprise!

Not going . . . down to Marshall Field's?

Surprise!

"But were you mad?"

"Of course I was. Just sullen."

"But—here was a party—ready-made. You didn't want a party?"

"They'd told me that— Well. Marshall Field's!"

"You were a dope."

"Of course I was. I felt that I'd been cheated."

"What did you do?"

"Oh, played some games. We had a peanut hunt. I found
the most, and clamored for the prize, but Mamma wouldn't let
me have it. She said Ruth Synwolt helped me find the most,
and probably she did. Poor Mamma—and she'd worked so hard
to have that party for me— Planned and cooked and— That was
the year she left us. She died when summer came."

She saw her mother lying in a final peace, and later on
the baby died, they took her in to see it. They said that it was
dead . . . Irene was sure that it was sound asleep. Her father
whispered, "This was your little sister," and she wondered why
he didn't say, "This *is* your little sister," and she wanted to
touch the sleeping child. But they said No, and led her far away.

5.

"Why do I keep telling you these things?"

"Because I keep asking for them."

"But you can't possibly be interested in my little-girl recollections. And many of them are so melancholy—"

"They were *you*, weren't they? I want to hear them all."

"But this is only our second date—"

"Are you sure, Irene, that it isn't our *twenty*-second?"

"Honestly, you have a remarkable effect on me. I don't think
I ever told these memories to anyone before—"

"You have a remarkable effect on *me*. And it's not all concerned with anecdote-relating or anecdote-listening-to. But—seriously—"

"Yes. . . . Seriously . . . ?"

"Sorry. I was day-dreaming for a moment. . . ."

"Night-dreaming, Mr. Kantor?"

"Night-dreaming. Thanks, Miss Layne. Seriously, I love hearing about your long-time home on Byron Street. It doesn't sound
like Chicago, with a yard and gardens and a barn and everything. It sounds more like the town where I grew up, in Iowa.

You said the Byron Street place is still there. Will you take me over to see it, some day soon?"

"Of course, if you'd really like to go."

"I'm dying to go. Say, Irene, this teapot is pretty cold. Shan't I ask the waiter to bring some hot tea?"

"Will it cost extra?"

"Course not. They'll give you as much tea as you want, if you have the regular Chinese dinner. Which we've just had."

"Well, a little hot tea would be nice. But— There's something else—"

"Hey. How about some fortune cookies?"

"No, no, no, I couldn't possibly eat another thing. No, the Something Else is— I'd like to hear about *you*. Your childhood. I've talked and talked about my own. And you said that it was droll—my living on Wilson Avenue now—because you lived on another Willson Avenue when you were a boy—spelled with two l's instead of one—"

6.

The peach has a flavor of all flowers and all candy. I have never tasted a peach before, it seems that each morsel is better than the last. "More, please, Grandpa," I say many times, and each time his sharp knife glides into the fresh-peeled golden glory, and a new sliver of peach is placed on the saucer before me.

. . . Mother stares from old snapshots in a ragged album. Her eyes are hollow and sad. She is a newly divorced woman, with no fortune, and no training in the art of earning a living. *My children,* her face says. *What shall I do?*

Grandpa is there, in the snapshots and in my mind: a stooped man with handsome silver head and silver mustache. He is only in his fifties, but looks old enough to be his own father.

We moved from the house where I was born, we moved when I was an infant; I hold only one misty recollection of the other

place. Grandpa has bought a white-painted house surrounded
by soft maple trees . . . their trunks are thick and scaling, the
upper limbs pale and smooth as young birches.

In the spring heavy masses of seeds hang among fresh leaves.
Even a tiny boy can reach up and knock them off with a long
stick. If the bulk of the seeds are beyond his reach, he cries an
appeal to Mr. McFarland, an agreeable middle-aged man who
lives next door. Mr. Mac comes sauntering out, tilts back his
greasy straw hat and examines the boughs critically. Then he
knocks down the juiciest wettest heaviest bunch of all.

Now the boy is armed. Each of these wingèd seeds is a pistol.
He has only to tear off the upper part of the green flake, aim the
seed at his target, and squeeze quickly on the fattest portion.
Pop, and the juice comes squirting like a bullet.

I repay Mr. Mac treacherously for his kindness. *Pop, pop*,
and he is shot, a couple of times. He holds up his hands and
flees in pretended terror. Into our house I go dashing, another
frail pistol between my thumb and finger. A smiling woman is
kneading bread dough at the kitchen table. She has light brown
hair and a blue calico dress—always she wears blues or pinks—
and she seems very tall to me, although she is of average height.
She is Grandma. . . . Virginia and I are rich, as if endowed
with two mothers.

"Hands up!" I cry. "Hands up, Grandma, or I'll shoot!"

She gasps, "Why, you— You dreadful wicked old— You *rascal!*"
and *pop, pop, pop* the loads of maple juice come spitting at her.
Her hands all floury, she rushes after me, pretending to be furi-
ous, actually delighted in her heart of hearts.

It is spring, I can go barefoot. All through childhood, from the
first days of steady warmth until the frost approaches, most
children of Webster City and of farms nearby go scampering
unshod except for the day which spells Sunday School and
dress-up clothes. Our fragile feet grow tough as the hide of boars.
In Fourth of July season it is fun to hold a lighted piece of punk
against the leathery sole of one's own foot; the burning callous

sizzles with a foul smell, the little girls shriek and cover their eyes; then the punk is jerked away. . . . *Ow!*—the red coal has burned all the way through. I've held it too long. . . .

Where is Mother? Gone to work—selling magazine subscriptions or books, substituting one day as a teacher in the schools, gone far out into the country to work for a week as a practical nurse. Or tending some woman of the town who's just had a new baby, or looking after an old man up at the hospital two blocks away.

Emptiness begins to leave her face, her widowhood is a challenge. If she has to make her way alone, and bring up her children, by gracious she will do it. Her tread is strong, quick. Her laugh rings briskly, her hands fly through every task they can find.

My sister Virginia has thick black curls and great brown eyes. We do not look alike: I am almost white-blond as a little boy, my eyes are gray, I am skinny and noisy, I run about violently all day. We both have infant chores and household jobs to do, but there is plenty of time for play. We adore each other, as small children. We will not adore each other in growing-up years to come.

Where is this strange place where Virginia and the elder children of the neighborhood have gone? School, they call it; and each morning I walk with my sister to the top of the hill in front of the McFarlands' shabby house, and there I kiss her goodbye. I'll be lonely until noon, but she'll come home for dinner then; and back to School she'll go again, and hours will seem longer and longer.

Grandpa gone to the grain elevator, Mother off working somewhere, Virginia at School . . . no one here but Grandma, and she has sewing and scrubbing and cooking to do. I am out in the quiet yard, grass tender between my toes, the tin sword from Christmas in my hand. "That's a good boy," comes Grandma's voice. "Just play in the yard. Don't run away."

But I do run. I trot down the path to Mr. Mac's barn. Perhaps he will be there, hitching up Prince and Molly; perhaps I can ride with him on a load of sand. . . . Ah, he is already gone— gone Uptown, Auntie McFarland tells me; and Uptown is a hundred miles off. And when will he be back?

I'm weary of maple squirters; my tin sword has come loose again, the hilt and blade are apart; maybe Grandpa or Mr. Mac can fix it for me soon. I go to the sandpile and dig with a rusty spoon. Here is the castle which Virginia and I and the Bale girls built on Saturday. A fine thing it is—half sand, half dirt, ornamented with parts of teacups and medicine bottles. Can I make a new castle? . . . Hours drone, wind sings in tele- phone wires beyond the trees, a solitary tune of open pastures and new planted fields. Robins populate the yard, many robins, running with nervous steps, listening for the faint sound of the worm, dragging out the worm, flying away . . . wind touches a lonely harp of wires.

Out of the sky an enormous voice starts shrieking, far across the town and its banks of greenery. *Woooooooooooo* . . . a scream up and down the scale, as if every tomcat in creation has joined in ghastly chorus. The fire whistle! Here are danger, drama, wonderland, sport, disaster.

"Grandma, Grandma! There's a fire! Where's the fire?"

She stands, her hazel eyes glinting, holding up one finger as she listens to the low steady growl of the signal whistle which has replaced the wailing alarm. One long long groan . . . three short ones. *Mooooan. Moan. Moan. Moan.* I cannot count with skill, but Grandma can.

"Thirteen!" she gasps, as if the living room were ablaze. "That's our box— This neighborhood— Thirteen!" While the steam siren squeals its gigantic warning again, we have sped to the front door. Already other doors are flung open, all up and down the street, and distantly sounds the faint *spank, spank* of a tinny gong. The fire team is coming.

We are out at the edge of dust and ruts, peering toward the north. On the slope appears a shiny spasm of red and brass, with prancing shapes of two black horses straining in their harness.

Bill Frazier is in his seat, tough arms clutching the reins, his big foot hammering the gong. Volunteers, men with their coats off, are running behind. Buggies and a few automobiles come lurching in the rear.

Bales, Gerbers, McFarlands—the neighbors are out. That new family, the Marvels, who have just moved from Illinois, come hustling from their brick house . . . dogs are clamoring in circles.

Past our yard the pageant pours in menacing beauty. Budge and Toddy, the foamy horses, roll their eyes as they lunge (and one of our fire horses will be sold to a farmer when he grows too old to pull the hose-cart at high speed; but he will go dashing in search of the blaze each time the fire whistle blows, scattering eggs and butter sky-high).

. . . It isn't a house, it isn't a shed. Smoke drifts from the door of the old stone brewery—an ancient deserted structure on the brow of a hill beyond. No brewing of beer has been managed in this hulk since Civil War times; nowadays it is like a perilous cave, haunted by rats and occasional gypsies or tramps. Only the bigger boys are allowed to explore it; thus later I will go adventuring with a blazing broom for a torch.

Today one of the wooden partitions is burning. Perhaps a tramp was sleeping there last night, or maybe careless youths left some coals smoldering after they roasted potatoes in the cellar. Out tumbles the brass-tipped hose. Men grab it and begin to unscrew a cap from the hydrant opposite our corner. The fire-wagon goes rocking on toward the stone brewery, more hose pouring out behind. The wagon halts, people flock around, suddenly the hose squirms and stiffens as water goes shooting through.

. . . Only some worthless boards, soaked and ripped aside . . . there is steam instead of smoke, then no more steam. Soon the hose will be repacked, the gaudy red wagon will come rolling in return, crowds will go away, branches will nod, shadows will be wide and cool. In late afternoon when Mother comes home from work we can tell her with bated breath, "We

had a fire today! In the old stone barn!" and before I go to
sleep at night I can build the whole enchantment before my
eyes, and imagine that I hear the wild whistle and galloping
again.

7.

We were married on Friday, July 2nd, three months from the
night we met. We would have been wedded sooner but for a
tragedy which struck the Layne family.

There was one child younger than Irene: a spirited youth of
fifteen named Kenny. One night we returned to 2200 Wilson
from the regular evening date which had become such urgency
in our lives, to find Mr. Layne hurrying out the front door with
the bent shape of Kenny cradled in his arms; and Dr. Billig,
family doctor and close friend, coming close behind.

What was happening? "Appendicitis," said the doctor, and in
moments they were gone.

Through years the white face of the youth and the agony of
his big brown eyes return to plague us. There are antibiotics,
there are other proven tools employed today to ease the threat
of a ruptured appendix; but such procedures were then unknown. Kenny died in the hospital. My first admission to the
family circle as Irene's recognized fiancé came at his funeral. I
met aunts and cousins who had presided over the household
through the decade of Charles Layne's widowerhood . . . the
country cousins were sober folk from southern Wisconsin, quite
devoid of hayseed . . . there came Irene's eldest brother, who
had been working with a mining company in Colorado . . . the
stepmother was by no means the shrew of former imaginings,
but an earnest woman devoted to her husband and his progeny.

The implacability of sudden death may tighten human bonds
among survivors or just as quickly destroy them. I became acquainted soundly with Irene's people through starkness of those

hours and days. As for her father, there had never been any doubt about our mutual acceptance from the first moment. He was a handsome somber man, with hair still jet black in his late fifties, whose ambition vanished with the loss of his first wife in 1912. Charles Layne was still a member of the Chicago Mercantile Exchange, but dealt only in small lots of farm products —eggs, chiefly—at a desk in the office of more opulent commission merchants.

Irene said, "He walked the floor after Mother died. My sister Ruth and I shared a bedroom next to his, and we used to hear him. We'd go to sleep, wake up and hear him walking still. It seemed that he walked for years."

I met him that first night when I called for Irene. Mr. Layne asked what I was most interested in. I answered, "Poetry, for one thing." He misunderstood, and almost jumped out of his chair in delight.

"Poultry!" he exclaimed with satisfaction, thinking of the egg business.

I was compelled to disillusion him, and we had a laugh together. But he learned that I was a woods critter at heart, and fell to talking about his boyhood spent in hills along the Ohio River near Ironton. He was glad also that I smoked a pipe instead of toying with the cigarettes traditional among the young. He despised cigarettes, and hated hard liquor with even greater ferocity. His own father, a cruel and indigent man, had been addicted to The Bottle.

There were others of interest in the Layne tribe . . . one was a police chief in Missouri. Our souls trotted out and met in pleasure when Mr. Layne spoke with envy of his Uncle Wat who lived up in a holler with a pack of hounds. It would be more than nine years before I published *The Voice of Bugle Ann;* but thanks to the genial bearded Lord who presides over hollers and hounds, he was still alive to enjoy it.

That future—or even a less salubrious one— Whatever future was in store, I could not face it without Irene. I was an amputee whenever she was gone from me.

We cannot have been said to haunt the friendly Chinese restaurant on nearby Lincoln Avenue—we didn't have enough money for that—but we were there as often as our financial law allowed. They had booths somewhat cut off from the main body of the restaurant by hanging chains of oriental seeds or beads. One of those booths made an excellent place for a couple to sit and eat, drink tea, and above all read manuscripts together, or favorite poems and short stories.

I sold the second piece of material which I had sold since meeting Irene. I read the little sketch triumphantly, and we marveled over the fact that it fetched twenty dollars. It told of ambitious fledglings visiting a "Chop Suey" (the common term for such restaurants) and being greeted by a benign elderly gentleman who finally quit operations in his old age and went back to China. I called it *King Ying Low,* but Swanson changed the title to *Young Shadows* when he published it in *College Humor.*

"Good night," said Quong, "I hope you very well." He counted rings on wire, and his face was old.

. . . Dear Quong, the ghosts of youths are on your stair. And let the peacocks laugh, the doves be silly pink.

. . . *They came and went, young shadows on the wall.*

Like the majority of unknowledgeable Americans, our notion of Cantonese food was limited to chop suey and chow mein. I thought that I didn't like either one, and always ate fried rice instead; Irene's partiality was toward chicken chow mein. I did not believe that it contained rat tails, but it rather looked as if it did, and one could never be quite certain.

Moo goo gai pan, war hip har, char sue ding and such succulent fare were well ahead of us and would be for some time to come. Nevertheless we inclined toward the belief that the Chinese, awarding dignity and importance to the past, managed to transmit a share of this philosophy to their food, and that we profited spiritually from the mere surroundings. Rice was fra-

grant . . . tea could be made hot . . . we were grinned upon,
and permitted to linger as long as we chose—or at least until
the staff decided to pack up for the night and go back to Went-
worth Avenue or wherever they did dwell.

8.

We went job hunting with success. Irene, deploring her role as
lamp-shade painter, visited Carson-Pirie's and found a situation in the picture-framing department which was then of considerable proportion in that store. She gave advice and directed customers in their choice of frames, and was glad to be
working in the Loop again.

I had been compelled to yield up my Dietzgen rod on the
Cook County surveying crew months before. Enduring osteomyelitis of the left femur area, my leg grew swollen from ardu-
ous tramping over summery dells northwest of Chicago, no matter how attractive they were to my other senses. Instead I must
go indoors where I could sit down, and the Highway Department had nothing of that sort open. They switched me to an
office where I joined a sedentary group of fellow workers in
stamping the signature of the County Treasurer on duns for
unpaid real estate taxes. Eventually I went to the American
Flyer, a toy train manufacturing company on South Halsted
Street.

(No necromancy informed me that I would ever wear the
wings of an American flyer myself. Says the Air Officer's Guide,
"The year 1926 was an important one . . . the Air Corps Act was
passed. This Act re-named the Air Service as the Air Corps. . . .
In 1927 notable accomplishments included the first outside loop
by Lt. J. H. Doolittle, and a transcontinental flight from Bolling
Field, D.C., to Rockwell Field, California, by Major Carl Spaatz."
A thin passenger rides the crowded streetcar in Chicago, and a
voice calls down from the sky, "You will fly in combat with the
bombers under General Doolittle's command. To serve General

Spaatz, you will tour the air of western Germany, and offer your
report on bombardment accomplishments there." The passenger's ears are deaf, he doesn't hear a word. When you consider
the entire circumstance, deafness in the young is a damn good
thing. And necromancers have rather gone out of style . . . I
hope.)

The title itself was imposing: assistant advertising manager.
What that meant mainly was that I drew up copy for Christmas
advertisements and catalogues of a winter to come. The salary
was only twenty-five dollars a week, and I could have done
with a lot more salary. However I got to do a good deal of writing for M.K. The factory had a top floor where a workroom
had been contrived among packing cases; and it was filled
with zinc-topped tables, and files of electrotypes to be used
in printing pictures of the various trains and accessories they
manufactured. I learned what was expected of me—how
many pages of copy should be prepared per day in order to
satisfy my immediate superior. I would work feverishly to have
this completed early in the day. Likely I was proceeding at a
rate of about four times normal human activity in such endeavor,
and had I been able to keep this up on a solid basis the
company would have owed me a hundred dollars a week
instead of twenty-five. But they wouldn't have paid it.

Seldom was I visited by anyone. Once in a long while a sane
and friendly individual—Mr. Arthur L. Chambers, the advertising manager—would come up to offer some direction or other; or
one of the young lady office workers might appear in order to
get a printing of some electrotype. Our big boss, also a big man
physically, was W. Ogden Coleman; but he came on only one
or two occasions. The real intrusion to be dreaded was that of a
brow-knitting corporal named Cuff, engaged as supervisor and
efficiency expert. He lurked near time clocks to see that no employee punched someone else's card as well as his own. His was
generally a sneaky tread, and he grew adept at frightening the
wits out of tenement girls who worked at benches and lathes
downstairs. However skulking his procedure, Mr. Cuff never

caught me in *flagrante delicto* on the top floor of the American
Flyer. The only means of access or egress except by fire escape
was a cumbersome freight elevator which swayed and grunted
as it made tedious journeys up and down. Infrequently did it
come to the top floor anyway. When the doors opened, it was
with a crash which fairly jarred the smoking chimneys of stockyards to the west. No one could sleep through such din, so I was
able to write or take naps as desired. By the time anyone arriving by elevator reached my boarded-off area, I would be
serenely at work with electrotypes spread before me.

Sleep hit me as abruptly as waking, in hot afternoons of the
dragging early summer. I needed sleep as I needed a monstrous
nurse, tender and invincible by turns. I had to be at work at
eight-thirty every morning of our six-day week, and that meant
being at the time clock well before eight-thirty: Mr. Cuff desired
to have us engaged in productive tasks by the time the magic
half hour clanged. I used to wonder with hilarity how many fits
he would have thrown had he guessed at my cozy naps,
stretched out on one of those zinc-topped tables. Zinc can be
soft when you are weary.

Irene and I tried to teach ourselves to terminate our dates by
eleven p.m., but that grew increasingly difficult; twelve or even
one o'clock was more common. She too had to rise early and take
transportation downtown, but at least she could go to bed the
moment after we broke apart at her hall door. Then ensued
my uncertain trip back to 2829 Cambridge. I would hasten the
four blocks along Robey Street, and tried to arrange to follow
fancied schedules of Lawrence Avenue streetcars. The schedules
were not well observed, they couldn't be. Sometimes with good
fortune I reached Lawrence Avenue just in time to see that
friendly round light bobbing from the west, with the little golden
bar up above the motorman's windows. Often enough, however,
as I scampered the last half block, an eastbound car would
plunge across the intersection ahead of me and be gone.

. . . Same way when it came to the transfer at Clark Street:
sometimes lucky, sometimes not. Sometimes there might have

been accidents en route. Cars would line up, nothing would come for half an hour or longer.

It was possible to get home from Irene's address in forty minutes, even thirty-five; that was the quickest which might come about. More often it took an hour, an hour and a half . . . a two a.m. or two-thirty a.m. going-to-bed, and then—it seemed instantaneously—arising at six-thirty to bathe. That was a slow business with my leg the way it was . . . have breakfast, prepare the lunch which I usually carried to work, and half-run the westward distance along Diversey Parkway to Halsted Street, and catch a car there.

As an ordinary detail of existence, I had from one to three open sinuses draining their serum on my left thigh, every hour I lived . . . during one fell week I had five of them open . . . always there was a single chunk of gauze to be tacked across each wound, morning and evening. Physically I was on the cadaverous side and, though blessed with an eager appetite, must have been underfed as a rule.

Like many determined and imaginative starvelings, I might have taken morbid pleasure in dramatizing the eminent situation to myself; in fact, I tried to do this, but usually was too busy thinking about what I hoped to write in any given day. Work—life-giving, salaried work— That was something you educated yourself to do; it was the means toward the end; although you didn't do any more of Other People's work than you had to. Were it to be appreciated and paid for, you would have done more. You found out how little you could do and still get along, and then you did that little bit. This was the common creed of the salaried: as practiced in Dickens' time, as practiced in 1926, as practiced today.

(Funny thing. When I scared up a better paying job downtown, and informed the American Flyer advertising manager that I was leaving, he took time out to try to persuade me to remain. He promised that he would intercede for me and attempt to wangle a raise in salary. I had deluded even Mr.

Chambers into believing that I was a valuable employee. Hurrah for my automatic response to the crashing open of those freight elevator doors.)

I am lucky, lucky. I can sleep at almost any time and in almost any position, and in almost any condition. The only sleeping pills I've ever absorbed were given me in hospitals against my wishes and counsel. I slept on that same zinc topping . . . have slept on chilly concrete, slept in luggage racks at the end of old-fashioned third-class British railway cars, slept on piles of baggage in transoceanic aircraft . . . have even slept stretched out on the welcoming grass of a cemetery. Thus I know, which most people don't, what it's like to wake up in a cemetery in the middle of the night. And when I did this, and stood up— I hold memory of the mortal couple who had crept there to exercise their very mortality, and who were the terrified beholders of that resurrection. Don't say that a dead man never rises from the sod. Somewhere there are, or were, people who saw it happen.

9.

We could never have believed that the stockyards industry would be so vulnerable to change as to be deleted from Chicago within the remainder of a lifetime. And railroads as well. . . . Our toy train factory lay almost directly across Halsted from the Omaha Packing Company, and beyond that were reared a host of other chimneys, drifting their smoke like tall censers, manufacturing a haze and solid odor which lay wadded over texture of the city itself.

Delvers within the American Society for Psychical Research are seeking relationship between sleep and full consciousness and the creative process. Half a century of writing has shown me that, in my case at least, a period of clear and conscious creative effort may follow directly on the heels of slumber. *The*

Romance of Rosy Ridge, The Good Family, Happy Land and
The Voice of Bugle Ann were all dreamed up shortly after
waking; and so were many characters and delineations included
in *Andersonville, Spirit Lake, Long Remember.* In stripling fashion of the 1926 time, I made obeisance before those chimneys to
the west, and put the clamoring of traffic out of my ears. It was
gone, it didn't exist . . . I yielded instead to Indian ponies and
cumulus clouds, and giddy flowers of the puccoon.

Maybe Eskimos had arranged a form of air conditioning in
their igloos, but nobody else had. At that factory we were even
cautioned about open windows. Mr. Cuff thought that dirt blew
in and fouled up the local universe, and probably he was right;
but whatever windows could be opened behind his back, we
opened them. In that box-like chamber with wire mesh nailed
up to the ceiling above partitions, to keep villains from crawling
over and stealing— God knew what. How much would a few
electrotypes bring at the junkman's? I had my paper and pencils,
and I wrote and wrote. I wrote *The Snow of the Okoboji,* wrote
Nebrasky Is So Far Away. I wrote *Turkey in the Straw* itself,
but had no inkling that it would be the title poem of a future
volume.

> And unseen eagles
> Yelled on a ridge,
> Over beyond the Deer Creek bridge.
>
> . . . And some say the little flags
> Snapped like stars
> To the drum, drum, drum
> Of those redskin bars;
> And I saw Yankee men
> Pushing up their stones,
> And dancing to our fifes
> On splinter-new bones.

One dulcet June day Mr. Chambers prescribed business for me
in the Loop. That was a great moment. It meant a trip downtown—where Irene was employed—and the nickels for streetcars

would be furnished by the American Flyer Company. Furthermore, in visiting the offices which I had to visit, no one knew how
rapidly such errands might be performed.

"Mr. Kahn may not be in when you get there, on Wells Street.
I've tried to find out, but they seem to be having switchboard
trouble. So, if he isn't in, you'll have to ask for Mr. McAcken. If
he isn't there, wait for him. There isn't anyone else who can
provide us with the exact sort of tracing paper we need. Then,
at the other place— Tell you what," said Mr. Chambers. "Go to
our cashier—here, I'll give you a note—and draw lunch
money. Then, if you can get back here by three this afternoon,
we can get our stuff in the mail before we close. There'll still be
time."

Time, gentlemen. Time. . . .

There was another errand which I contemplated, one of a
deeply personal nature. It was something I had to dare myself
to do. And yet, and yet— I moved to an empty portion of the
streetcar—no rush hour now—and examined the few dollars in
my billfold. Today should be the day. . . . In benevolence of
spirit I tried to concoct a lithesome June-time summer-time
romance-time set of verses, to make my journey more than pay
for itself. But I hadn't progressed much past initial hawthorns
and roses and the slim feet twinkling under petticoats, before I
was on the edge of the Loop, seeking the first scheduled address.

Everything broke favorably. Mr. Kahn was in, and supplied
essential materials on the spot. . . . I went on to the other place.
Mr. Leinmunster was home—he had the grippe, his secretary
said. I clucked in sympathy along with her. But now, just what
did Mr. Chambers need? Oh yes, she remembered . . . the correspondence was right here . . . she produced it, and found what
was necessary to fill the order.

Two large envelopes I toted along with me. The County
Building was only a few blocks yonder. I went over there, stood
in a short line, and in ten minutes was out of the office. In many
places the two of you have to appear together in order to secure

a marriage license—but not in Chicago, not in those days. I held the pink certificate worshipfully . . . wanted to kiss it, did kiss it . . . folded it into secrecy in the back pocket of my wallet.

I believed A. L. Chambers to be a noble man. I still thought so twenty years later, when he came to us in Florida and we sat with cocktails, and had affability together.

10.

One night when I left Irene and turned the Robey Street corner, she went immediately to her room on that side of the building. She was drawn to the window by a snarl of automobile tires, sound of a car skidding to a stop, and the forthright yell, "Hey, you. Put up your hands!"

Irene looked down to see that I had put my hands up most obligingly. Two policemen had their revolvers aimed against my body.

"You ran over from Lincoln Avenue. Don't deny it!"

"No I didn't. I just walked out of this building, here on the corner—"

"Blue shirt, black pants! You just stuck up a cab, two blocks west of here—"

"Nope. You've got the wrong guy. I just took my girl home to this apartment building—"

They went over me for weapons and found I had no gun. "We followed you east on Wilson—"

"You must have followed someone else."

"What's the name of the apartment where you say you took your girl home?"

"It's there in the lobby. *Layne*, on the second mailbox."

One of them still kept me covered, the other went in and returned quickly. "It's O.K., Ed. That's the name. He wouldn't have had time to go in there and read it."

They drove away, probably to scour the neighborhood for

the fugitive in blue shirt and black trousers. I hurried toward Lawrence Avenue, unaware that Irene had witnessed the incident from her window. This was the second occasion in a few months that the police had aimed at my belly. The other time they were searching for Marty Durkin. That was no fun either, because Durkin was marked as a cop killer . . . trigger fingers were somewhat itchy. I didn't look much like the picture of Durkin which appeared in newspapers. But one night another young man was picked up in northern Indiana; and that fellow, falsely accused and placed under arrest, could have been my twin brother.

I had told Irene about this and persuaded her to laugh at the idea. Nevertheless I was sufficiently shaken, on going down to Richard Henry Little's in an evening when the central and lower North Side were crawling with cops, to hang cardboard signs on my chest and back: *I am not Marty Durkin.*

Also, in stupid style I had spoken jauntily to my idyllic idol of encounters with individuals who were already outside the law or who were being watched by it. Those were names you saw in the press. Peter Von Frantzius ran a sporting goods store on Diversey Parkway; he was considered, at least by reporters, to be an armorer for various North Side hoodlums. I knew Mr. Von Frantzius slightly. Once, when especially broke, I had tried to talk him into buying a revolver I owned; but he said the gun wasn't worth much. . . . Hymie Weiss was a neighbor. . . . I had met Schemer Drucci in his flamboyant panama hat. . . .

A man named Cliff Palmer lodged frequently at 2829 Cambridge. He was a former Federal agent, and held reputation as a gunman. He'd been a buddy of S. Glenn Young. Palmer and I struck up a friendship. . . . Once in a while I treated myself to a chocolate malted milk in the pharmacy of the Rienzi Hotel, also on Diversey— I shared the fountain with another avid chocolate malted milk drinker: Frankie Foster. He was considered to be a professional trigger man.

Such braggadocio I dispensed to the innocent Irene. No

wonder the gal was at her wits' end when she saw me below her
window with my hands in the air.

A few nights later, around three a.m., the Layne family and
other tenants of their building were brought from bed by the
stammering of shots . . . cries of, "I'm a police officer and need
help! Somebody call the police!" A wounded patrolman was on
the ground in a yard across Wilson Avenue, waging a battle
with some character crouched in front of 2200. The bandit
escaped by running up our sacred stairway and out through a
trapdoor on the roof. Reinforcements arrived tardily, an ambulance came for the wounded patrolman, and later the neighborhood regained its normal quiet if not normal aplomb. This
strife conjured up a series of terrors for Irene, as she envisioned
me in the role of runaway outlaw. Asleep or awake—mostly the
latter—she spent miserable hours.

During the forenoon I was summoned from work to receive
a tremulous telephone call.

"Are you all right?" she asked.

"Sure, I'm fine. What's the trouble?"

"There was a policeman shot, across the street from our
building—"

"Oh, yes? Was it fatal?"

"We don't know. They took him to the hospital. But— Are
you *sure* you're all right?"

"Of course I am." This went on for several minutes.

It seemed that if the activity of banditry continued menacing
us, our romance was in trouble. Should the city keep smelling of
burnt smokeless powder—the odor was high right then—it was
going to play utter hell with my fabled hawthorns, green lanes,
and with Irene's petticoats. The ribbands had best be knotted
together, and quickly, or I might be doomed to a life of bachelor-
hood with a hollow-cheeked countenance displayed on *Wanted*
posters. Should the betrothed lady suffer an attack of the me-
grims every time a pistol banged—and they were banging—I
had best join the connubial ranks or else some priestly community. The former sounded more attractive.

11.

On that important Friday I presented myself as a victim of illness, bereavement, mayhem, and general hostility, and managed
to get off from work half an hour early. This made it possible for
me to be standing at the Madison Street entrance of Carson-
Pirie's when Irene left the store. A few doors to the east we
halted in a deserted alcove, and I presented a fervent appeal.

". . . But if we ran off and got married, my father would
never forgive me."

I was confident that Charles Layne would forgive her and
forgive me, and swore to it.

"It would be too disturbing for him, coming just after Kenny's
death—"

"You wouldn't be running off. We'd just be getting married,
but telling no one about it. Call me a coward if you like: our
family is in debt as a whole, and personally I owe what seems
like ten million dollars for unpaid doctor bills. What have I got
to get married *on?* Nothing. But that's one of the ten million
reasons why I need to marry you. *With* you, I know damn well
we can go a long way. *Without* you, it might be a different story.
Yes, maybe I'm being selfish in demanding that we marry now.
But maybe, when men are this deeply in love, they're always
selfish."

Irene whispered, "What would your mother say?"

"My mother's not well, and she'd faint dead away if she knew
it, so she mustn't know it. No one must. I guess by this time
you should understand the situation. My mother is confident
that nowhere in this wide world does there exist a creature who
is fit to be married to her talented and devoted son. Every girl
I ever had— When Mother realized that our hearts might be
fluttering, she'd start talking about someone else. If I busted
up with the first girl and went to a second, then Mother would
start telling me how Number Three was better yet. It went on

that way indefinitely. I became engaged to Andrea when I was
twenty. In no time flat, Mother was sure that Andrea was not
the girl for me, although she had always praised her to the skies
before I started going with her. That's the way it is. It'll always
be that way."

"But what about the future?"

"She'll be as much in love with you as I am."

"I mustn't do this to Dad."

"What will you be doing to your father, anyway? You'll be
getting married. Surely he's always expected that of you."

"We haven't got any license—"

"Oh yes we have," I crowed. "Take a look!"

Finally we removed our discussion to the Polly Tea Room
on Wabash, around the corner . . . Irene was weakening in her
rejection. We had the sixty-five-cent *table d'hôte*, and I told
her that that was our wedding dinner, and she said, "Well,
maybe," and the pianist sped early to her piano on the balcony
and played "Nola" and Percy Grainger's "Country Gardens"
which she always played; and I told Irene that that was our
wedding supper music, and she said limply, "I'm not sure."
They gave us little dabs of perfectly vile baked cocoa cake for
dessert, and I said it was our wedding cake, and Irene said,
"Well, possibly," and I smoked my last Melachrino cigarette
and wadded a chunk of cake into the little cardboard box,
and wrapped it in a paper napkin and took it along in my
pocket (we had it put away for years, laughing about our
wedding cake; and then the box in which it was housed got
crushed in storage, and amid dried wreckage we discovered
the mummies of two maggots, so that's what happened to our
wedding cake).

I hustled Irene off in search of a parson. My ideas on the
subject were high. In recent years I had heard only one Chicago
minister preach. He was a burly Presbyterian named Thompson,
the dominie of a millionaires' church on North Michigan Avenue.
With effrontery I escorted Irene there. The office was open, and
an amused janitor said that one of the assistant pastors might

be along soon. Perhaps he would be willing to marry us, as I practically demanded.

We waited . . . Irene showed signs of losing heart . . . during one of the janitor's absences, we retreated. We tried an Episcopal church up the street: nobody home there either. They had a Swedish janitor, and I didn't know that any Swedes were Episcopalians, but maybe he wasn't an Episcopalian anyway. He thought the curate might be coming in "pooty soon," but the curate didn't show, so we went over to Rush Street. Anyway Michigan Avenue was a little too close to the Graeme Players for our consciences.

At a drug store I consulted a telephone book and wrote down several addresses of nearby clergymen. The first one turned out to be a clergywoman, and Irene wouldn't even let me approach the entrance. She said that if she were married by a woman, she wouldn't feel married at all. The next address also brought definite refusal. She said haughtily, "I wouldn't be married by anyone who lived in a dump like that." We traveled northward.

After several more starts and false starts, I caught the reflection of a lighted sign on a Chicago Avenue building. It was a lodge hall. According to symbols on the illuminated glass, the Knights of Pythias were about to hold a session.

"Here, honey, you wait in the lower entrance. I'll run upstairs. Bet you the chaplain of that lodge is a minister, and I'll ask him to marry us." I went up, to be halted by the Pythian sentry. He was early on the job, with two or three other members gathered near.

Yes, the chaplain was present. I told him I thought it would be like the Masons . . . the chaplain might be a minister?

He said, "I'm a plumber by trade," and they had amusement. This considerate man had also a suggestion.

"Look, son. Do you know where the Moody Bible Institute is?"

"Somewhere west of here, isn't it—?"

"That's right. Corner of Chicago Avenue and LaSalle Street.

Why don't you go over there? There's bound to be some ministers around the Moody Institute."

"Are they open at night, sir?"

"Sure. I live not far away, and there's always lights on, and a whole gang of future missionaries around."

I ran downstairs and dragged the quivering bride along the several blocks to LaSalle Street. Here indeed was the Moody Bible Institute, so lighted up that it seemed the ghost of old Dwight L. must be holding forth in person, with Ira D. Sankey pressing out organ notes in the background.

A fainting damsel collapsed upon a bench outside the library door, and I proceeded to make inquiries. Good Christian spirits appeared—first in the shape of a vigorous young man named William Shoemaker, and secondly in a future missionary to whom he appealed, one Martha Cunis.

They looked at each other doubtfully. "Say," said Shoemaker, "how about Doctor Harold Lundquist, our secretary? Upstairs. Isn't he an ordained minister?"

"I'm almost sure that he is," said Miss Cunis. "Let's ask someone else."

"Don't bother," I told them in desperation. "You say his office is on the second floor?"

"Yes. Right opposite the stairway."

Irene was pale as a Washington Irving lass about to be carried off from Katzenellenbogen by the specter knight. I left her in stupor and ran up to encounter Secretary Lundquist. He seemed a pleasant soul, equipped with desk, round countenance, spectacles, a sweet-smelling pipe, and a genial smile.

"Well, yes. I am a minister, although I haven't married anyone in some years. What's all the rush, young man?"

"There are circumstances . . . it isn't what you might think: we don't *have* to get married. But I'm determined to marry her tonight, and had a hell of a time persuading her to do it. If we don't— Lord only knows—"

He extended his hand. "License?"

I gave it to him.

"Bring the young lady here to my office."

She was in a trance, although she didn't fight or cry out. Lundquist said, "You'll need two witnesses, according to law."

In the library again I captured Miss Cunis and Mr. Shoemaker. We came back to Lundquist's office where the Reverend Mr. Secretary delivered himself of a lecture on the perils of hasty marriage. To the best of my recollection we received this in utter silence. I was too exhausted, and Irene too stricken, to make even feeble reply until the end.

He asked us, "You're positive that you still want to be married?"

"Yes," I cried with force. Irene uttered bird-like sounds which could have been interpreted any way he chose.

"Very well. Will you please stand over here? And you witnesses— There."

The ceremony was direct and simple. For a ring we employed the cameo which Irene was wearing. She treasured it, it had belonged to her mother. I had indeed thought about a wedding ring, but that would have to be put off. The one I examined at Lebolt's, on State Street, was ticketed at eleven dollars, and might have to be bought on Time. Irene wore a dark-blue georgette dress, and a blue cloche on her head, and overall one of those oilskin raincoats which the girls were wearing that summer: yellow, with a ribbed corduroy collar and narrow leather strap at the neck. Her eyes were big as plates. She swayed while we stood there, and I feared she was going to fall over.

(It turned out that this diagnosis was one thousand per cent correct. As we approach the half-century mark in relationship, she recalls keenly that the room and people went dark before her eyes. In language of modern pampered murderers, she blacked out and couldn't recall a thing.)

Harold Lundquist signed his proper portion of the marriage license, and said that he would return it to the county office as required. We asked for some sort of certificate. One of the witnesses affirmed that those could be bought in a bookstore adjacent to the library downstairs, if it was still open . . . it was, barely. I requested a wedding certificate; they had only one kind, complete with doves, lilies, and a few Crosses and sunrises. It looked hallowed and not very official, but it was all they stocked. Secretary Lundquist filled the certificate in, and presented it to us . . . we ran, we had to get to rehearsal. Before departure I placed in the minister's hand the little American Flyer envelope prepared that afternoon.

I'd called the Players while we were at the Polly Tea Room, and Joe Driscoll took the call. I explained that some unforeseen emergency had arisen, and we would be late—maybe even quite late—for rehearsal. They would have to rehearse around us. . . . Can't remember which play we were working on at the time, but we were in it, and that last-minute change of schedule practically pulled up boards from under the cast. Miss Graeme reminded us of this in a firmly bitter speech. I started to remark offhand, "If you only knew what we've been doing," but my new spouse adroitly kicked me into silence.

Our wedding journey was made by bus, and cost twenty cents. We rode to the end of the Wilson Avenue line and walked several blocks to Robey Street in silence, holding hands. Irene felt she had done something indescribably wicked, yet was unable to explain it herself. I thought it a deed well done, but corrosive to the nerves.

I kissed her goodbye in the hallway. "Wife, there's something. A little matter—"

"What on earth, darling?"

"A little matter of money."

"But you don't need to give me any money *now*."

"No, I want you to give me some."

She began to giggle, with a quality of hysteria.

"I could spare only three dollars for the minister: there were three one-dollar bills in the envelope I gave him. I hope he doesn't laugh his head off about that. But— After the restaurant and wedding certificate and bus fare— See, I'll get paid at the factory tomorrow. But in the meantime— You know. Carfare?"

Silently she opened her bag and offered her purse.

"Can you spare a quarter, Goodwife Kantor?"

"Certainly, because I'm rich. But now I realize that you married me for my money."

I robbed her of twenty-five cents. She unlocked the apartment door, we looked at each other a long moment, and then she went to her room and I out into the bandit-strewn police-infested night. I was dog-tired by the time the Clark Street car reached my neighborhood, and rode past the Diversey intersection. Then I woke up and had to walk back.

(Two years later I sent Dr. Lundquist a copy of my first novel when it was published . . . once we visited together, and enjoyed a scattering of correspondence . . . a few later books went his way. Eventually came that silence which we assumed meant Departure.)

Irene was so tired that night that she thought she would never sleep. She passed out as soon as her head hit the pillow. In the morning she walked to the El and took an express train down to Carson-Pirie's. She had bought a *Tribune* before she entered the car and in force of habit opened it to the editorial page. There was the "Line O' Type" column, and this was July 3rd, and the next day was the Nation's birthday, and my Fourth of July poem appeared at the head of the column. Dick Little had put a row of flags at the top of the piece, and a row of miniature cannon at the bottom. I'd been intent on bringing the Revolutionary War to life.

Jefferson's out of Virginia with foxhounds at his heels,
And all of the black guns lumbering on crooked clumsy wheels.
Tories are up in the orchard to see what may be seen.
Ho, for an oath at Monmouth—and the queue of General Greene!

She said that she sat quietly and said to herself, "My husband." A warmth of compassion and pride came over her, and I was ready to cry when she told me this.

II. *AN EXTRY PLATE FOR CHARLEY*

1.

We had no Colony or State of Virginia to come storming out of, and no hounds to follow on our heels. We did have city lights, and stars to admire and live with . . . stars or moon or both. They were our signal lanterns, and we walked or lay under them, and spoke beneficially. We found meager wildernesses, mostly along Lake Michigan, where land had been filled and grass was growing; but people and parkways had not yet intruded in quantity.

Our real wedding journey was maneuvered when the Graeme Players rented a cottage at Deep Lake, and everyone went up for a long weekend. Irene and I were invited, but sagaciously we left one day early and joined the Graeme Players one day late, and nobody ever learned the difference. We had been at quite another scenic pond: Gray's Lake, with an entrancing (to us) down-at-the-heels hotel on the main street. We honeymooned in all fact. We found divinity in every bite of food we ate, every sound we heard, every step we took together, every motion in which we joined. Only lack of money kept us from repeating such rapture.

But her brother's passing was still silhouetted on Irene's memory, and to lesser degree on my own. The more eager and active the young, the more indelibly does the flow of death stain them. This phenomenon is like a figure in cerements lurking behind . . . it is difficult to step away from Him. With contemplation of the morgue ordered upon them, the young can scarcely tear their gaze loose. I heard with shock that my wife counted eight funerals held from the house on Byron Street. Four of them were in a single year: her mother; the baby sister a little later; her maternal Grandmother Lawrence; her uncle Harry Layne.

"It must have reached the point where, if people down the street saw folks arriving, they asked, 'What's all that crowd?' and someone replied, 'Oh, probably just another funeral at the Laynes'.'"

Irene mused again. "But you're acutely sensitive to the process of death yourself. You write obituary poems, one after the other. Now we have that pretty girl from Montana, killed in the rodeo down in Grant Park. And you've written a tender poem which Dick put in the column: 'Lovely Louise.' You've done so many of those that Snowshoe Al calls you in print, 'a charnel-house bone-rattler.'"

"There was something . . . when I was real young."

"Surely not in your family? You never saw your Grandmother Kantor; and your father's still alive, though you're estranged; and your Grandfather Kantor's still alive too. Your grandparents in Iowa are both alive, and your mother, and sister Virginia—"

"No," I said, "it was another boy."

2.

Charley Morean like myself came from a broken home. His father was divorced and gone away somewhere, his mother re-married. Charley lived with old Grandpa and Grandma Morean. The name was pronounced in three syllables: *Mor-e-an.*

We called him Chink as a nickname, and he did look a trifle like a Chinese boy, with slanting eyes. But his eyes were blue and merry, his hair sandy and usually clipped off short. He was tall for his age, round-shouldered, and spoke with a drawling nasal voice.

For some reason still unrecognized, I thought that Chink Morean was someone to poke fun at, to make a joke about. We had for years one of those weak distant acquaintanceships which small-town children possess when they do not live in the same neighborhood, attend the same Sunday School, or meet commonly in any other place. Then, after I began to carry our local newspaper, the *Freeman-Tribune*, as a regular job, I saw Charley every weekday. He was one of the dozen other paper boys, and had a route down near Union Street in his own section of town.

He held a dream of organizing a boys' club. I think he was lonely much of the time, living in a small house with his gray-haired grandparents. Doubtless he imagined how fine it would be if there were a club of boys organized especially to go on hikes and picnics, to have wienie roasts and bonfires, to hold meetings and originate secret badges and signs. Perhaps, lying in bed at night before he slept, and entertaining fancies, Charley actually saw himself as President of such a club, with a whole troop of loyal followers.

We paper boys earned one dollar each week. Chink Morean must have spent thirty or forty cents of hard-saved money on the advertisement which he inserted in that same daily *Freeman*.

> WANTED. Boys to join a boys'
> club. Inquire of Charles Morean.

His address followed.

At that time I had not enough imagination or understanding to see anything but the ridiculous in Charley's appeal. I said to friends, "Did you see that crazy ad Charley Morean put in the paper?" Together we sneered.

The following week I was alone when I met Charley in front of the paper office, and he was alone too. I was cruel enough and bold enough to scoff openly. "Well, how's the wonderful boys' club doing?" with the meanest scorn of which I was capable.

His eyes opened, wide and innocent . . . his face showed only bewilderment. "You know," came his high-pitched voice, "I just can't understand it. A lot of fellows talked to me about my

club, and I told em we'd go on a hike on Saturday. I told em
where my grandpa's house was—just go east from Superior Street
until they saw a white stone rabbit at the edge of the yard, and
that was it."

He shook his head. Into that slow squeaky tone crept a note
of pain. "They didn't come. I waited and waited, but nobody
came at all. I had the wienies all bought, and everything."

He went away, lugging his heavy paper bag with his long
thin-legged stride. If a stone cornice had fallen from the roof of
the building above I could not have felt more crushed. The
knowledge that you have deliberately hurt a fellow being, without reason, is worse than any toothache in the world.

(I remember feeling like that one other time, though there
was less excuse for shame: this other thing was more or less of
an accident. At a circus, crowds were edging out of the tent
after the performance, and my grandmother and I walked high
on a plank above the topmost tier of seats. We were passing the
reserved seats which cost extra, and were merely chairs placed
in orderly rows, and—in our town—seldom occupied. It occurred to me that if I upset one of those folding chairs, it would
fall against the one below, and that chair would upset the next
one, and so on down through rows, like domino soldiers in a
line. Deliberately—but pretending that it was merely a happen-
stance—I upset the top chair. *Click, click, clack, click, clunk:*
thus the chairs went, with precision like clockwork. The lowest
and last chair shot forward, smacking against the arm of a little
girl who happened to be passing at that moment. She gave a
shriek. It's a wonder that her arm wasn't broken. Her mother
and other people all looked up at the top row to see how
such a thing had happened. But by that time I was well past
the place where the first chair had toppled . . . apparently no
one suspected that it was my fault. Later, outside the tent, I
saw the girl again. Her arm was still hurting, her face red and
wet with tears. . . . I stalked home beside Grandma. "Didn't
you like the circus, honey?" she asked anxiously. I had earned
my entrance ticket by scrubbing white-painted wooden balls

which the polar bears used in their act, but Grandma had
spent a huge fifty cents for her own ticket. I mumbled that the
circus was wonderful . . . the little girl's name was Esther Yaus.
She's been dead for years.)

Truly I felt that I needed to be whipped when I plagued
Charley Morean, but there was no one to whip me. This was a
private woe which I dared not talk about, not even to my mother.
I thought of running after Charley, falling on my knees, sobbing
that I had never meant to deride his little dream. But that
would have been a lie in itself. I had indeed meant to mock—
heaven knows why.

One thing I could do, and that was to go out of my way to be
nice to him. The next day I asked Chink if he'd like to go on a
hike, the following Saturday—go early in the morning, and get
back at three-thirty or four o'clock, just in time to carry our
papers. He was radiant at the suggestion. On Saturday we were
up at the crack of dawn, trailing excitedly down the railroad
tracks to Essig's Woods: three of us instead of the usual two—
Herbert Arthur, Chink Morean and myself. In those days Herbert
was a well-knit blond of my own size, though a year and a half
older. Herb welcomed the idea of Charley's joining us; he said
with his usual terse calm that he thought Chink was a swell
fellow—always had liked him.

When my birthday came, I demanded that Chink be included
in the circle of guests. "Charley Morean?" echoed Mother, mysti-
fied. "Why, you've never had him at a party before." He came,
and six or eight of us played games in the slush, then bounded
into the house and sat telling stories through the February dusk,
while my sister Virginia served us bananas and coconut cookies.
To our combined astonishment Charley told the best story of all.
I was not even jealous, although it was commonly supposed that
I was the finest yarn-spinner in any group of boys. He gave us
"The Black Cat," by Edgar Allan Poe; none had ever read it,
and we hung on every word. Perhaps if the ghost of Poe stood
in the shadows of our parlor the ghost didn't recognize his own
story, but we could find no fault with Chink Morean's telling.

That was the year we all joined the Boy Scouts. Herbert had waited for me, though he could have joined earlier. But now I was a Scout, Herb and Charley were Scouts. Any one of our group could have passed his Tenderfoot tests when he was nine or ten—most of us could have passed the Second-Class tests as well. The town's Scoutmaster, Murray McMurray, was aware of the situation, and had written to headquarters urging that ten- and eleven-year-old boys be admitted. But Murray was crying in the wilderness: no one of the national powers-that-were dreamed of Cub Scouts then, or considered lowering the Scout age to eleven.

With tests and contests, Charley Morean found rare happiness. He was seldom a leader in patrol work or games, but he possessed something finer and rarer than a particular skill: an enormous love for the world and for his fellow men. He was easily the most popular boy in the Troop, if popularity might be measured by affection and not by admiration of physical strength or a knowledge of woodcraft, or the wearing of a sleeve colored with merit badges.

. . . Our 1917 camp. Charley didn't show up at the school-house yard, where we went to have bedrolls and knapsacks checked, and to await the cars driven by fathers or friends who would tote us toward enticing greenness of the Bell's Mill timberland.

A cry arose. "Where's Chink?"

Murray reminded us, "Didn't you know that his grandfather had moved back to his old farm? He said he'd drive Charley over to our camp from there."

So they came at last, an hour or two after we had taken possession of our site and erected the tents: an iron-faced man, driving in an open buggy with Charley beside him. Forty boys swept around horse and buggy in a welcoming horde. I think the world should have loved Charley Morean all the days of his life.

So the world did, the world did.

Mr. Morean told my mother that he and Grandma Morean

had decided to return to their farm purely for Charley's sake. Chink's legs were longer than ever; he was only fourteen in that year, but stood six feet tall. "He'll get a lot of benefit, working out-of-doors," said the grandfather. "He's strong, but he's skinny and flat-chested and kind of high-strung."

People who owned farms used to retire when they grew older, and let younger folks do the work instead. Mr. Morean had some small business which he had conducted for years—farm insurance, if I remember correctly. But now he went back to black-earthed land beside the Boone River, because he thought that life there would be good for the thin-faced youth who was leaping so rapidly into man-size.

Their old-new home was in the Bone's Mill region, some six miles south of town. The river curved behind the Morean place, and across the stream was a sloping forest where stood an old summer shack and picnic camp called Jones' Cabin. It was a lovely area for any sort of woodland wandering. Herbert and I treasured the notion that there might be especially rare butterflies in that region.

The possibility of a day with Charley was a joy hanging ahead. On Monday morning, July 9th, 1917, we started out on our bicycles. "Shouldn't you call up Charley, and find out whether he wants to see you?" Grandma suggested. "Maybe he has to work today." But the Moreans boasted no telephone. And as for work— Well—

We pedaled speedily down Millard's Lane and over rolling hills to the south. It was a bright hot day, with the remembrance of rain a night or two before—not the arid burning Iowa prairie summer as yet—but lush and scented, like June. We hopped from our bicycles once or twice when a clover field tempted us with myriads of small yellow butterflies flickering. Long ago we had acquired most of these as specimens—male and female of each common *Colias* species, dried neatly on pins or flattened in glass-covered Riker mounts, with no notches in their wings and no scales rubbed off. But there was a chance of acquiring a rarity, such as a Southern Dogface or a Clouded Sulphur.

Briggs' Woods lay behind us; so did the old log cabin of pioneer days, which stood out in a field and now did duty as a pigsty. Late in the forenoon we reached the Morean farm, and a country mailman had just driven down the road ahead of us. We opened Grandpa Morean's mailbox, to fetch his letters. There was one with *German American Insurance Company* printed on the envelope, and we made serious faces over this. We were newly at war with Germany. Should we report Grandpa Morean to the sheriff, or perhaps to the Iowa National Guard? Herbert knit his brows; then suggested that probably the letter was from an honest and loyal company so unfortunate as to still bear such a name.

We rode down the long side lane, whooping at Chink when we saw him in the farmyard. He was as tall as his grandfather or taller, skinny in faded blue overalls, his bright face gleaming a welcome. Yes—Charley could have the day off. His grandfather had expected him to plow corn that afternoon, but it didn't matter. Weather was fine, the last plowing of corn was almost finished; Chink could ride the cultivator next day instead.

He scampered into the house to put on his Boy Scout things. Chink would not consider going into the woods in overalls; he was determined to dress properly for an excursion, no matter how ragamuffin the attire of Herbert and myself. Soon he was with us, armed also with a knapsack of lunch and a homemade butter-fly net and killing jar (a glass jar in which to properly retain our specimens). Sun was past its height when we splashed through a shallow ford and entered the timber opposite.

Here grew the peaceful trees of our region: cottonwoods and soft maples on low ground, oaks and butternuts in higher places, with grapevines twisting down from many trunks, and a wealth of wild gooseberry and hazel bushes in between. Green woods smelled of bounty and anticipation, and every moment abounded with the flash of an oriole in flight or the haunting whicker of a flycatcher. And a rarer, darker jewel than these: an enormous black butterfly drifted above horsemint weeds like a runaway handkerchief of velvet.

We saw it, we whooped identification. *Spicebush swallow-tail!* They were not commonly found, so off we went in full cry, tangling legs and arms and nets as each tried to get the prize for himself. The spicebush swallowtail would have none of this. He lifted gracefully out of the turmoil and sought higher safer avenues among walnut trees. He left us panting through the bushes, and went off to make a bit of dinner for some eager bird, no doubt, instead of a flake of richest ebony embalmed in a collection.

Somewhere below Jones' Cabin we settled ourselves on the grass, and fed our starving bodies—trading extra radishes or crumbled cookies back and forth. It was too hot to build a fire, so we had brought no meat to cook as we usually did. Grandma had made me a package of beet-pickle sandwiches. Sounds like an odd sort of food, but I did love them.

I have never eaten a beet-pickle sandwich since.

. . . We swam in cool contentment in a broad patch of quiet water opposite the old picnic cabin. Here the river, so shallow at a bend below or around a bend above, spread brown and slow-moving. At intervals along that stream the current had gouged to considerable depth among glacial boulders, and these natural swimming pools were called holes. Some of them were ten or twelve feet deep normally, and still deep enough to drown a man even when the river had shrunken in drouth and lay scummy beneath the press of dog days in August.

The prescribed hour-and-a-half or two-hour interval after eating had been observed while we explored the woods at a slow pace. Then we took off our clothes and flung them on a dry gravel bar. No boy ever thought of donning a bathing suit unless he went swimming at Scout camp, or in one of the holes near town. In ordinary fashion we were naked as at birth, though it paid to keep an eye out for the approach of a picnic party or a group of country women and children come fishing.

None of us had ever had a swimming lesson in his life. In some manner or other we had learned to swim, crudely but effectively, when very small. We used the primitive dog-paddle stroke, and tried later to teach ourselves side-stroke, back-stroke and a floundering sort of crawl.

Thus we ambled and rolled in the water, wading the shallows to hunt for fresh-water clams or crawdaddies, then romping back to tussle and splash and try to duck one another. Growing tired of these antics, we swam across to a mass of rocks below a high claybank on the opposite side, and sat on the largest stone. We talked about everything from war to butterflies.

I shut my eyes and let the sun pound me. There was an enormous satisfaction—at thirteen, and after four years of snow and heat drudgery—to find myself freed from the stern demands of regular paper route hours. Generously my mother had let me stop carrying papers after I entered high school the previous fall, so that I could have time to join in dramatic and glee club activities. I even "went out for" cross-country running, but soon gave it up. The other runners were all seniors grown to the stature of manhood; they loped far ahead while I trotted miserably along the road after them. I was only five-feet-two, and the next-to-the-shortest boy in our class. No long pants for me, though I begged unceasingly.

There were plenty of ways to earn money—far better than a paper route. In any gardening season our truck-farmer neighbor, Wesley Frank, was glad to hire extra hands for hoeing or strawberry picking. He paid a notoriously small wage, but at least it was money. And during this very summer I had gathered in a satisfying sum for taking the school census; and there were always trees to be trimmed or lawns to be mowed for old ladies who lived alone and needed such tasks done. . . .

The river chuckled softly at a distant rocky sluice which we called riffles. The lunch had given joy to my body, just as the voices of my friends brought pleasure to my ears.

Pioneering. . . . Herbert and I planned to build a shack soon, or a bridge, and thus qualify for that particular merit badge. And the Terry's Uncle Tom's Cabin tent show would be coming to town soon, and a yellow-haired girl named Leona Teget had hinted that—well, almost, not quite, she wasn't

sure—but, if her mother would let her—maybe she might go
to the tent show with me. And we would each have a box of
Cracker Jack; and the Uncle Tom's Cabin people announced
on their advance bills that they had *two* Markses and *two*
Topsies. If one Lawyer Marks and one Topsy were funny,
two ought to be twice as funny. . . .

The sun stared. Idly we sang ditties aloud, the river talked,
the flycatchers chittered in faraway thickets.

Herbert said, "It's getting kind of late."

"Sure is."

"That's a long way for us to ride, back to town. Hadn't we
better get going?"

Chink asked eagerly, "Why'n't you guys stay all night? We
could go over to Pierces' place and call your folks—Pierces' have
got a phone. Grandma'd be glad to have you."

But Herbert had to accompany his mother to Fort Dodge
early the next day, and a date with a lawnmower awaited me.
So back we swam to get our clothes. We would carry shoes and
socks, and thus wade through the ford on a return trip after we
were dressed.

In leisurely file we crossed the serene river—Herbert first, then
myself, with Chink coming after us. Herbert was already out,
and on the gravel reaching for his clothes, when my hands
began to touch bottom. I stood up in shallow water, then turned
quickly. Chink was still out in the middle of the river, and he
was making dreadful sounds.

He skirmished and flapped, his hands were splashing aimlessly, his mouth seemed pulled half below the surface. He was
saying, "Hey, guys. Hey, guys," or this is what we thought he
was saying; but it was a croaking and gobbling noise, as if he
cried in a foreign language.

And for Charley Morean, of all people, to do such a stunt.
Any boy ought to know better than to pretend that he was having trouble, when of course he couldn't really be having trouble.
Drownings: those were things you read about in the paper. They
happened off at summer resorts and such places.

Clear Lake, Ia.—May 31, 1917. A tragic accident occurred here yesterday when Miss Louella Wethred, 18, of Mason City, was drowned while swimming with a group of friends. The party had come to the lake for a Memorial Day picnic, and Miss Wethred, who could not swim, had—

But Chink could swim. Why should he be flopping his hands, and bobbing about, and making that uncouth appeal?

I heard my own short laughter rise and die, and Herbert's laugh did the same. Suddenly we knew that this was truth, this was dangerous, there was no jest in it. Then we were both in the river, swimming toward Charley as fast as we could go. Since I was closer at the start, I got there first.

Try to approach the person from behind.

That was what it said, or words to that effect, in one of the handbooks. So I tried. But he whirled around as I reached him, and his eyes were nearly shut, and his face looked like the face of an utter stranger. This couldn't be Chink. Something had happened to him. Sunstroke? We didn't know.

A great claw seized me above the left knee. It clamped as the arm of an octopus must clamp, or the coil of a boa constrictor (my leg was black and blue afterward, where those talons had gripped). Under we went, and down, and down, deep, deep. Silver lights came bursting inside my skull. Even amid those frantic muddy depths I tried to speak to Chink. But water was in my nose and eyes, and he seemed stronger than one of the horses he should have been driving with the cultivator.

I remembered vaguely something about breaking a clutch. *Put your foot against the stomach, and shove—* My right foot went twisting around, seeking, and then it found Charley's body, and I shoved. The metal clutch broke free, I was swimming back and up, and breaking surface at last. I sobbed for life and air again. As I blinked I saw the sun above, round and glaring— the kind sun now a demon.

Herbert was near, swimming in circles, watching for Chink to come up.

I gasped, "Don't try to handle him. He's too big."

"He hasn't come up—"

"Maybe he'll come—"

Herbert lifted his arm in the middle of a stroke. "Stump!" He pointed.

A stump it was—old, bone-dry, lodged on the edge of the stream. Curling roots lifted like parched fingers. The stump would float like an enormous misshapen piece of cork, and might serve as a raft or diving platform when we sought to bring Charley up from the bottom.

But he was up before us, washed closer toward the lower end of the wide pool, and how he had forced his way from such depths we might never know. We sped to shore, wrenched the stump loose, towed it back. Not only a diving platform—it might now be a lifeboat for Chink Morean.

We saw the top of his wet head as he struggled, one hand scattering the water, and he was making those ugly sounds no longer. "Chink! Chink!" Herbert yelled at the top of his lungs, but it was like trying to call to someone at the other end of a long field. By this time Charley was off in some hidden wilderness of his own, unhearing and unheeding.

Just before we had the stump fairly within his reach, he hoisted both arms on high and went straight down. He did not appear again. Herbert swam desperately about, hunting beneath the river as long as he could stand it, then coming up to gulp for breath again.

I was on shore, pulling on trousers and shoes.

"Get down to that riffle," I yelled over my shoulder, and began to run. At such a narrow rocky rapids the current always poured stronger . . . perhaps it would catch Chink's body and roll him along in the gush so that Herbert could find him, drag him out, and maybe save him with artificial respiration.

The Ruppel farmhouse and barns stood well up a timbered slope behind the old Jones' shanty; it was at some distance; when you were well away from the riverside you could barely see a pale small house on a ridge above. I tore past basswood trees, then found the twisting track by which automobiles or buggies

An Extry Plate for Charley   59

might drive near the cabin. Along this path I raced, watching
ahead as I neared the house. A telephone wire sagged from the
eaves. Thank God, the Ruppels had a telephone.

"Anybody home?" as I reached the nearest barn. "Anybody
home? Help! Boy drowning—" For answer came only a squawk
of guinea hens, and the roaring of a big brown-yellow dog.

He came raging toward me. I snatched up a spoke or tool
handle and drove him off. No one was at home. Not a flicker of
life from the house—and wheel-tracks creased the dirt toward the
lane, to show where the Ruppels had driven away. No hired
man, no anybody. Sun and shade patterned the little house,
horribly silent, horribly cozy.

I tried to enter. My soul was striving toward the telephone
instrument, but the big dog resisted. He was nearly as afraid of
me as I was of him, but he was snapping; I ought never to have
struck at him in the first place. He circled swiftly, tore my
trouser leg, dodged away, came snarling back. This wouldn't
do—I was losing precious minutes. And maybe the house was
locked. The Pierce home must be the next nearest place, and it
was a mile away or such a matter, back on the Moreans' side of
the river.

The Albright bridge was built to take a back road across the
river, two bends above the hole where Chink had vanished. It
was a long way from the Ruppels' by road, but half the distance
could be saved if I cut across a lower pasture. I rolled under a
barbed-wire fence and dashed down across the field. Cattle
lifted their heads, watching. Then I heard a growl and flurry of
feet, the dog was after me again, he thought he had me on the
run.

He came worrying along, clashing his jaws and trying to
nip my ankles. Then the cattle charged. They hated the dog as
cattle often do; they plunged with lowered heads, pouncing and
stamping, swinging their tails. The dog and I were become a
single enemy of the herd, and more big beasts were swinging in
ahead to cut us off. I darted to the left. Behind me rose the
dog's *yipe, yipe* as he was hurt by a flying hoof. I flung one

glance as I staggered through the fence wires, tearing my trousers again and gashing my leg. The dog was headed for home with steers after him.

. . . I thought of cross-country training at high school, and brawny seniors speeding with their giants' stride ahead of me. Dully I wished that one of them were with me now, to run with good success the awful race where I was plunging toward failure. I knew it well, felt it in aching legs and red-hot chest and gaping mouth. Chink was dead. No use . . . but there was nothing to do but shove my feet high and forward, a *thump-trot-thump* across the red-painted bridge.

And summer weeds of lowlands crushed up solid along that road, higher than a man's head . . . weeds smelled of peculiar wet mysteries. I pounded my way toward the hill. Crows were hollering in woods over back of the McConnell farm, and the sun glared and punished.

The hill road turned and taunted. It was like Pike's Peak which I had seen on a postcard: a mountain which hurt, blindly, powerfully. Then I was at the top and the barricade of weeds was gone. Ahead on the right loomed an orchard of fat cherry trees, round and reddened, stuffed with purest fruit. The Pierce house . . . not too far . . . I could see the road junction ahead, where Herb and I had spun so gaily a few hours earlier.

Voices beside me—they came from on high. Mr. and Mrs. Pierce, up on ladders, laden with baskets, picking cherries, and never knowing that Death had come to bathe in the river close at hand. I heard them, and then I was on the grass with dust in my nostrils.

"Boy drowning," I heard a dry voice saying.

Mr. Pierce clambered with fright and suspicion through the fence. "Come on, what's this? What's the matter?"

"Boy drowning. . . ."

They put me on their sofa in the house, while Mr. Pierce talked to the fire department in Webster City over the telephone. Officials had a new Pulmotor at the firehouse, for use in cases of drowning and asphyxiation; I believe that it had never been used before.

Mrs. Pierce gave me some sips of water. I felt able to accompany the farmer in search of further help. He cranked up the engine of his Ford, and we drove into an adjacent cornfield. There was no sense in going for Grandpa and Grandma Morean: they could have done nothing. Instead we sought out Orville Berryhill, a broad-shouldered red-haired young man who had a neighborhood reputation as a good swimmer and general athlete.

He was plowing corn in this field, and the ground was dry enough for the Ford to churn its way through. Orville drove his cultivator and team into some shade, and went with us toward the claybank cliff of the river, unfastening his clothes as he sat in the bouncing Ford.

Scarcely had we reached the brink above the river when we could see a touring car rocking down through trees on the other side of the stream. How those men had ever gathered themselves together, gathered up the Pulmotor, and driven six miles from Webster City in a 1917 car on 1917 roads, is something to wonder at. Yet here they were, only ten or fifteen minutes after the urgent telephone summons: Bill Frazier, the fire chief; one of the firemen named Ora Newman; and Dr. W. W. Wyatt.

"Where is he?" they called, laboring along with the weight of the Pulmotor. They cursed when they found that Charley was still in the river. Through that weak buzzing on the country line they had gained a notion that the drowned boy was already removed from the water.

They hunted steadily. Fire chief and fireman were stripped down to their underwear, so was Orville Berryhill. They brought a broad wooden door from the picnic cabin and used that for a raft—our stump could not carry their weight. Dr. Wyatt and Mr. Pierce stood on the shore and offered advice, and Herbert and I were ordered to dress. "Pretty soon some women might be coming down here," we were told. We stood aimlessly, crying a little . . . brown depths so sullen . . . how did Charley feel now?

One of the men's voices called, "Think I've got him. Touched something right about here," and Orville dove down to catch hold of the boy and tow him toward shore. No resistance from Chink now, no movement, no mighty hand clawing to grasp you. I never saw anyone look so thoroughly soaked. It was as if that long-ribbed body could hold nothing but water within it. He didn't look frightening and disgusting, he merely looked soaked, like a little girl's doll lost in a garden pool.

His eyes were squinted more than ever, and one foot was twisted. The doctor said that this might have been a cramp which caused his first struggles; on the other hand, it might have occurred after he sank.

For nearly an hour the men plied the Pulmotor handle, trying different speeds and pressures. They had dumped a surprisingly small amount of water out of Chink's lungs, and swaddled his face with the rubber mask. Even Herbert and I were allowed to relieve the men at the pump under their supervision: we wanted to do something. . . . We were past crying. We could only stare, and move about in silence.

Questioning us closely, Dr. Wyatt estimated that it was at least forty-five minutes from the time Charley went down for the last time, until he was pulled to land. The doctor shook his head, and motioned for the men to cease their work with the motor. Tenderly he opened a vein in Charley's arm. The blood was black. "Must have been dead all that time," said Dr. Wyatt. "Could have been a heart attack."

We put Charley's clothes back on him, and draped his face with a handkerchief. One of the men fastened Charley's Scout hat on the boy's head, though Herbert and I thought it would have been better if they had left the hat off, and I still think so.

My mother told of it afterward . . . the first thing she saw, when she and Mrs. Arthur came through the woods by the Ruppel farm, was that tan slouch hat, bobbing along as men carried Charley.

Mother was editing the weekly *Herald*, owned by Senator Cady Chase. Someone had called her at the *Herald* office, and told her they thought she ought to know, for the paper— A boy had just been drowned, swimming down below the Albright Bridge. Mother knew that corner of the country well, she had been born in it. She knew also that Herbert and I had ridden to Charley's for the day, and that we were bound to go swimming.

She called the widowed Mrs. Minnie Arthur. They got a man to drive them, and rode in the back seat along those hot miles, holding hands, never knowing which boy was drowned, each woman fearing that it was her own son.

. . . Funeral at the Methodist Church in town a couple of days later. Herbert and I were honorary pallbearers. We couldn't be active pallbearers because we weren't big enough and strong enough to help carry Charley's gray coffin. We escorted him to a slope just behind the old soldiers' memorial plot in our cemetery. Every Boy Scout bore a bouquet of flowers to cover Charley with. There he lay then, there he lies today.

. . . Grandma Morean kept begging for Herbert and me to come down and get our bicycles; she'd feel better just talking to us boys, she insisted. But it was long before we could force ourselves into going. Then we went, hiking and hitchhiking in a morning as bright as the July 9th through which we had first ridden.

Grandpa Morean, looking years older than before, stood under a tree in the farmyard with a knowing look on his sad face. He was just throwing an empty shell out of his gun.

He touched a motionless squirrel with his shoe. "Close enough to autumn, now," he said. "Squirrel will stew pretty well. Come on in the house and Grandma'll start to fix some dinner."

He lowered his voice, and his piteous and pitiful old-lined face came close to us. "Don't mention about that extry plate to Grandma, when you see it on the table. She always sets an extry plate, for Charley."

III. THE COLUMN AND THE CROWDS

1.

Rapidly I became ruled by desire to hold a job in the Loop. Then Irene and I could be together at lunch each working day; and, hopefully, I might earn more money than I was making at the American Flyer.

I arrived at this elite status through the offices of The Phantom Lover. The Phantom Lover was one in R.H.L.'s stable of minor writers who filled the "Line O' Type" column with their contributions, and his true name was Henry V. Stevenson. Big of frame, golden-gray of hair, and thickly bespectacled, he cut a figure when the "Line" crowd appeared in public—say, at a radio station or lyceum engagement. His appearance and his delivery of stanzas were cooed at and over by susceptible ladies.

He appreciated verse forms all the way from Herrick to Leigh Hunt and back again, and applied those styles lightly in an ironic and somewhat limp-wristed gait, thereby winning an amused following of readers. We called him Harry. I have never been able to conclude just how my own friendship with him came about, because I was definitely interested in the female sex, and the female sex only. The Phantom Lover shared his apartment with a nervous companion who stamped the floor when he was peeved, and cried, "Harry, how could you *do* such a thing?" However, the fact that our romantic inclinations were not akin had nothing to do with the high regard in which he was held by other members of the group. Snowshoe Al

Bromley, a hard-boiled little satirist from downstate Illinois, liked Harry immensely; so did I, so did several of the tough-scarred war veteran relics in our crew. We all loved to play poker, and played it assiduously whenever we could get enough money together. We did not play for extreme stakes, but high enough to make a loss hurt and to make a win mirthful.

Henry Stevenson served as private secretary to Mr. Coyne, manager of Mandel Brothers. He appeared in this function with diplomatic elegance. I had visited him at his office a time or two previously, but now I was hatching an idea.

The first time I was again sent on an errand to the downtown district, the task was performed with speed enough to permit a sortie to Mandels'. In accord with my needs, Mr. Coyne was gone out of town, and Harry presided in regal state—not too occupied to welcome me with cordiality, as a duke might greet a more-or-less faithful commoner.

"Harry," I said, "I've heard about claim correspondents in stores. Also I've heard about advertising departments in stores. Do you think I could get a job here? I'm a writer, first and foremost."

He turned on me a gaze benign and searching, and stroked his waved hair in thought. A former Notre Dame student, he had entered the novitiate in one of the Church Orders; but some shrewd priest persuaded him into what might be termed a course of lay activity.

"My dear Mack, I can scarcely envision you in a department store!"

"Oh, come on! You must have four thousand employees: they're not all going to turn out to be Marshall Fields. There must be something to do here, where whatever aptitude I possess at writing can benefit Mandel Brothers. I've written advertising copy before—"

He said, "The advertising department is sacrosanct. Furthermore, I'm continually at war with them. Except for the employment of casual sales help, it would petrify you to find what a closed club a large department store may be. There are all sorts of juntos and cliques, in various capacities. A friend is introduced, and then a friend of the friend comes along, and, if fortunate, is introduced to the reigning dignitary—"

Harry shook his impressive head. "No advertising, I fear. But you mentioned claim correspondence. A gentleman named Russell is the manager of our adjustment bureau. Actually I feel that he might like to talk to you. I'll find out whether he is free. . . ."

Quickly I was sitting with Mr. Russell, a bullet-headed Scotsman with iron-gray hair, an intense stare, and an authentic brogue.

"Young man, Mr. Stevenson tells me that you're a writer—that you have capability in handling the written word. What is your experience?"

"I more or less grew up on a small-town newspaper, sir."

"Why aren't you working on a newspaper in Chicago?"

"Because it's very difficult for a small-town guy to come to Chicago and get a job on one of your big city dailies. They've got waiting lists ten miles long . . . people graduating from journalism school up at Northwestern. . . ."

"Aye, I suppose you're correct, it must be difficult. What else have you published?"

I spoke of *College Humor,* and he shook his head about that. But when I mentioned the "Line O' Type" column he responded warmly.

"I know you now, I've read you there. You're not bad, not bad. And your Christian name's MacKinlay. Tell me, how did you get that to go with the name of Kantor?"

I explained that it was my mother's name. When I mentioned that her father's family came from Dunfermline in Fife, he smiled.

"I know the place, it's a fine wee town. Well, young man, so you'd like to try your hand at being a claim correspondent? I don't know whether you could be one or not, but we'll give you a trial. Here—I'll scribble a note to the proper person."

In parting, his shaggy brows went up and he peered over

his spectacles. "'The king,'" he quoted, "'sits in Dunfermline town, drinking the blude-red wine.'"

I bowed in reply. "'O whare will I get a skeely skipper, to sail this new ship o' mine?'"

Mr. Russell slapped his hand on the desk. "You know it, lad, you know it. It's good for any man to know Sir Patrick Spens!"

In that hour I became the first airman to fly via helicopter from the northeast corner of Madison and State streets to the east side of Halsted Street at 2219–39. I confessed to Mr. Chambers what I had been up to. That was when he tried to dissuade me, but admitted candidly that he didn't believe I'd have much of a future with the American Flyer. So he rejoiced that I was to earn a whole thirty dollars per week, and also— guess where?—across the street from Irene.

"Phone an ad in to the papers for me," he directed. This I did with glee. It didn't come at too bad a time: already we'd got the jobbers' catalogues out of the way . . . it was just the slow business of Chambers having to break in a new man on a job where I had served only a few months. I agreed to finish out the week and to help him in interviewing applicants, since I wasn't due to begin at Mandels' until the following Monday morning.

Departing on Saturday, I observed Mr. Cuff pacing close, and concluded that he was on the job to prevent me from stealing stationery. I did have some, but the tiger missed his kill: the stationery remained inside my shirt until I got home. If I looked a little bulky, the public probably concluded that it was merely a bulletproof vest underneath.

2.

In fleeing the toy factory and exchanging it for an imagined sinecure on State Street, I gave up certain benefits. No longer could I get my work out of the way, and then sit and dream before the misty odoriferous horizon, and stipple it with pioneer

shades to populate my ballads. There existed no zinc-topped
tables, no fenced-off cubicle, no freight elevator to warn a dozing
writer with its clangor. I sat at a desk in an area where other
correspondents sat at theirs, and with regularity the information
regarding each letter to be written was placed in a basket. A
slim pool of secretaries took our dictation and typed the letters.
I had hoped that the routine might prove exhilarating—like all
adventurers, I was eager to peek into a new compartment of
existence— But there ensued small thrill in explaining to Mrs.
Nimbkin that Mandel Brothers deeply regretted that her ashtray
was delivered to her in a broken condition; or in informing Mrs.
Dumbunny that Mandel Brothers deeply regretted the fact that
they had sent her six pairs of 8½ beige stockings, rather than
the six pairs of 10½ off-black hose which she insisted she had
ordered.

The first day of my department store career was celebrated
with Irene in revelry of luncheon at the nearby Stevens Tea
Room, where moderate pomp and circumstance accompanied
a fifty-five-cent *table d'hôte* meal.

Next day the well-meaning Henry Stevenson performed a
distinct disfavor in inviting me to lunch at that same tearoom.
I knew nothing of the fraternities and sororities which abounded
in organizations like ours, and thus became the target of contempt in the eyes of colleagues nestled near. I was absent
from the office because of a notation, "See Buyer on this, before
writing letter," and I had gone, true to trust, to see the Buyer.
When I came back, there was a note waiting. "Mr. Stevenson,
secretary to Mr. Coyne, would like you to lunch with him
at 12:15." Fellow correspondents regarded me with suspicion
and cynicism to say the least, and in some cases with downright
dread. Why had I been singled out for a social engagement by
one of the Austere from Upstairs? Why had I been put here in
the first place? Probably I was a spy . . . they were determined
to regard me as such.

We were not supposed to use our telephones for personal
conversations. I scooted out to one of the public telephones

placed for benefit of customers, called Irene in the picture-framing department at Carson's, and explained that I couldn't have lunch with her after all. I went along and joined The Phantom Lover and his associates.

I didn't know just who they were . . . several junior executives from upstairs . . . Harry did his best to make me feel at home among them, but that was impossible. They nailed me with barbed glances. One or two managed to say, "Oh, yes, I've heard about you. You write rhymes, don't you?" and then they went off into the deeper business of store politics. It was no wedding of angels. I pleaded that a mound of work awaited me, and excused myself while they were still at the table. I tried to reciprocate socially to The Phantom Lover a time or two, but he was always dated up, and thus ensued a certain relief. I acquired the tacit knowledge that a claim correspondent should not invite the boss's secretary to lunch, although the boss's secretary might choose to invite *him*. Nor had anything occurred to lull the suspicion of my associates, or decrease the hostility they bestowed.

Along with the common mass of customers, I had gained the belief that department stores banded together in a campaign to defraud the public; but now I was sitting on the other side of the desk. I found it true, believed it reverently: customers were banded together in a common campaign to defraud department stores.

I was a larcenist: stationery stolen from the American Flyer, a teaspoon filched from the Ontra cafeteria, and I was considering a pair of salt-and-pepper shakers from Stevens'. But such defaults seemed petty compared to the cumbersome misrepresentations of our patrons. I took it upon myself to protect Mandels' pocketbook with the stability of a Negro slave who had been owned by the same family for seventy years. If those jayhawkers sought to dig up Mandels' silver, I must brandish a scythe to prevent them from doing so.

There existed a couple of supervisors in our department who lost little time in bringing my correspondence to the attention

of higher authority. For a few days I saw my letters being
carried off somewhere, instead of being sealed and stamped to
go out with the regular mail. Next I was told, "Mr. Russell wants
to see you at three p.m." and there shone a few anticipatory
smiles in the background.

With alarm I approached the interview, feeling that I might
be turned out into the street before achieving my second pay
envelope. Seated in Mr. Russell's office, it was obvious on the
instant that he was the dentist and I the patient who had a
very large hole in his tooth or in his head or somewhere.

Several of my letters were spread before him.

"Lad." He motioned for his secretary to leave the office. "How
can I say it? Your letters are vastly incorrect—"

I murmured that I had thought they were well written. . . .

"Well written? Ah, no," and he made a face. "The English is
all right, I'll grant you that. But you're not polite."

"I— I thought they were courteous—"

"Courteous? What is courtesy, if at the same moment you
are punishing the customer? Actually *castigating* her! What
then, laddie?" He shoved a letter toward me. "Here, take a look,
and read it back to yourself this very minute."

I read it, and nodded. "Yes, Mr. Russell, I remember this one.
The customer is Mrs. Squitt, and she ruined a two-piece knit
dress. She claimed that she never even tried it on. It said *See
Buyer* on the claim, so I went to the Buyer. He said they couldn't
take it back in stock. 'Look at this,' he said. 'Here's the garment
in question. Look at that: all the little threads pulled out by
hooks on her foundation garment. Of course she tried to squeeze
into it, and she was just too damn fat. Why, I've got here a piece
of merchandise which I can't sell if I take it back in stock. I won't
do that.'"

It seemed that Mr. Russell and I might share a common
Scottish descendant devotion to Killiecrankie, Culloden, *Rab and
His Friends*, or the unfortunate Jerome Russell who was burned
at the stake in Glasgow, for heresy, in 1539— We might contain
mutual faith in Sir Patrick Spens and Sir Walter Scott, and in

heather and collies; but we were vastly apart in our knowledge of the handling of Mandels' customers.

"You see, the customer was asking for *credit*. She wanted full credit on the garment—"

"But the Buyer wouldn't—"

"I don't care what the Buyer said. This should be taken care of by other means. Did you look up the details on her account? Naw, you did nothing of the kind. Do you realize Mrs. Squitt spent a total of two thousand, two hundred and eighty-seven dollars and sixteen cents—here, across the counter in Mandel Brothers—during the calendar year just past? God, lad, if we sent *your* letter to her, in which you were censuring her severely for this performance—"

"But, Mr. Russell, when a customer—"

"I don't care what a customer does. You've got to consider the average. You've got to consider what it costs *us*. Costs us? We refund completely, if it's a cheap dress like this, down in the basement. She took it home and then she tried it on; and it'll cost us but seventeen dollars to write it off. What would she do if she read your letter? She'd close her account at Mandel Brothers and go to Marshall Field's, that's what she'd do. She might even go to *Davis* Brothers! Think of that! A customer of Mandels'—An over-two-thousand-dollars-a-year customer at Mandels'—And she goes to Davises'!"

I sighed. "O.K., Mr. Russell. Shall I leave the store now, or wait until the end of the week?"

He peered through his glasses, shook his head, muttered something, and then strangely he reached across the desk and took my hand.

"Don't be absurd, MacKinlay. I said nothing about your leaving the store. You've got a good mind—at least I think you have— and you can learn. Now, here's what I want you to do: I want you to go into the third subway where the claim tracers are, and really learn something about claims and the tracing of them. You've got to learn about the store, you've got to learn about the customers! You've got to learn about the various departments and their ways and means. You've got to learn about nondeliveries, and breakage, and all the ramifications that exist in dealing in the mercantile trade. I tell you this: I think you can catch on to things. Tracers earn but twenty-four dollars per week, but we'll keep paying you thirty, as agreed in the first place, because of future possibilities. And—"

His homiletics concluded, he arose in emphasis.

"Now, then. Run down to the third subway, find Mr. Frank— he's in charge of tracers there, and tell him— Never mind, I'll have my secretary give him a ring and say that you're on the way. We'll make a merchant out of you yet!"

In leaving Mr. Russell I tried to remember . . . was there anything personal in my desk or on it, which I would need to retrieve? I had no wish to go back among those correspondents again, to witness their smirking. . . . On the other hand, wouldn't it be more of a satisfaction to them, to witness the fact that I *didn't return at all?* . . . My pipe? I felt for it; it was in the side pocket of my jacket. Tobacco pouch? Yes, in the hip pocket. Anything else?

I knew now: a knife which I'd owned in boyhood and treasured ever since. I'd used it to cut the grime off an eraser— Didn't I have a couple of poems, come back with rejection slips? I'd stuck those in my top drawer. No use—I had to go in.

Everybody was busy, or seemed busy . . . two people dictating. They left off dictating when I rose from my desk. Suddenly I felt intrepid, and desired to yield to showmanship. I needed a good exit line, and found it.

"I'm going to be a claim tracer," I said, "in the third subway. I'll see if I can't raise a little more hell for you correspondents," and they were frozen as I went out.

Down the escalator, down a second escalator from first floor to basement, down a stairway to the first subway which was also a basement bargain-counter; down a second stairway; along a ramp. I'd never been in this catacomb before . . . it was a dark place, with caging surrounding an amphitheater where parcels were wrapped for delivery. A row of metal lockers . . .

these belonged to tracers and telephone girls . . . then into the bright tracer bureau itself. Desks parceled out along the walls, and a second room beyond where switchboard girls sat.

Mr. Frank, a large owlish young man, held court at the head of the first room. "Yes, they told me you were coming down. You can take that desk over there next to Dubrowski. Put away that pipe. No smoking here."

He lowered his voice in the first cordiality he had shown. "None of us dares to smoke down here," he said. "But maybe you'll learn to put a piece of thin Climax in the side of your jaw, the way some of the rest of us do. There's a big wooden box here behind my desk, to use. We can't have spittoons out in sight. You just read a bunch of claims for the rest of the afternoon. Then in the morning I'll send you out with one of the tracers, and you can see how he works."

His eyes roved the room, and he called out, "Popejoy!"

The young man sauntered forward, languid and nonchalant. Soon I would discover that he wished to become a composer of popular songs, and held talent in that direction.

"Here, Pope," Mr. Frank said, "this is Kantor." And to me, "Pope knows his onions about claim-tracing."

He continued, "Pope, take Kantor with you, beginning to-morrow morning. Let him follow you on your rounds and see what you do. Then he can take claims of his own the next day, and start in. I understand"—Frank scoured me with ascetic gaze—"that Mr. Kantor was a claim correspondent *very briefly*. Now he'd like to really learn something about the adjustment bureau."

Boy. Did I learn.

3.

Irene and I quavered amid a matrimony which wasn't quite matrimony, and this didn't seem fair. True—we could have most noontimes together, which wasn't commonly the lot of newly-

weds in a city, and we could have our evenings. But it seemed
ridiculous to continue spending the nights apart. This was a
cringing existence which neither of us admired. At least I was
the tenant of an eight-dollar-a-week hall bedroom into which I
might escort my wife officially. What was I waiting for, anyway?
Divine intercession?

Surely Irene had nothing to fear from parental or family disapproval. There might be a scene—might be exclamations and
adjurations, even tears; then it would be over.

What was scaring me? My mother principally, I had to con-
fess. Oh, there were the debts and creditors . . . the voiced
disgust at a young man's taking on fresh obligation when already
he had obligations which he couldn't fulfill. But if our marriage
was to be the treasure which we hoped it would become, then
let it glisten in the light of acknowledgment.

One Saturday evening we sat in darkness and thick summery
fog, on the shore north of Lawrence Avenue. This was a lonely
spot, with waves murmuring at the foot of nearby jetties. My
jacket had been spread over a patch of dry sand, and we were
huddled on it—arms wrapped, voices muted—when suddenly a
man and a woman materialized out of the night.

They went directly past us, unseeing, contending. The man
came first, the woman scrambled behind . . . staggering a little
. . . she could have been drunk, we didn't know. The man
stalked with purpose, the unhappy female trailed lugubriously
on his path.

She was opposite when she burst into frantic plea. Her words
seemed especially shocking, wrenched out as they were with no
preliminary, no introduction.

"If you leave me now, I'll just lie down here on the sand and
die!"

His reply came floating within seconds. "Die. I don't care,"
and then they were both gone into blackness.

. . . Instantaneous peek at minor romantic tragedy, at least
momentary tragedy, as if it were the single frame of a talking
motion picture (not yet circulated) flashing swift. Being sedate

in affirmed and practiced love, we were selfish enough to find only amusement in this witnessing. Whatever cleavage had come between those two, we did not know; in heedless fashion we did not care. We saw only a man pressing forward, a woman abject in her following.

Lie down . . . and die. . . . Die. I don't care.

We indulged in laughter all the way to the Layne apartment, and were still a-giggle the next afternoon. However, we began to find a lesson in the sadly distinct words as remembered.

Irene voiced belated charity. "You know, perhaps it's not as funny as we think."

I agreed, and carried it further. "Suppose one of us should die in the night. It doesn't seem likely, but just suppose. How would the other one know? And when?—and where?"

"And how?—and why?" she cried. In that moment we found no further logic in remaining apart.

It was a question of informing the Authorities, so we filed away to inform them. I would make a telephone call to Iowa that evening when rates were cheaper.

Charles Layne was reading the paper, and Jessie the step-mother was in their bedroom, putting on her hat to go with him for a walk.

Some of our bravado had vanished. "Dad," came Irene's small voice. I said, "Mr. Layne," as limply.

He looked up, glancing from one face to the other.

Irene said, "We've got something to tell you," and turned to me.

"We want you to hear some news, sir. Irene and I are married."

He half-rose out of his chair and then slouched back. "Jessie, come here! Come here this minute!"

Mrs. Layne dashed through the hallway, wondering what catastrophe had befallen.

He gestured toward us. "Do you know what these two—darn fools—have gone and done?"

"Charles—not married?" and Mr. Layne bobbed in affirmation. He wiped his eyes, but was smiling as he did so. Affectionate embraces were awarded . . . no blessing requested or bestowed. Irene's three surviving brothers were informed, then and during the next few days. *Well. Congratulations!*

We went up to the apartment of her considerably elder sister, Ruth, on Winthrop Avenue, to tell our story. Ruth began to cry, and I demanded with vigor, "What the hell are you crying about?"

"Oh, I always wanted Irene to have nice things!" wailed the poor woman. She burst into a real boo-hoo, just at the moment when her husband Bob Bennett had come over to shake hands.

The bride kissed her sister, while I was ready to make a fight of it. Irene shook her head, and kissed Ruth again.

"Of course you've always wanted me to have nice things, and I know it and appreciate it. But let me tell you a secret: Mack is going to see that I *have* nice things."

No bridegroom could desire sounder confirmation than that. We ended up with Ruth's drying her eyes, and our all going out to a dairy lunch together.

Irene had packed a bag for the night; in lively mood we swept to Cambridge Avenue. My landlord and landlady, the Albert H. Norrises, were playing the usual nickel-dime ante which they played often with several lodgers. I left Irene in my room and went back down to see Pop Norris. We had grown to be friends.

"Pop?"

He came out into the hall, wiping his glasses.

"Yes?" His wife was right behind him, fearing lest some minor disaster had taken place. One night a drunken tenant sought to brain the gentle Mr. Norris with a galvanized garbage can, and I'd managed to prevent such disaster by knocking the assailant flat. I was skeletal in shape but necessarily had learned to give battle under urgent conditions.

"I wanted to tell you: Irene and I are married. We were married on July 2nd, and she's going to live with me now."

He cried, "For goodness sake! Wonderful, wonderful!" and patted me on the back. Mrs. Norris said flatly, "That's nice.

She's a lovely-looking girl. But I hope you understand that your room, double, comes at ten dollars. Wear and tear. Extra linens —towels and—"

I said, "It won't be essential for you to put in a bed for us, Mrs. Norris. We'll just use the same day-bed which opens out—"

"Yes, but when the room is double, it rents for—"

"Lillian," said Pop, "you go back and fill that inside straight of yours." When she was returned to the poker table, he whispered, "It'll just be the same eight dollars, the way it's been before. Don't worry, I'll talk Lillian into it. I always have to talk to her about these petty things. You know how she is. But— Suppose I give you the extra laundering on towels for a wedding present?" He clapped me on the back again, and we were happy.

The big worry was Mother. I didn't want to talk to her on one of those public telephones which sat on shelves in side halls. No, thanks.

It was a chilly evening, and I went up and lit a fire, which was ready on the hearth for any grand occasion. There were plenty of splinters in the basement—pieces of old packing cases and the like. Sometimes I'd find a fallen branch in the park, and break off pieces and carry them home: we'd have logs to burn.

I hugged Irene, said, "I'll be back pretty soon," and went over to the United Cigar Store at Diversey and Broadway. Got my change, and piled it up in the booth.

Mother was half Scottish, with a bit of English and Pennsylvania German in her inheritance. But one of her grandmothers was a Bryan, and bogs and emerald hills and thatched cottages were often in her face. She could look and sound like a banshee with a lost voice, and I knew how her eyes were brooding.

Our telephone conversation was unpleasant in many ways, and extremely one-sided.

"Mother, are you still on the line?"

Remote wailing from the fens. . . . "Yes, son."

"I was afraid we'd been disconnected. Well, I know what the

creditors in Webster City are going to say, and I don't give a damn. Sorry—you hate profanity—but I want to make this as emphatic as possible—"

(Mother abominated profanity up and down the line, and came close to swooning when she heard an obscene word. Her attitude was taken with some good reason, since Grandpa McKinlay employed such language only when he was in fury, and wife and daughter had best keep out of his way. Once, when I was eight or nine, I got in a fight with a gang of children. During the melee someone tossed my paper bag up into a tree, and I couldn't get it down. The householder alongside, one Mrs. Mills, promptly telephoned my mother at the *Freeman-Tribune* office. "Effie Kantor, your little boy's out here in front of my house, and some kids have thrown his paper bag in the tree—he was fighting with them—and he's saying the worst things. It is perfectly *horrible* what he's saying!" "Oh, Mrs. Mills, I'm sure it's not Mack. It must be some other boy. I don't permit Mack to use language like that—" "Don't permit?" bellowed Mrs. Mills. "Why, Effie, everyone knows that he's *the worst-talking boy in Webster City!*")

If my parent herself had burst into opprobrium, it would have been preferable to the mourning aloofness she maintained.

"Look, Mother. When our family contracted so many debts, and then when I had them with all the operations and stuff, there wasn't any agreement that I would never marry. I love my wife, and I've got a right to be married to her. I say this frankly: I won't be able to pay any of those debts next week or next month. I don't know how soon I'll be able to pay them. But I will pay them all, and pay yours and Grandpa's and Grandma's as well. I'll be able to do it a lot sooner, now that I'm married to Irene, than I would be if I weren't married to her. Mother, you don't say anything. What on earth is the matter with you?"

". . . Son . . . I don't know what to say . . . what is there I can say? . . . You've told me that you're married. I suppose that's it." Her voice didn't emerge from St. Patrick's tomb, because I don't think St. Patrick has any tomb, but it came out of somebody's sepulchre. Up in those green Reeks of her soul the banshees were groaning.

On the way back to Cambridge Avenue I lectured myself. "She'll get over it, she'll accept it. But I guess it's a shock for any mother to receive a call like that."

Resentment was red-hot. Resentment that I—miserable weakling—should be so tormented by dread of creditors, by fear of disapproval, that I had deliberately cheated ourselves out of the satisfaction which Irene and I might have attained in being together from the start. I squeaked, "I'm a mouse," but that didn't do much good.

There was this feeling as I climbed steps in front of the old stone building: "Your wife's waiting upstairs in your room, with marital fire burning on the hearth. It's up to you to earn your own way and your wife's, in confidence and respect."

That sounds very old-fashioned Sunday-school paperish, but those were my sentiments. It might be wished that they were endured more commonly today. But we can't all be among God's lucky few.

4.

Richard Henry Little, in his middle and late fifties, had been cast in the role of eccentric round-shouldered giant. He played the part to perfection. If his stooped shambling body had been straightened out (impossible) it would have measured six feet five inches from tip to tip; and his bent shoulders were proportionately broad. No one ever saw him truly drunk—again, in those days. Coming to know him intimately, I never felt that he was wholly sober. The odor of bootleg bourbon surrounded him like a cloud. He had bottles with Sunnybrook labels on them locked in his office desk, stashed away down in The Case at the *Tribune,* hidden behind books in his hotel suite. He still held a fine appetite for food however. He might be a consistent nipper during all his waking hours, but when he ate, he truly ate, and thus a good set of internal organs held him together until he neared eighty.

I contributed to his column first in 1924, but did not meet him until the following winter, after "Floyd Collins' Cave" appeared. The entrapment of this hillbilly in a remote Kentucky cave, the fevered efforts to rescue him, and the discovery that he could not be moved from beneath a slab of rock which brought about his termination: these captured attention of that Humanity which presses forever against barricades to watch disasters go parading by.

Rescue shafts had been sunk, pipes had been put close to the victim. With wintry air and hot soups and prayers, the regional population flocked round, and big city reporters and photographers assembled in droves.

Known previously only as a bumpkin who liked his moonshine, and who cut an ungallant figure at church meetings, Collins became almost overnight, and through weeks which followed, the master of headlines across the Nation. His death throes were attenuated, and shared down to the final gasp and quiver by millions in faraway towns. People blocked traffic to throng before bulletin boards and observe hour-by-hour announcements flashed on screens.

Radio was become a medium to be reckoned with. Beginning with crystal sets and climbing on up to the status of superheterodynes, the public twisted knobs and bent toward amplifiers to share Floyd's struggle and final grief. There was not yet a radio machine in every living room, but in small towns there were one or two on every block . . . in each metropolis, in every building.

Doctors risked their lives; again they wormed their way inside, and spoke and touched. No use: Floyd Collins was dead. His body could not be moved (they thought then). Concrete was to be pumped, and this international shrine would become a mausoleum in fact.

The news reached us on Tuesday, February 17th, 1925. I was thirteen days past my twenty-first birthday, and still lame and sore from another profitless operation the previous month. I shut myself off in the living room, turned on a storied green-shaped lamp, and appointed myself poet laureate of Sand Cave.

> Down in the earth thar was fairies and elves
> And they tole him secrets that he wouldn't tell. . . .
> What's jest beyond, in the turn of the slide—
> Thar in the damp whar the cave crickets hide?
> Less' go and see, Floyd, less' go and see—

Oh yes, dialect, and that was the curse of my youth. But at least I owned the good sense to make preface with a line, "Written as the ancient song-ballads of Kentucky were written." Late the next morning I hobbled to mail my verses through the letter slot of the noon train. My offering might reach R.H.L.'s desk on Thursday the 19th. It did, and he printed it at the head of the column on Friday the 20th.

> And thar's moaning—a moaning
> Back in the cave,
> Floyd Collins' cavern is Floyd Collins' grave!

My life had changed. This was the first great alteration brought about by my writing. I could not recognize this at the time, any more than most people recognize a crucial happening while it is in the process of occurrence. I knew only that I became by turns proud, amazed, overwhelmed, flabbergasted.

R.H.L. sought me out via long-distance telephone. I remember his deep mumble and the ardent words, "Well, well, well, you're raising Ned all over the country!" and that was charm for any writer's ears.

The press of America subscribed on the instant. In New York City (fabled visionary place inhabited, to my mind, principally by Diamond Jim Brady, Eddie Cantor, and a great many publishers) the *Daily News* ran my verses as its editorial of the day. All over the country this was happening within the week. Either the poem was reproduced itself, or it became the subject for

profound editorials on life, death, Kentuckians, caves, and the
mercy and heart of Mankind. There were cousins of my grandmother's, or nieces or nephews who were mere names . . .
they sent clippings from the West Coast newspapers. Here was
an editorial from the *Daily Oregonian*. Even people in distant
Portland were now aware of what I had thought and written.
We were dizzied by the knowledge.

Dick Little telegraphed that I must come and be his guest at
the Virginia Hotel, and recite "Floyd Collins' Cave" over the
microphone at the Chicago *Tribune*'s WGN studio. He didn't
know whether I could read the lines with any skill, was utterly
unaware that I would rather recite my own poems than eat . . .
and I had an abounding appetite.

We scratched together what few dollars were available, and
I limped to the Illinois Central depot. It was the noon train
again. Grandma had prepared a ceremonial lunch, in the
ceremonial shoe-box, although it didn't need to be that big. Miss
Elsie Heiden, a kindly lady who worked at the First National
Bank and was an admiring friend of Mother's, hastened along
the platform just before the train arrived. She stuffed an envelope
into my pocket.

"Don't open it now. Wait until you're on the train."

"But what is it, Elsie?"

"Just some good wishes from your friends at the bank."

The bank? Oh, God, we owed money to the First National
Bank. We owed money to the Farmers' National Bank. We owed
—I held vague fear that somehow the bank's officers had decided
that, in this nationwide glare of publicity, I must also have
acquired a fortune, and they were dunning me for payment.
Then their faces rose in mind, and I laughed, even while waving goodbye to Mother and Elsie through the coach window.
I saw Will Clifton, plump and affable, and never dreamed—
nor did the rest of the town—of his suicide in a year to come. I
saw the handsome Mr. Earl Mason, the fabulous black-eyed
Elston King who had been cowboy and killer, out West, long
ago. I kept the envelope intact, promising that I would open

it only when I'd finished Grandma's lunch . . . I couldn't eat much, I saved it for Later On. One deviled egg, deviled with the boiled dressing which she concocted so skillfully . . . some olives, half of a cold meat-loaf sandwich. Then I relaxed, sipping milk from a paper cup, and thinking, "It's time to open the envelope, and read their good wishes."

Their good wishes were expressed in the form of currency: green bills printed by Uncle Sam. There was even one gold certificate among them.

Dear Mack: Please do have a good time in Chicago. We're proud of you.

Afterward, it seemed like a long time afterward, the conductor was bending over me with concern.

"Young fellow—"

"Yes?"

"You know, there was a doctor got on back there at Jesup. I know him pretty well: Doc Keatley. He's a homeopath, and he's got his pill case with him— Maybe he could give you something—"

"Thanks, Conductor. I don't need a thing."

He was a fairy-tale official, had wan pinkish eyes behind gilt-rimmed glasses; his was a triple chin, his was a musty voice contrived for soothing worried mothers; his watch charms had been dandled before a thousand babies; he went out of existence when the last locomotive ceased to smoke and clang.

"Well, now, I saw your cane and all— Figured you was having some pretty severe pain—"

I said, "And I was crying."

"Yeh. A little—"

"It's all right, Conductor. No pain whatsoever. Those were tears of appreciation."

He smiled, shook his head, gave a semi-salute, went jingling away with charms and ticket punch . . . went to join Casey Jones, Brave Kate Shelley, and that other Conductor who said *God Bless you, just sit right where you are.*

In late evening we reached the Park Row station. I took a

taxi to the Virginia Hotel. That was at Ohio and Rush, one
small block away from another building at 541 North Michigan
which was to become of exceeding importance thirteen months
later.

I approached the desk at the Virginia and gave the clerk my
name. "Mr. Little said there'd be a room—"

"Yes indeed, Mr. Kantor! Your room is ready, and we're happy
to have you with us! You are to go to your room, according to
instructions, make yourself comfortable, and then go down to Mr.
Little's suite. He has a few friends with him, and they're waiting
for you."

Fellow contributors were packed into Dick's small quarters:
they sat on the floor, leaned between bookcases. They held
their glasses high when he put his arm around me and proposed
a toast to the memory of Floyd Collins.

These were his nearest and dearest. They included Shelby
Melton who would become his wife a few weeks later. She
was a downtown secretary who spent every possible extra waking moment in Dick's company, assisting him with the column.
Her pen name was Helen Henna; in addition she wrote acres
of little squibs, signed with weird signatures, supposedly the
product of other contributors.

"B.L.T. got twenty-seven hundred letters per month with his
column. I get over eight thousand." The rough voice, voice which
ambled as its wounded master ambled when he strode. "People
say I'd take a hundred thousand circulation away from the
Tribune if I walked out the door. Some say I'd take more than
that. I don't know how many I'd take. I am not going to walk out
the door. I have no intention of walking out the door! I'm going
to stay, and print the wonderful things you dear people write for
me. Yes, you, God damn it, Snowshoe Al, you rabbit from Strea-
tor! Yes, you, God damn it, Colorado Pete! Yes, you, Lun Dee!
Yes, you, Le Mousquetaire!" And then, bridling against me with
the gaze of his protruding blue-brown deer-like eyes— "And
whom have we here? A cave cricket! A cave cricket come from
Kentucky by way of Ioway! God damn it, MacKinlay— What

do they call you—Mack—? God damn it, Mack—we're going to
have another drink of Sunnybrook, and then we're going to hear
you recite 'Floyd Collins' Cave!'"

Our fondness, begun so auspiciously if noisily, increased in
warmth and even acquired dignity as days went by. I had never
met anyone like Richard Henry Little before (or since) and was
overwhelmed by the rambling excitement in which he walked.

My broadcasting of "Floyd Collins' Cave" was an unqualified
success in the opinion of the WGN radio audience, as sheaves
of telegrams attested. There had been or has been no phenomenon comparable to the popularity of Dick's column before
or since. Eventually I was to dwell upon this in my first published novel, and would recall with amusement how various
New York critics reacted in scorn and disbelief. The fame of a
well-read and brilliant Franklin P. Adams, or of a mincing
Isabel Patterson, was comparatively limited in its scope. R.H.L.
affected the herding mass of newspaper readers with his senti-
mental outspoken emphasis on native Americana and wartime
reminiscence. (It must be remembered—and today's people
may find it difficult to believe—that this latter was an acceptable
and even enviable commodity.)

Several of his most popular contributors were veterans who
wrote about their military past. One thinks especially of people
like Leonard H. Nason, who wrote for Dick under the pen
name of Steamer. I was bewildered but thankful when it became obvious that my own popularity with this audience ex-
ceeded even that of the veterans, who were a young and ardent
factor in the newspaper-reading public. The balladry which I
extolled was a kind of hard cider, and the public drank it willingly. I was paid only in the shekels of approval, but even those
were valuable currency for a beginner.

This was the heady age of the personalized newspaper column.
There were several such published in the Chicago press, including the more literate expositions of Keith Preston and Richard
Atwater. Their combined readership was fragmentary compared
to R.H.L.'s.

Radio stations other than the *Tribune*'s WGN were brandishing offers for Dick to bring his "Line" gang to their chancels,
and broadcast over more powerful circuits. We went trooping off
on two such enterprises. The money received for these activities
—above expenses incurred—stoked a fund which Dick maintained to provide cigarettes and other tiny luxuries for hos-
pitalized veterans. These experiences were bewildering but in-
finitely satisfying.

"Why go back to Iowa, Mack? You belong here with us. I
want to keep printing your stuff—"

But I had a novel which I was intent on finishing. I planned
to enter it in a contest held jointly by a magazine—*Pictorial
Review*—and a publisher and a motion picture studio. The prize
was ten thousand dollars.

"Probably you won't win. Probably you'll be too God damn
good for them. Who the hell can please a publisher, a magazine,
and a motion picture studio all at once? They'll want something
about love life in country clubs, and you don't write that kind of
crap. In fact, I doubt sincerely that you know anything about
love life in country clubs. Am I correct? Of course I'm correct!"

My novel still might be a door opening on an important future.
I went back to Iowa and did finish the book. Then I returned
to Chicago to meet with Dick and Shelby after they came from
their Mexican honeymoon.

Mine was not the only such commitment in R.H.L.'s fumbling
gregarious life. There ensued some bleak days and weeks when
I searched for work in vain. Dick had thought that the *Tribune*
would want me, but my virtues as a possible sensation were
unappreciated and practically unscanned by the powers there.
Finally a letter to Anton J. Cermak, president of the Cook
County Board, did the trick: I got my surveying job. Through
the ordeal, friendship with the Littles prospered. Soon it was
possible for Mother to come and live with me for some months
in Chicago.

Dick and Shelby moved to a new apartment, one much
larger than the hotel suite, and Mother's advice and assistance

lifted her to favor. The rambling quarters selected were in an old building at the corner of Chicago Avenue and Rush Street, close to the lodge hall where Irene and I were to receive advice from the Knights of Pythias chaplain on our marriage night.

Mother scrubbed and advised. She was never happier than when assisting other people to form a new home. She sewed curtains, selected kitchenware, cooked stews, concocted salads to surprise the pair when they came home. Dick, delving into lore of ancient Peterkins, called her The Lady from Philadelphia. Under this title in time she was honored by minor inclusion in the column, and thus became one of the "Line" gang in fact. She joined in festivities, none of them particularly rowdy, but forever high-spirited. In no way did she approve of any drinking which went on; but one had to accept or reject Richard Henry Little as he was; she merely looked the other way.

Planets swung and traffic roared, and the Graeme Players advertisement was read and acted upon . . . Irene's advent was welcomed wholeheartedly by the Littles. They had seen me going from girl to girl, and sometimes exhibited strong disapproval. But they were Irene addicts from the start. They enjoyed her gentle dignity and the impishness which she could display in fun. When finally we burst upon them with news of our marriage, the confession was greeted with cries of enthusiasm, and a bottle of champagne was produced from God knows what source. Dick felt sublime when he gathered his cohorts about him, and his wife (we believed then) embraced the same affinity.

Irene and I worked hard and longed to play hard as well, but rapidly we were losing interest in participating in theatricals. I was to be a writer, not an actor, and trivial productions put on in odd small theaters throughout the suburbs did not hold much appeal any longer. Briefly we walked a social tightrope between the Graeme Players and the Littles and their people, but it was easy to recognize where our preference lay, and our enthusiasm and ambition as well. Sunday afternoons came to be a great thing in the Little household. We had to choose between those gatherings and the Players, and did choose.

That autumn the rains and chill were persistent. Tree leaves turned dull brown instead of coloring brightly; dampness prevailed, and probably gloom as well. But we were too ambitious and too delighted, we did not succumb to mildew.

Sundays became a bliss to be held in reverie with recurrent tenderness. No running on Sunday, no gulping a hasty glass of juice or eating half an orange, and then scurrying to the Sheridan Road bus. No snatching the remainder of breakfast in a cafeteria before turning to our respective stores. We had achieved the loan of a small electric plate, and enjoyed leisurely toast and coffee in our room . . . we savored bits of cheese or sausage we'd fetched home as scraps from other meals . . . now they assumed mystic jollity.

A woman named Bertha White, with singular silvery hair, conducted a tiny candy and nut shop not far from our apartment building. It was fun to go to her on Saturday evening and fetch away a huge sack of popcorn, and stop for a quart of milk at a grocery store on the way home. Here was our cereal for Sunday morning. Irene selected a parcel of Chinese bowls, and we unpacked those from their Oriental wrappings, and used them for popcorn and milk. We bought fabulous raw tomatoes for breakfast greenery (commercial tomato juice was as then unheard of). Irene did laundry and ironing while I sat at the typewriter. Then at late noontime we would stroll to one of several favorite restaurants on Broadway or Clark Street.

These were the elegant, the seventy-five-centers; these were the ones where we could afford to eat only once a week. We considered our Sunday dinners to be fabulous. Hot roast veal . . . chicken pot-pies . . . slabs of white roast pork over the mounds of dressing . . . steaming browned potatoes . . . the salads, the slabs of butterscotch or cherry pie.

In vigorous dream we wandered down across Lincoln Park, stopping alongside the zoo, admiring bears, lions, wolves— In boyhood I had learned to howl like a timber wolf, and so, circumstances granting, I would howl, and have a chorus of wolves answering in no time at all. Keepers hastened in suspicion, and we'd need to flee. We'd stroll the little conservatory, scent blossoms, watch alligators in their pool. Then on across the middle and lower North Side, a region of imposing houses turned into apartments and clubs. Elm trees brown, mist coming down, dun leaves pasted across sidewalks; the buses going swish, streetcars grating at North Avenue and Division Street. On to the Littles'.

We had a peculiar knock which we used on coming to that second-floor door, and Shelby knew who was there before she saw us. This was agreed upon: there were rare times when they did not wish to see others, when Dick was tired or had a headache or felt suddenly that he wished to withdraw from mankind. But those days were rare. Most times he'd come limping, waving his arms, making uncouth and affectionate sounds, wrapping Irene against him, glaring at me, saying, "Whom have we here? What are you doing with my *other woman?*" And to Irene, "What is *he* in your life? A poet or a poetaster?"

It is unlikely that most of the "Line" people thought of themselves as being Bohemian or deliberately exotic in manner of life and thought. Most of them proceeded naturally on given bent, and were sincere in application to please the huge master with their efforts. Only a few would tally much accomplishment in the end; but they had the joy of producing, and knowing that sympathetic ears turned their way.

Shelby hated to cook, knew next to nothing about the process; but her huge pots of coffee simmered interminably. We were not plied with liquor. Drinks were offered seldom except on "Line" nights . . . those were growing to be display nights as well, with various Social Registerites invited along. The new Mrs. Little held dreams in that direction, and more and more she insisted on their accepting invitations which her husband had ignored previously. But we were still a crowd of ambitious folk and behaved accordingly. There was an air of freedom and *laissez faire* in the place, and we sank into it gracefully and gratefully.

In that sprawling apartment the Muse was apt to fling missiles. One afternoon we had been discussing Rudyard Kipling. Kipling had spoken with his usual savagery about America's belated entrance into the World War. I felt inclined to explain at least some of his bitterness, and how he could not walk abroad in Sussex without seeing fancied coffins crowding the ditches at the roadsides. The fact that I had never been any nearer Sussex than East Chicago, Indiana, did not deter me. I was a Kiplingite just as a throng of Sir Rudyard's characters were Janeites.

(A dozen years later we'd come to know Beatty Balestier, his brother-in-law, and would learn firsthand why Kipling hated the United States with such intensity. Still . . . no one might ever appreciate being threatened and injured in a brawl on Vermont's quiet Pine Hill road.)

Shelby Little went on a tour of the apartment. Withdrawn to a far corner of the living room with paper and pencil in order to celebrate Kipling at the moment, I vaguely heard her speak when she came back. She was a coffee fiend pure and simple. Even the great whites of her eyes seemed yellowed with caffeine, and ludicrous gossip held that she used coffee instead of the usual henna to dye her hair.

She stood in green smock, cup in hand, and gave report.

"David Sortor is in the rearmost bedroom, writing a poem about a crystal cat. George Carroll is seated at the dining table, writing a poem about James Stephens. Mack is over there, writing a poem about Kipling. And the inescapable thing about it is, Ricky, that you will have to print them all!"

That same George Carroll became a fellow honoree at the Army-Navy game. For the first time in sports history this football epic took place at Soldier Field, on the edge of Grant Park in Chicago. Excitement reached fever pitch, with special trains coming in from all over the country. You had to be well heeled to go to that game. Scalpers were selling tickets for a hundred dollars apiece.

A Montana politician ambled into the *Tribune* newsroom and sat down opposite Little at his desk. "Dick, I got called back home, and here I am holding two tickets for tomorrow. Can you use my tickets, and take Mrs. Little along with you to the game?"

Dick groaned. "God damn it. Tomorrow, at the very hour of the game, Shelby and I will be en route to Milwaukee, where I've got to deliver a speech in the evening."

"Then give one of them to that guy who wrote about the Montana girl who got killed here, in the rodeo last summer."

> Louise was the string of a Montana bow . . .
> And she saddled her horse for the big rodeo;
> With her hair in the sky, with her hair in the wind,
> She headed her horse where the corral gates grinned.

Irene could not use the other ticket; it was awarded to George Carroll. Shelby held ardent conviction that he would be The One in the entire "Line" group to be remembered by posterity.

Surely the idea of selling my ticket came to me, and was as promptly rejected, and I felt chagrin at even entertaining the notion. It would have been a flagrant betrayal of some sort of trust imposed. Carroll chuckled later when I talked with him, and confessed that he had endured the same reasoning.

Work halted momentarily in our department when I took leave the next afternoon, bound in frost for Soldier Field. This was unheard of: the fellow tracers swore to take up writing verse at once. Even Mr. Frank, the overseer whom we dodged adroitly most times, shook hands in congratulation. He told of certain upholstered bigwigs in offices upstairs who had been turned down in their efforts to secure admission to the game.

In ordinary season an employee was docked for time taken off from his prescribed duties . . . no one considered any other possibility. Those of us who had political connections, and went to work at the polls during election season, expected to be thus docked; so were workers in almost any other situation. But I had toiled mightily, and turned in the full allotment of claims for a day's work. Even the grim Frank did not suggest that I be penalized. I was cheered on my way, and went out to catch a cold. It was miserable weather, and I didn't particularly enjoy sitting there.

Neither did a certain Army scrub. He was revered as a lacrosse player, but the coaches considered him a bit light for the mauling conflict which ensued on that particular gridiron. I saw him sitting there; indeed I saw all the scrubs on the bench in front of us, draped in their blankets.

He got into another somewhat larger and more important brawl later on. His graduation from the Academy was an event of the future, and so was his marriage to the beautiful Liz, both of which occurred in 1928. What did Fred L. Anderson know of aerial bombardment on that dreary day in 1926? Not one thing. What did I, who would fly with the bombers under his command, and report their activity, know of aerial bombardment? Even less than nothing. Fred hoped to become a fighter type pure-and-simple, and it was when flying a blazing fighter plane across crowded San Francisco and into the icy bay that he would win one of the few Distinguished Flying Crosses to be awarded in peacetime. Neither of us could guess about other perils which we would encounter, nor of the rewarding friendship which would endure, terminated only when the volleys rapped above Fred's grave in Arlington.

"Oh, richest wisdom!" I'd write in a future novel, "that the terror of the future shall never be revealed to us who are powerless to avoid it." On me would devolve the happy responsibility of informing his wife that he had been promoted to two stars . . . that was a great luncheon in our lives. But far away from this moment in the sleet at Soldier Field.

One figure, huddled beneath his blanket on the bench with the scrubs; the other, drenched and shivering, sitting twelve rows above him, with cold feet jammed into a soggy paper bag.

5.

As in all regions where people of the same age and general classification act together in common effort, there were rules of behavior which prevailed at Mandels', and which if consistently ruptured brought about a vicious form of ostracism.

Promptly I had learned how many claims to turn in as settled, in the course of a day's work. As low a figure as fifteen claims—whatever the difficulty involved in tracing them—would bring glowering and censure from Mr. Frank. . . . Seventeen claims? He might shrug at that, but keep an eye on you if this still minor figure was observed with suspicious consistency. Eighteen, nineteen or twenty claims?—you were above criticism, and if especially fortunate might dare to go as high as twenty-two.

. . . Never, never, never turn in more than twenty-two claims as settled and as proof of one day's activity. Keep it around nineteen or twenty.

"But what," an experienced tracer might be asked, "do you do with claims if you have good luck and settle—? Well, say twenty-five or twenty-six. What do you do with the others?"

"Turn in the oldest claim first. Oldest by date. Mix them up a little. You have a lot of easy Deliveries Not Received? You simply call up the customer, and often find that the goods have been received subsequent to the customer's filing a claim of nondelivery. 'Customer received O.K.,' and that claim is settled. Maybe it took you all of five minutes to find it out? You go on, and you get into some really rough stuff: damaged goods, Customer Reports Damage When Package Opened, all that sort of stuff. You can run your legs off all day on some of those, and be no nearer to a settled claim than you were at the beginning. That's the reason you have to have a backlog."

"Backlog?"

"Certainly. That's what I'm trying to explain to you. Keep a backlog of easy claims, those you've got all fixed. Don't turn them in—not until you have to."

"But what do you *do* with the settled claims which you don't turn in?"

"Hide em."

"Where?"

"You've got to figure that out to suit yourself. Some try one stunt, some work another way. I can give you a few tips. Don't put them in your desk drawer: Frank always goes and looks there. He gets snoopy whenever he thinks the claims aren't coming in fast enough. People have come in after hours and found him going around, peeking into people's desks."

"What about our lockers, where we keep our hats and coats and—?"

"That's up to you again. The lockers are supposed to be safe places, and only we people who are given the combinations have access to them. That's *supposedly*. Rumor tells us that Frank—or possibly somebody else—has a master list of all the combinations on the lockers assigned to us. Be that as it may, lots of people do hide claims in their lockers. I don't know what would happen if a bunch of settled claims turned up in a guy's locker. I just don't know. They'd have to have some excuse for prowling in there, you see, and I don't quite know what that excuse would be. But, as I say, there are rumors about folks sneaking and peeking. I've got various secret places myself, and I don't use the same one all the time. Didn't you say that you've written a detective story or two? Well then, you ought to be able to figure out a way to hide the settled claims which you don't want to turn in."

Good advice. I figured out a way.

In essence, however, I was finding reaffirmation of a hideous truth. Most people didn't like the jobs which life compelled them to hold, and they cheated their employers whenever and however they could manage to do so. If in no other way, they cheated in time and effort withheld. We had done this in the Cook County surveying crew (that's enough bench marks for today; let's stop at Gus Janecek's roadhouse before we drive back to town, and he'll give us a couple of free beers apiece)—had played our little games of elusion and vanishment in the County Building itself. I had given liberally of the American Flyer's time to my own concerns; and now here were the tracers at Mandels' impeding the store's effort with plotted deliberation, and I was one with them.

Far cry from the small town newspaper effort of an earlier epoch . . . Mother and I worked day and night and—whatever our complaints about stupidity demonstrated at the city hall or Iowa Farm Bureau offices—we truly loved every minute of it.

I looked at my battered rebuilt L. C. Smith with fresh and ardent gaze. If there existed any contrivance to help me escape from the futility in which I trotted, it was that typewriter.

If it were necessary to learn to please editors rather than merchants, I must learn how. . . . Stay. Weren't editors, in turn, essentially pleasing their advertisers who were also merchants? I chased this notion down the trail for a way, but then it went to ground and I felt no inclination to dig it up. An advertiser might be brooding beyond my typewriter in general effect, but I would not hear him complaining because I told a good story. In all fact he would wish me to tell one.

In divulging these observations and meditations to Irene, I found her to be entertaining an attack of giggles.

"Well, what's so damn funny about what I was just saying?"

"Me," she said.

"You?"

"I don't suppose you've ever considered your devoted wife as a candidate for those same charges?"

"Why— No. You go to work, and do your job. I don't see how you'd ever have a chance to— Well, what did you *do?*"

In glee she informed me. Time itself: she had stolen copiously of it. During the several months following her initial employment at Carson's, there was little opportunity for us to ever breakfast together. She'd sleep until the last possible moment at home, sip her fruit juice while she dressed, then run to the elevated station . . . check in at the store, greet the other gals in her department, make whatever preparations for the day's activity which might be made . . . then, bag in hand, depart for the ladies' room. There were several such institutions within easy reach.

"But I wouldn't be in the ladies' room at all. I'd be in the customers' cafe, having a luxurious breakfast. By that time I'd be very hungry, and they had so many of my favorite things. You know how I love fish, and their cod was excellent, and not truly expensive. Also the roast beef hash, with poached egg— Superb! And some leisurely cups of coffee— Then I'd go back to the department, and feel like a new woman."

"Didn't you ever get *caught?*"

"Why, no. Who was there to catch me?"

"But didn't you realize that you were cheating the store out of your *time?*"

"Not necessarily." She turned her lovely eyes on me. "I just felt comfortable," she said. "And rather elegant. And relaxed."

6.

During earliest phases of employment at the store, before we were dwelling boldly on Cambridge, more often than not I was still dead for lack of sleep. Those nighttime hours on surface cars consumed their toll. Downtown I didn't have the lofty retreat which had endeared itself during factory days, but— Wait.

We possessed a Returned Goods section on a balcony next to the delivery court. There all shipments which were damaged in transit or were refused by customers, found their way home. A lot of them were more than packages: crates and huge boxes— and they were dumped uphill from trucks into this domain. The operation was excessively noisy during afternoons, but there would be many hours each day when no such deliveries were made.

This performance was presided over by a black-browed individual who shall be dignified by the name of Tartini. I didn't know a Neapolitano from a Piedmonteso, or a Genoese from a Siciliano. All I knew was that Tartini was Italian, and that he sang long and loud with the dedication of an entire chorus—spear-bearers, dancers, magicians, principals, libretto writer, and composer.

Part of his job lay in rending open the crates and boxes, that goods might be inspected . . . part, of course, in keeping records. Another essential chore was in his submitting to interviews, mainly with assistant Buyers or claim tracers who sought him for specific information. He was dark-faced, bespectacled, surly-looking. It must be chronicled that Tony Tartini delighted to trade on his grim appearance, and frighten the wits out of certain employees with whom he came in contact.

I loved his singing, and had some small familiarity with many arias or choruses which he essayed, because of Mother's devotion to opera, and her own skillful piano performance and vibrant voice.

If he weren't singing, and I came there on business, I'd profess disappointment at not finding him vocally engaged.

"Don't worry. Just let that son of a bitch from Department 17 come in, and I'll be ready to go!"

His domain was L-shaped, broken into two sections, with a desk situated at the rear. When you were at that desk you were not visible to anyone who might come through the outer door. Wonder of wonders, a big shaded light hung over the desk . . . it had an enormous bulb. Also Tartini loved to entertain company, and I was fortunate in quickly becoming one of his intimates.

From then on the procedure was simple. I would rush through hours of work and earn my sleep before I took it.

"What's the situation, Tartini? Are you busy at your desk?"

"No, no, finished twenty minutes ago. Go on, go to sleep. You look like you needed it."

I'd go to the rear, fling myself down in his chair, and spread a

few claims and one of his checking sheets before me. I'd reach
up, pull the chain on the light to become swathed in semidark-
ness . . . fold my arms on the desk, drop my head on my arms,
and be unconscious in another couple of minutes. If one of
the tracers came seeking advice or assistance—O.K. The code
was definite and intense: one tracer never offered information
against another. I'm not sure what would have happened to him
if he'd done so, but at the time we held strong suspicion that
he would have had an accident on an escalator.

Claim tracers, then, were nothing to worry about. Mr. Frank
was someone to worry about, and so were Buyers or their assist-
ants, with a few notable exceptions. Let one suspicious soul
appear, and *"M'appari"* would burst forth.

> *Marta, Marta, tu sparisti,*
> *E il mio cor col tuo n'andò!*
> *Tu la pace mi rapisti—*

Before the intruder had reached an area where the remote
desk was visible to him, the roar awakened me. Automatically
I'd reach up, pull the light chain, and be sitting at work with
papers spread before me. It was a beautiful system and never
failed. It held dangers . . . there were times when even store
executives had reason to seek the advice or assistance of Signor
Tartini. But those occasions were rare. The system was infallible
unless, in slumber, I were suddenly to become stone deaf.

After Irene and I cried our news to the world, we could behave
like civilized participants in matrimony, and no longer needed
to spend our evenings drifting about the lake shore or riding
streetcars. I was trying to work on two more novels (neither
of which amounted to anything in the end) and also stubbornly
attempting success in the field of the short story. Irene had
her tiny wardrobe to keep up, her hair to wash and curl . . .
divers other feminine activities, all of which took time. Our
evenings could now be devoted to domesticity instead of the
eternal streetcar riding. Also there came occasions when we

declared holiday, and read aloud in bed, consuming enough apples and popcorn to stock a fair-sized Halloween brawl.

Suddenly, however, I found myself entertaining a business proposition offered by none other than the tuneful Tartini. One afternoon, blinking his big eyes mysteriously, he suggested that I might find it worth while to drop in at his business quarters when work ended that day.

"Make it at five-thirty. Your wife won't mind if you're fifteen minutes late, will she?"

"Not if I call her in advance."

"Better call."

I came to him at five-thirty, and he locked the door from the inside. From some hideaway he produced a tall bottle and said merely, "You like wine? Of course you do. Have a nice drink of wine."

I took the drink. He was right: dago red, but even better than that served by the immortal Giovanni in our little La Boheme cafe.

"Like it? Let's have another."

"Tartini, it's simply great!"

"How'd you like to take some orders?"

"Take orders?"

"For this very wine. I've talked to you a little bit, and you'd know a lot of people who might like our wine. Five gallons, ten gallons. How about your 'Line O' Type' people? How about your people where you go— You know, dramatic activities? How about your own neighborhood? You know, people in the stores? How about your own building? You said your landlord was precinct captain there. Well then. What are you waiting for?"

He had jotted down a price list, and awarded this to me, and also noted the extent of his profit and my profit which might ensue.

I went to find Irene, and she wondered why I was so silent during the homeward trip.

"What on earth have you got in that brown paper sack? It looks like a bottle."

"It is a bottle."

"Goodness sake. What's in the bottle?"

"Wine. It's still three quarters full."

"You mean you've been drinking *wine?* At *work?*"

"Tell you all about it when we get home."

We dined at a nearby cafeteria. Then I walked with Irene to Cambridge, saw her in, and retreated to Diversey Parkway, wine and all.

There is no need to embarrass the descendants of folks whom I visited, by telling exactly where I went or to whom I spoke. At one delicatessen in particular I knew all three proprietors, and had heard them longingly express desire to handle this very commodity on the side. They tasted and believed.

When I went home I was dizzy. Sat down at the desk . . . Irene and I finished the last taste of wine, and I did a lot of figuring on scratch paper.

I said, "Listen to this," and read off my figures.

"I don't understand."

"It's very simple. I can clear at least fifty dollars a week, minimum, in taking orders for Tartini."

She listened, while I went over the account again. I suggested how the amount might be increased—

Irene asked, "Who already handles the wine in this district? I mean, which bootleggers? Is it the Capone crowd?"

"Oh no," I told her. "Not Capone at all. This is too far north and east. No—there are some brothers named Genna—"

"And just where, my dear, would this activity put you insofar as the Gennas are concerned?"

"Why, I wouldn't have anything to do with them. It wouldn't be necessary. Tartini and his brother will take care of all deliveries. We won't be working through anyone else—"

I expatiated wisely. "Look, Irene. The big bootleggers are not interested in piddling little sales—piddling at least by their standards. They're jobbing out lots in the thousand of gallons: big accounts, big deliveries. They— This is just little stuff. Private individuals. The Gennas don't sell to individuals. They job it out to other people, and the other people get orders from big handlers: hotels, syndicates. Baby stuff like this wouldn't interest them. There are probably a thousand individuals going around Chicago right now, taking orders for wine in tiny lots— Well, maybe not a thousand, but at least several hundred—"

Irene said serenely, "In which select lot my husband shall not be numbered. I do not choose to become a widow when I've scarcely become a wife. Where's that bottle?"

Our two windows opened on an air shaft, but one window was long painted shut and could not be moved. The other operated readily. I had fastened a box outside to serve as ice chest and storage chamber when autumn weather cooled into winter. A few stray items were secreted there even now. Also, like most city air shafts, this was a depository for junk. There were windows in opposite buildings farther down, and we had heard glass broken there before.

Irene added her private wreckage to the sum. She opened the window and, reaching past the storage box, tossed Tartini's offering into space.

We listened. *Smash.*

My wife turned with a seraphic smile. I have never heard that Carry Nation looked particularly beautiful when she was in a bottle-busting mood, but— Could have been, could have been.

"Now then, my dear Mr. Tommy Gun," Irene told me, "please inform Tartini that you are wedded to the self-appointed president of the Diversey Parkway Anti-Wine League."

7.

There ensue occasions when mere sweetness and warmth become nobility. A common man without conscious pretension to seraphic status may walk as a savior.

One particularly gloomy day I received a slip of paper: *See*

Mr. Whiteman, customer, upstairs, and that sent me flying to the booths near Mr. Russell's office. I'd had no customer named Whiteman in relation to any recent claim. A friend was come.

(He had less than three years of life left to him in which to exert his innate kindliness. A freight elevator in his own warehouse would be the instrument involved—operated, I firmly believe, by the Devil disincarnate.)

Plump figure, beaming protuberant gray eyes, baldish head: he arose, waving a small package in his hand. I came into the booth and closed the door.

"You see, Mack, they said that there was a rule against pulling claim tracers up from your office for meetings with personal friends. They said that if I were a customer and needed to talk about a possible claim, I could send for you." He brandished the package again. "So I became a customer. I went and bought an evening bag for Metta."

Metta was his wife, Dick Whiteman's mother, also overplump and affable. Dick and I had known each other in Webster City when we were small boys, but our true friendship waited until the teens; then we became close. After our mutual graduation from high school, the Whitemans moved to Cedar Rapids, where the father was president of the Howard Holt Drug Company. His firm specialized in dealing with veterinarians who preferred to buy their drugs direct rather than through a retail outlet. Mr. Whiteman was as substantial in native affection as he was in body and in purse, and had grown popular in Masonic circles.

In utter and peculiar contrast to such business activity, his family were the only ardent Christian Scientists to whom I'd ever felt closely drawn. If queried no doubt they would have maintained that their spiritual gentility was gained from ardent study of Mary Baker Eddy; but non-Scientists would have rejected such explanation. It came from innate geniality of spirit and affection for the human race.

We sat down and faced each other across the little desk. "Mr. Whiteman, are you all right?"

He beamed. "Wonderful. Just had to come to Chicago for a

couple of days on business. I'm going home—" He looked at his watch. "In about an hour and a half."

"How's Mrs. Whiteman?"

"Wonderful."

"How's Dick?"

"Fine. They'd both send love, if they knew I were seeing you."

"They send love. I can feel it."

But he shook his head. "Mack, you look tired."

"I am tired."

"Hope you won't mind," he said. "Dick let me read some of your letters about Irene. She sounds just great."

"She is just great."

"I'd like to meet her. Only wish I had more time, but maybe on the next trip—" He stared at me steadily. "If you're still here," he added.

My pulse felt uncertain. "What do you mean," I asked rudely, "if I'm still here?"

"Oh, I don't exactly know. I just had a feeling that you were . . . well, kind of desperate, and ready to take off for some other place—"

I told him, "I'd like to. Take Irene and go . . . any other place."

"You don't like this department store business?"

"No, I hate it. I'm just not equipped for it by inclination or by any acquired interest. But it's the best job I've been able to find, and so— Oh, hell. I'm sorry to have you see me like this. I'm worried to death about money, as always. A letter came from Grandma McKinlay and— You know: as in tradition. It was tear-stained. Literally. I could see where she'd cried, and the water of her tears had muddled the fresh ink where she'd written. It was about their real estate taxes. She kept saying that she didn't want to bother me—"

He said gruffly, "If you need money that desperately, you have only to—"

"I know, I know, Mr. Whiteman. You're going to say again that you'd be glad to lend me whatever I need. It isn't as easy as that. I wish it were."

Perspiration had come out on his face. He unfolded his breast-pocket handkerchief to wipe it away. "But it's hard on the rest of us."

"Thank you, sir. And thank you for feeling that— But in my case it's just not a matter of adding to obligations. They're too severe for that. . . . God did smile a little. I just received a check for a poem sold to *Adventure,* and I was able to endorse that and send it."

He said explosively, "I think you could make more money in Cedar Rapids."

"How do you mean?"

"Newspaper."

"But I don't know any of the newspaper people in Cedar Rapids. Wouldn't know how to go about it."

"I do know them," he said. "I know Verne Marshall of the *Gazette,* and I've met the other fellow that's publisher of the *Republican.* Want me to make some inquiries?"

"Good God, yes! But . . . would it be better if I wrote to them myself?"

He thought it might be more practical if I let him proceed with inquiries in the first place. Then, if anyone became interested, he could let me know, and I could write a letter of application.

His gaze swept around the little office, as if he listened to damp moaning of the city outside, and wondered about it.

"No." Talking to himself now. "This isn't your sort of place. It's intensely commercial, and you're not intensely commercial. Or do I mean intently?"

We both chuckled. I spoke, quoting: " 'Here's to lying, stealing, swearing and drinking.' "

He began to laugh. "You still remember that?"

"Of course I do."

It had happened a couple of years before, when I was lugging a busted heart down the road, and came through Cedar Rapids. A rampant toothache was worse than my momentary heartache. Mr. Whiteman shook his head over this, and went down to the basement to return with wine. He poured out a stiff drink, asking only, "Do you like muscatel?" with my replying that I had never tasted it in my life.

He lifted his glass and made his toast.

" 'Here's to lying, stealing, swearing and drinking. If you must lie, lie to a beautiful woman and she'll be glad to believe you. If you must steal, steal away from dull care, and it will do you good. If you must swear, swear by your friends, and they'll be glad to swear by you. And if you must drink, drink with me, and I'll be glad to drink with you.' "

I'd asked at the time, "Mr. Whiteman, did you make that up, your own self?"

"No, I picked it up somewhere or other. Some acquaintance said it, and I had him write it down so I could learn it. I don't know where it comes from or who said it first. Nice little thing, isn't it?"

I'd learned the toast then, and instantly, and have never forgotten it, and never will.

This day he said that he had a little more shopping to do and might as well do it there at Mandels'. We went down together and stood on the main floor.

"Mack, I'm a merchant. This is an exciting place, this store. There's just a little bit of that pre-Christmas feeling beginning to get under way— Do you truly hate it?"

I explained that it was mercantile endeavor, and I was just not cut out for it. "We have some really swell people employed here, and I've got to know a few of them. So it isn't the people. It's the surroundings, the enterprise. I've had enough of Chicago for a while. I'd like to get off somewhere else and maybe—you know— eventually write about it? Or write other things. I'm confident that I'm destined to make my way by writing."

Harry Whiteman said, "I think so too." He looked at me and held up one finger. He repeated a few words as if he'd known them long and lovingly, and again wished to share.

I supposed meditatively that they were an expression first uttered by Mary Baker Eddy, or at least ascribed to her. I wasn't a Christian Scientist, and owned no intention of becoming one;

but the line came from this man's lips in saintly quality. For all acquaintance with the New Testament, I didn't recognize that this was from the Third Epistle of John.

> Beloved, I wish above all things that thou mayest prosper and be in health, even as thy soul prospereth.

That night when I met Irene as she came out into chilly dimness, I asked, "How would you like to go to Cedar Rapids?"

"Where?" she demanded. "You mean where Dick Whiteman lives?"

"His father came to the store this afternoon, and I got to talk to him a while. He thinks it's just possible that I might be able to get a newspaper job there."

"Why, how wonderful! When?"

"I don't know. He's going to try, and I've got to write to Don Farran. You know, the poet who comes from that little town of Rowan—"

"Oh yes, I met Don when he was here at Dick Little's. But what can he do about it?"

"He knows a guy named Farquhar who's publisher of the Cedar Rapids *Republican*. Maybe he can put in a good word for me too."

Suddenly the world had grown brighter, the splintery rain less stinging. It was a fortunate moment to be alive, with folks going around putting in good words.

8.

Election day that year was rarely bountiful and bright . . . air blue-gold, temperature unseasonably high. Our polling place of the Second Precinct, 44th Ward, occupied the same area where it had been housed through previous campaigns: the laundry rooms and onetime storage space in an apartment building facing directly on Diversey Parkway. No machines. Votes were registered by paper ballot.

I had risen from lowly ranks of watchers and clerks, and now held one of the positions as judge of elections . . . five dollars knocked off my salary at Mandels' for absence on that day, but twenty dollars to be paid in hand by the precinct captain.

Thank heaven this wasn't registration. I had suffered through one of those.

Prominent in our precinct was a dignified hive fronting on Diversey, called the Brewster, tenanted almost entirely by gaffers and widows. We'd have a procession of them stretching out through a concrete courtyard. Many were so infirm that they had to be supported in their tracks by companions, and there were enough canes to stock a store.

"How long have you lived in the United States, ma'am?"

"All my life. I was born here."

"How long in the State of Illinois?"

"All my life!"

"How long in Cook County?"

"All my life!"

"But, ma'am, we have to put down a *date*. How long in this precinct?"

"Well, I was born just around the corner, where those Pine Grove apartments now stand. Is that in this precinct?"

"Yes indeed, ma'am. But you see, we have to put down how *long* in the precinct."

"Sixty years!"

They were eighty-five years of age if they were ten, when they caterwauled such falsehood.

Our precinct, whatever its proximity to persons who operated in or on the fringes of the underworld, was avowedly a quiet one. But trouble was fostered by a watcher representing the Bertha Bauer organization.

Mrs. Bauer had been a perennial figure on the political scene. In this occasion of her candidacy she achieved vast press coverage, and was reckoned as a power to be dealt with. Nevertheless, through some manipulation of chicanery or plain stupidity, her watcher at our polling place gummed up the procedures.

The idea seemed to be to retard the balloting as much as possible in certain regions which Mrs. Bauer knew were already lost to her. Proceeding on this plan, her watcher challenged in mechanical routine.

Challenging the ancient Brewsterites was an inhuman act. It kept those crones standing in line until they were in a fainting condition. It meant trotting out the voting lists to see that each and every voter was properly registered, and to review their personal histories.

Albert H. Norris, our precinct captain, was driven wild by these tactics. The ward committeeman, a short husky middle-aged man—call him Gillian—looked his disapproval. Quietly he voiced it on the side, but was powerless to do anything to retard the retarding.

My fellow lodger, Cliff Palmer, with his Treasury Department and S. Glenn Young background, was disposed to do something about it.

The Bertha Bauer worker asserted her tactics to the limit of bladder capacity, and then she had to go to the bathroom. Obviously inexperienced where voting procedures were concerned, she went away and left her watcher's list exposed on an old laundry tub converted into a table in emergency. This formed an irresistible challenge to anyone of resource and opportunity.

When she came back she gave an explosive shriek. "Where's my *list?*"

It wasn't there, and a watcher without her list of voters to be challenged just wasn't any watcher at all. Most of us exchanged wise professional glances, but this woman romped away in search of a telephone.

"Bertha Bauer shall hear about this!" and Bertha heard.

She both heard and acted with precision. Sooner than one might have believed possible, the trim figure of the busy little candidate, magnificently hatted, stalked among us. She was escorted by a uniformed cop.

"What's this all about?"

Her watcher explained wildly. She'd gone to the bathroom,

she'd not taken her list. "It was lying right here! Somebody stole it!"

There piped the voice of a clerk who was serving her first term at the table. I think it unlikely that she wallowed long in the jungle of Chicago politics. She just wasn't cut out for the job.

"I saw who took your list. It was Mr. Palmer."

"Officer," screamed Bertha Bauer, "find Mr. Palmer and arrest him!"

"And," the informant stammered, "I think I saw him give the list to Mr. Gillian." Even this nitwit spoke the name with some awe. A ward committeeman!

"Officer! Find Mr. Gillian and arrest him too!"

The cop stood scratching his ear. "Look, Mrs. Bauer, you got to tell me where to find these people. I just can't go around arresting thin air."

It was time for the voice of experience to speak. And anyway, we weren't Bertha Bauer people; and anyway, we didn't like the watcher; and anyway, we wished to terminate the silly episode as adroitly as possible; and anyway, I was conscious of the fact that Bertha Bauer and her henchwoman formed an extreme minority; and anyway, everyone else was dying to get rid of them too.

I said, in the tender tone of the most helpful Boy Scout who ever scouted, "Who is it you want to find, Mrs. Bauer?"

"That Mr. Palmer and that Mr. Gillian!"

"Why, I saw them together a few minutes ago. They were talking on the sidewalk, up at the corner of Surf and Pine Grove."

Away they went—north along an alleyway behind the building, and thence heading by alley and court for the destination I'd described. The cop trailed reluctantly . . . the women kept turning, beckoning in fury, urging him on.

I waited until they were past the last corner and no longer visible, then hastened to Cliff Palmer and Gillian. They were sitting together in a car on Diversey, smack in front of the polling place.

"They're looking for you and that list. I just sent them up to the Surf Street corner."

Palmer and Gillian bounced out of the car. "Got a minute to spare?" and Palmer beckoned me along. I went with them up the block to our Cambridge Avenue building, and watched Cliff burn the voting list sheets above a lavatory in the corner of his room and flush the black flakes down the bowl.

"I guess that takes care of the evidence," he said.

Gillian agreed. "I guess it does. Who the hell is this young man, Cliff?"

I felt pleasurably cute, and said, "Bye-bye," and left Palmer explaining me to Mr. Gillian in glowing terms. I heard the Chicago *Tribune* mentioned, and kept retreating.

Things had quieted down. Policeman, Bertha Bauer and watcher were vanished, after returning from their futile sortie and—incidentally—inquiring vainly for me. I kept a weather eye turned on the door the rest of that day, but they did not return. The precinct assumed its normal peace.

It was a long day and evening. I remember the transporting of our locked-up ballots to the County Building. Standing in orderly mobs until all hours; the long wait; the people from wards of the North Side, South Side, West Side; black faces sprinkled liberally among the white; the slow shuffle-shuffle as we edged forward to halt again, to wait long, to shuffle-shuffle more, and eventually to be admitted to locked sacred regions where we delivered our cargo.

I described the scene in verses written about Paddy Carr when he died later that month. The poem was called "Chant in the County Building," and carried some of the same sad walking rune which Chicago retained in its streets and chancels.

(Black and sleek as river tides, or white as Drive hotels)
In the halls the voters veer, their steps a-chime like bells,
Crusted with a stockyard smoke—or smooth as girls who play
Devil-slick in satin at a haunted cabaret!
Up from Cicero they troop, or down from Maywood far,
Weighted heavy with their horns to blow for Paddy Carr.

Well, I had served—had earned my twenty dollars, and thought that was the end of it.

About a week went by. Then, when Irene and I came from dinner one evening, we were informed that Mr. Gillian had been inquiring.

"I told him that you're usually back here by eight o'clock," said Mrs. Norris. "I think he'll come round about then."

He did appear—elegant in new blue autumnal coat, elegant in his felt hat with its dashing brim, elegant in immaculate linen and shiny shoes.

I welcomed him into our bedroom and introduced him to Irene. He stood appraising us.

"I very much appreciate what you did on election day. Perhaps you will remember speaking to Palmer and to me," and his eyes flashed merrily. "Well, then. I've come to make you a proposition. We cannot offer you the precinct captaincy here—"

"That's Pop Norris."

"Yes. However, if you are willing to consider moving into the Fourth Precinct of the 44th Ward—that will mean over beyond Clark Street—we can give you the position of precinct captain there. The work will consist of getting out the votes: purely and simply that. You are to round up the voters, get them to the polls."

"What else would I have to do?"

"Not another damn thing," said the honest Gillian. "I'm told that you want to write, and you'd have plenty of opportunity to write. The pay would be two hundred dollars a month. What do you say?"

My jaw dropped a mile. Wistfully I considered my typewriter, not during tired hours in the evenings, but daytimes. *Daytimes,* when I was filled with energy and strength.

Rounding up the vote, guiding the voters to the polls . . . that would be a lark. I wanted to shout to the skies.

I turned to look at Irene, I'd thought she'd be ready to dance a jig. She wasn't ready to do anything of the kind.

She observed Mr. Gillian coolly . . . oh, Christ . . . Tartini and the wine. . . .

"Mr. Gillian, wasn't there some trouble on election day?"

"Not here. Nothing but the business about that silly watcher's list. Your husband is a resourceful young man, Mrs. Kantor. That's the reason we're offering—"

"There was a killing. Someone was machine-gunned to death."

I exploded, "That guy Granaday. Sure! But that was down in the 22nd Ward, on the South Side. You'd expect that to happen down there. But—"

"Thank you, Mr. Gillian," said Irene. "You've been very kind. I'm sorry, but we would not be interested in moving."

Gillian took a long look at her, and then nodded. "I see." Without rancor he looked at me squarely. "Your wife makes the decisions, I see. They like to do that. I know my wife does. Good evening, young people. Mrs. Kantor, it's been my pleasure to meet you," and then he was gone.

The air hung tense for a few minutes. Irene didn't know what I was going to say or do, and I didn't know either. I went over and stood looking out of the window, and couldn't see anything but blank blackness and reflected light.

Then I heard her say, "Darling, are you going to hate me?" I turned around and told her that I wasn't going to hate her.

"But, my God!" I yelled. "You won't let me do anything! First the wine, and now this! I could still take them both on—"

She said airily, "Oh, write a book about it," and I exploded with a few obscenities.

"Sure! Some day—if I ever get a chance to write! If you keep getting in my way, I'll never get a chance!"

Irene took a dancing step and twirled on her toes. "Don't you understand? By my getting in your way I'm helping to *give* you the chance."

Three or four years later a fellow named Chic Young started to draw a cartoon strip called *Blondie*. Mr. Young was born in Chicago, and I'm positive that he must have known Irene somewhere along the line.

9.

That might I told Irene about the first job I ever held, following paper route days. The three and a half dollars earned weekly kept me in spending money, minor school items, and helped to purchase some of my clothes. I was filled with a sense of responsibility, which, next to an awareness of urgency, is gold and jewels to the young.

My boss was Seymour Eichman, who had come to Webster City and opened a women's ready-to-wear clothing store a few years before. He was, when I went to work for him, unmarried; I thought him very handsome, and so apparently did most of the young women in town. Never was an eligible bachelor more cooed at by girls of marriageable age, but it didn't seem to go to Mr. Eichman's head. He remained efficient and even-tempered —tolerant of people's mistakes, but still a man who would stand for no nonsense.

Perhaps the fact that half my own inheritance was Jewish built a small bond between my employer and myself. At any rate, our relations were of the pleasantest. He would always show me, personally, just how he wanted a job done; afterward he expected that I would do it in that manner. I was porter, errand-boy, sweeper-outer, general handyman.

Mr. Eichman's slogan or motto for his shop, "A City Store at Your Door," was not far from the truth. There were at least five girl clerks, together with a seamstress and alterations expert.

Very early in the morning every weekday I was on the job, delighted to carry the store's key fastened to my belt. I would sweep and dust, cleaning off the sidewalk in front, washing the show windows whenever they needed it. There were a number of mirrors, and these had to be polished to a high gloss. One series was a novelty in our town—one of those closets or cubbyholes into which you could step, with long mirrors on both sides and in front, and see yourself from a dozen different angles.

This cubicle was my especial dread. I was beginning to grow up, my appearance was altering, I was getting taller and bonier—certainly not "bonnier" to any eyes except Mother's. My hand would be working away, wiping off soapy polish which dried over the glass almost as fast as it was rubbed on. Thus, through chalky white walls, gleaming holes would appear; in these holes I would appear to myself—a dozen Mack Kantors, all equally unbearable and incredible. I would stop working for a time, staring fearfully. No one could ever love a face like that, I thought. Surely no woman would ever want to marry me after I'd grown up.

If I had known that practically every boy or girl who ever lived suffered the same pangs, there would have been some reassurance. But I didn't know. . . .

Mr. Eichman appeared about eight a.m., correct and serene. How well he held himself, how splendidly he was dressed! I longed in those days to be like Mr. Eichman, although I had no ambition to own a dress and coat and ladies' underwear store. And here was a man who gave his employees the same smile he offered his customers, or sometimes even a better one.

He would produce the key to the mailbox and I would sprint down the alley to our post office, a block away, and bring the mail. There might be another quick errand or two, then at eight-thirty I ran to school. At four p.m. I was on the job again and worked until six. Saturday was scheduled as a long day: the agreement called for me to work from seven to twelve o'clock noon—from one until five-thirty. Then I was expected to work from seven p.m. until closing time—around ten or thereabouts. There were no union rules in our town then, at least none that affected me.

Never once did I work all of a Saturday evening. Mr. Eichman had surprised me about this the first time, but I didn't give him a chance to surprise me again. I was way ahead of him after that. At five-thirty I would speed along the eleven blocks of Willson Avenue, and reach home in a lather of Saturday evening excitement.

Saturday night—those were big hours in any small town. Every store stayed open—even some of the professional offices. The banks were open: this was the day when hundreds of farmers drove into town with their families and did their week's shopping and business. This was the night when every boy and girl of high school age who could walk or ride, came ready-dressed for the social fray. Lines waited at both pop-corn wagons, customers were banked three deep in front of the soda fountains in drug stores or in the Greeks' candy shops. Pool halls echoed with shouts and brayings; young people clustered thick in restaurants and magazine stands.

Years later I came to know cities in Latin countries where the youth of the towns promenaded in the evening, boys and girls giving each other the flirtatious once-over as they passed. Surely a Saturday night in our town in 1918 offered much the same spectacle. Taller stronger older males were gone away to the war in droves—they were at Camp Pike, Camp Dodge, Camp Mills—and many were even slogging along the roads of northern France with the 168th Infantry of the Rainbow Division. But we slighter teen-agers strove willingly to pick up where they had left off.

Our girls may have been skinnier and shriller-voiced than theirs, but they were beautiful to us. With care I would scrub my face and comb my hair—with frowning contemplation I would use Mother's little manicure scissors to clip the rim of tiny hairs now showing on my upper lip (I wished that they were thicker and more bristly; then I could shave as my school-mate Charles Mason was already shaving. Of course he was very dark . . .).

A hasty supper, then the jaunt back to Eichman's store. If I had a new necktie, so much the better. A time or two I was even wearing *a new shirt*. . . . There might be wastebaskets to be emptied, a bundle to be carried; always there was the evening mail to be fetched. Then I would plant myself—not in the back room or basement, my regular quarters during business hours—but conspicuously at the back of the store itself.

There I would stand rigidly at attention, like a soldier or foot-man in a play.

Customers all over the place, women gabbling in dressing rooms, luscious lady clerks hastening from rack to counter to drawer to rack and back again. I scented the odor of their perfume and face powder, and thrilled to all the feminine rustle, and wished hungrily that I didn't look like *me*—that I was handsome and careless and assured of manner, like Chester Maag or Gerald Wiese or one of the popular upper classmen.

Mr. Eichman himself would be busy as the rest, greeting incoming customers, adding up bills, directing his clerks. He never seemed to observe me standing back there . . . yet before too long he would make it his business to stroll coolly toward the back of the store, where he might make some agonizingly extensive calculations at the big cash register. Then he would look up, and seem to discover me for the first time.

Always he gave a calm appraising look, and then his mouth bent in a smile. "Well, Mack." The ritual never varied. "You look like a million dollars, tonight."

I would grin my thanks.

"By the way, I don't believe you need to stay on the job any longer. There isn't much for you to do tonight." With impressive gesture his hand would smite the cash register; a drawer would shoot open with the friendliest clang in the world. One, two, three he would count them out: silver dollars, and a fifty-cent piece also. With this pleasant weight in my pocket I would jabber a word of thanks, and get out of the store as fast as I could without knocking down any old ladies.

Second Street—it was Broadway, State Street—it was London and Paris and the busy shining world. The squawk of motor horns, the howling of a tired country urchin, the prattle and calling, the grating of wheels—the challenge flung from sidewalk to sidewalk, the scent of Bill Corisis's fudge sundaes, and salty hot odors from Mac's popcorn wagon (he was an ex-cowboy, not our next-door Mr. Mac; and he had a rhyme printed on his popcorn and peanut sacks, about a man who was dying of starvation, and who finally said, "Give me one more sack of Mac's popcorn, and then I am ready to die.").

Second Street was all beauty and all mystery and all carnival. The kids . . . where were they? Probably over at Channer's drug store. Howard Sheldon was keen on Ruth Blankenbuehler (that was a name for the book); and Kempster Pyle was keen on Marie Garth; and most assuredly I was keen on Elizabeth Tormey. The three girls were devoted friends and always strolled together; perhaps sooner or later we might stall them . . . ah, 1918 slang.

And over all the sense of spring, and the awareness of an ever-talking river bending beyond . . . fresh memory of hepaticas growing under last winter's matting, the strong knowledge of oak forests where now the pink oak leaves were as big as a squirrel's ears.

A fragrant recollection to entertain when the city was perpetually so sooty, dank, chilling.

10.

The key landed in the dungeon cell with a clang, sooner than had seemed possible. On my desk appeared a note concerning the publisher of the Cedar Rapids *Republican*.

Call Mr. Farquhar at—

A local telephone number followed. I hurried to a public booth, gave the ring, and reached him immediately.

He told me, "I'm at the office of a friend; you probably know the name. He's active in real estate—" Then I thought that he said his friend's name was Dixon.

"Oh yes. Reminds me of *The Birth of a Nation*—"

"What say?"

"You know, the author of that book on which *The Birth of a Nation* was based. Isn't it *The Clansman?*"

"Well," he said, "I don't recognize that. But anyhow, can you come over here and talk to me?"

"Of course, Mr. Farquhar."

"When? Now?"

"Certainly, sir."

"It might be well if you could stay in the Loop, and we could have an early dinner together."

I crowed, "Splendid—and thank you very much. I'll be there soon," though it was only four p.m.

This became critical and no mistake. I had not expected to hear directly from any newspaper, and for a publisher himself to call me— Apparently Mr. Whiteman had been busy. So perhaps had Don Farran, the railroad telegrapher who owned ambitions as a poet.

To tell Farquhar that I dared not leave the store until five-thirty would have been just too much. I thought it over quickly, then put together the claims already settled that day, and from my hoard drew a few more—enough to make a fat full day's work.

I sought out an earnest young man who had joined us recently. "Susskin, you remember last Tuesday? You asked me to punch you out at the time clock."

"I sure did appreciate it. I had to go to the dentist—"

"Well, I don't have to go to any dentist, but I've got to go somewhere else, and it's damn important. Can you manage to perform the same favor for me, at five-thirty this afternoon?"

"Of course I can."

I gave him the large envelope containing my claims. "Just drop that on Mr. Frank's desk when his back is turned."

He grinned. "Yes, and I'll have to visit the time clock when his back is turned, as well. But don't worry: you did me a big favor and I'm glad to pay it back."

(Susskin offered an enlivening description of his activities when we met the next day. He'd resorted to considerable skulking and speedy clock activity, in order to accomplish the feat. Frank owned that awful skill which Mr. Cuff had demonstrated at the American Flyer, of being everywhere at once. All in all, it was a good thing for us tracers psychologically: it put us on our toes. A dangerous game, but rewarding. There were only a few casualties.)

This meant going without an overcoat, but I was used to that. A lot of us habitually wore caps to the store instead of hats: they were easily concealed in our pockets. So I jammed cap and gloves into one side pocket of my suit coat, rolled up a woolen scarf and put that in my hip pocket. Then, with a claim in hand as if headed for duty in a portion of the store beyond the delivery court, I walked boldy past store detectives who lounged forever near the court entrance. Pretending to be bound for the section specializing in men's haberdashery, I saw it was a question only of dodging behind a couple of delivery trucks and vanishing amid throngs of shoppers who trooped Madison Street in early twilight and slow-falling sleet.

A plague on all people designated as Dixons. I thought I'd heard the name before, and how could any real estate office be so elusive? I rushed to the address which Farquhar had offered. It was on Dearborn—or Clark Street—near Monroe. But—lo and behold—there wasn't a single Dixon listed in the lobby directory of tenants.

The elevator starter shook his head. "No Dixons here."

I went to a telephone book and searched for Dixons. They were numerous, but any real estate firm such as I sought seemed unlisted. It took me all of forty-five minutes to find the proper address as I combed from building to building along those blocks. Then, across the street, I happened to glance up, and there was NIXON reflected in gold-lettered bounty along a whole string of windows on the second or third floor opposite. (I was somewhat more delighted at seeing that repetitious name than Humphrey would have been, say, in 1968.)

It was anybody's guess what Mr. Farquhar would think about this extended delay, but my own opinion of my investigative talents was not exalted. As a possible Henry M. Stanley searching for Dr. Livingstone, I presumed that I had been batting around Asia instead of Africa on two very stupid feet.

I raced upstairs, made myself known to a guardian angel, and she passed me on to a secretary who escorted me into the private office where Farquhar sat with his friend. They were old pals, lounging, genial and relaxed.

An apology was stammered out . . . something had come up at the store. . . .

"Oh, that doesn't matter. We've been having a grand time, talking about old days—"

I managed to unclench my hands while they talked about old days a while longer.

James Farquhar turned out to own the manner and intensity of an urgent shining-visaged driver. Such men often demonstrate ambition beyond the reach of their own talents, but I held no worry about this . . . I was experienced and wise! . . . good Lord, I was twenty-two!

He asked, "Mind having a fairly early dinner? I'm a country boy, you know: we're used to eating the evening meal a lot earlier than you Chicagoans. I'm hoping that you can stay in the Loop and dine with me, and we can talk—"

"Oh yes—that'll be fine—thanks a lot—just let me make a telephone call—my wife—"

I caught her at Carson's as she was about to leave the counter. It was as if I saw her smiling charitably over the phone. "But you already called me, honey. Half an hour ago."

"*I did?*"

"You said you were hunting for that Dixon office, and you couldn't find it, and it was driving you crazy. You told me that you'd find it if it took all evening. You said for me to go home alone—"

There ensued an explosion of groan and laughter in the same breath. "Looks like I'm going to be a sensation in Cedar Rapids, if we get there." But gigantic pressure was relaxed now, and soon I was making better sense.

Farquhar asked, "What—no overcoat? Don't you wear one habitually?"

"Oh, you know—dashing away in a hurry—"

He looked at me keenly. "Or maybe not wishing them to know that you were leaving for the day?"

"Mr. Farquhar," I said, "you are now a member of the Chicago Detective Bureau," and we burst out laughing.

He took me to a downtown club where either he held membership or where guest privileges had been arranged for him. We drank a little needled beer and talked with enthusiasm. He explained that he did not own the *Republican,* but was engaged by the owners to serve as hired publisher. He was ambitious— So was the whole staff—he wanted ambitious people, not mere drudges— He'd looked up some of my work, and friends had shown him more.

What about my duties with Mother on the Webster City paper? What were my chief interests, my preferences? Obviously I doted on what he called Americana . . . should I come to him in Cedar Rapids, I might concentrate on such local phases.

Nothing could have suited me better, and I said so.

"Would it be possible for you to leave Mandels' at once?"

I sighed, thinking of the wintry rush. "They wouldn't like it if I left immediately," and it was essential to explain a little about the adjustment bureau.

"Well, then— You'd really like to come?"

"Of course I would. I'm dying to get out of Chicago."

"Very well, we've got a job for you. Now then—about money. How much will you have to have?"

I considered rapidly. "It's expensive for us, making the change—"

"Don't worry about when you first land in Cedar Rapids. We hold a lot of due bills at the Montrose Hotel. You and your wife will have a place to land until you can look around and get settled."

"Thank you, that'll be fine. But— Would you go for fifty dollars a week?"

He thought about this.

"You see, I'd like to better my condition—"

"Look, Mack. Forty dollars a week will buy, in Cedar Rapids, what fifty dollars a week will buy in Chicago. Everything's cheaper there than what you're confronted with. Would you go for this? Start at forty dollars. Then, if you prove as valuable as I think you will, next year we'll go higher."

I said wearily, "I really ought to stay through the Christmas rush and immediately thereafter. The adustment bureau is in a panic over the seasonal business, and so they'll be immediately following the holiday."

"Can you start as early as Monday, January 10th?"

"Yes, sir, I can," and my heart was dancing, and all the waiters in that taproom where we'd had our beer and dinner— They were dancing too, and so were mighty old chandeliers on the ceiling; and out in a frigid street the traffic was jumping up and down; and over on the icy lake congealed ships were dancing; and critters in the Lincoln Park zoo must have been leaping. And all those thousands of people thronging round— Oh, they were singing in streets, and uniting their hands in grasp, and going round and round; and there were Maypoles, and I heard the clatter and puff of fireworks; and seals were flipping, and wolves with whom I'd howled— Oh revelry, concertinas in the street, in mighty buildings, the squat ones . . . blossom colors tinting the morose clouds above.

. . . The quickest way to 2829 Cambridge and Irene?

Farquhar and I stood near the corner and talked a few minutes longer. "You'll think I'm quite a club man," he said. "Now I've got to go over to the Press Club and meet somebody else."

I knew where the Press Club was, Dick Little belonged there. "Let me drop you off." Grandly I stepped from the curb and held up my hand. "Oh, taxi!" One of them skidded to a stop. I felt like William Randolph Hearst, James Gordon Bennett, or maybe Joseph Pulitzer.

It seemed twenty days later . . . actually it was only twenty minutes before Irene and I were holding hands and going round and round in our narrow bedroom. Her face became a daisy's face. "But is it *true*? Is it really *true*? I can't *believe* it!"

11.

We were asked over to the Laynes' for Sunday noon dinner. Such invitations might postpone activity with the Littles but they were greeted with high favor.

Jessie Layne's kitchen enterprise I held to be little short of marvelous. She'd gotten me over a young lifetime's aversion to baked beans— Made me into a bean hog pure and simple. She'd select the firmest fattest dried white lima beans; anoint them with onion, Worcestershire sauce, sugar, and a bit of mustard; simmer them overnight with a generous slab of pork in a huge iron kettle . . . I can smell them, see them, taste them, with rivulets of golden juice running off to be absorbed by boiled potatoes. Would there perhaps be baked lima beans on Sunday? I screamed over the telephone that I hoped there would be; and she responded with those assured chuckles which a master chef in full consciousness should be allowed to award. Her pot roasts as well, her mixed veal-and-ham loaves, the dulcet potato salads with bits of red onion and slices of sweet pickle, generously peppered with celery seed. Deep-dish apple pies, crusted tan with cinnamon. . . .

We'd accepted ardently, like big cats in the menagerie mentioned above after their weekly day of fasting.

. . . But where was Irene?

I sat with Mr. Layne and the sons Charles and Lawrence, who were still unmarried and living at home. Charles worked for Montgomery Ward; Lawrence had left off his Colorado mining endeavor after Kenny's death, and decided to stay in Chicago. He was working for a firm which installed tear-gas chambers in the vault doors of banks.

I held forth in conjecture about future newspaper operations. True, Irene and I were earning forty-five dollars per week between the two of us, in Chicago; but I treasured Farquhar's assertion that forty dollars out there would buy what fifty

dollars bought here. Lawrence, thinking of Colorado, quickly
affirmed the opinion. It was close to a step upward in earning
capacity, and there was the possibility that Irene might find a
promising situation as well.

"Where's she gone, anyway?"

Lawrence pointed with his pipe. "Out in front, on the
porch. Some mail came for her. I guess she's reading it."

Indeed she was reading it. When at last I went out to inquire,
her face held a weird mixture of pride and calamity.

"Lawrence said you had some mail."

"Yes. A letter from Aunt Nettie—she's owed me for a long
time. And one from Dorothy Jane . . . you know, my old
school friend. She went away on a trip with her mother.
And—Well. Here."

She offered a sheet bearing the letterhead of Meyer-Both,
a well-known advertising art agency.

Dear Miss Layne:
　　We recall with interest your application for a place in our
company made last winter. At the time we felt ourselves to
be overstaffed, and could offer nothing better than a hope
for the future.
　　However we are now checking previous applications. We
recall with favor the work which you submitted, and hope
that you are still able to come into our organization.
　　Should your talents be available to us, will you please
call the undersigned as soon as possible—

I said weakly, "Congratulations."

"Don't be silly."

"They'd pay you—?"

"At least twenty-five to start—maybe thirty dollars—"

"Then, if I remain at Mandels', we'll be earning fifty-five or
sixty dollars between us."

The small voice whispered, "Yes."

My words floated in space. "Maybe eventually I can go
back to being a claim correspondent. We could have an apartment, and get out of that single room—"

Now the tears were coming. "And what would you be giving up?"

"The newspaper job in Cedar Rapids."

"And your ambition to make your way by writing! It's— Oh," she cried, "why did this have to happen now? It's—so— I can't find the word."

I asked, "Taunting?"

"I'm afraid so. I'll write to them and tell them I can't possibly consider it."

Her stanchness was loosening the tentacles in which I'd been wrapped. "Well, is everything just the way it was? You'll go to Iowa in good faith?"

"Course I will."

"You won't be angry? Jealous? Resentful because I made you leave town?"

Her voice still trembled. "I'll just take pride in the fact that these people did want me after all. Now, it's chilly out here— Let's go back in the apartment—"

"Are you going to tell your folks?"

"Please, no. Not now. I don't want to discuss it any further."

She was intrepid. She believed loyally that she must fill her husband's needs, must demonstrate dependence upon him and his choices. Those years of struggle to attend classes at the Chicago Academy of Fine Arts and the Art Institute had borne only this small and suddenly sweetly bitter fruit.

That night I would awaken to find her crying.

I formed a hard resolution that some day I must build for her a studio in which she might paint and prosper to her heart's content. (Did, too.)

What we could not know was that in effect she was saying goodbye to painting for a long time to come. There'd be no opportunity to achieve by this means when we reached Cedar Rapids. Then new perils would ensue, along with her dedication in aiding me with my first-to-be-published novel. Hard after this, more complex problems . . . the process of maternity, homemaking . . . maternity again. . . .

Only when I went off to a then-inconceivable war in a distant future would she sit alone and feel again the blinding desire to take up brushes and assert herself in such manner, and never cease. Then and only then would her palette be freshened—not with lamentation, but with inherent oils. The long-needed perfumes found amid emerald, cobalt, rose madder.

12.

My intentions had been liberal when I told Farquhar that I felt I ought to remain through the Christmas season.

Rumors ran like cockroaches behind a quick-lunch counter. By this time I understood the department store jargon, not to say superstition, of the period. The ghost would walk (we would receive our weekly checks) on Friday, December 24th. A broad axe was to fall at that same moment with keenly whetted blade. All the temporary help, numbering some twelve hundred, would be notified that their services were no longer required. But worse: it was the annual firing date for more permanent employees who had been weighed and found wanting.

Had Miss Gargoyle been giving consistent trouble to the assistant buyer in the imported china department? Had Mr. Blitz evinced a surly attitude to his immediate superior in bookkeeping? Did the junior Mr. Sullivan consistently refuse to mend his ways in producing petty discomfort for the senior Mr. Gilbert? Little blue slips appeared in their pay envelopes, and those were the last pay envelopes they'd get from Mandels'. It was a moment of worry for some; in fact, for all employees except the most serenely well-established . . . a time of walking death.

Nervousness extended like a plague, it affected even those originally convinced of their own importance to the establishment. People snapped and bickered where they had not done so before. Petty squabblings were a way of life to many, but seasonal angels seemed caroling a litany borrowed from all the witches on the moors.

Irene said that it was the same over at Carson's. "They're all twittering. Even many of the older and more firmly entrenched employees seem fearful of their jobs, and they communicate their uncertainty to the rest."

In agreed concert we tracers were turning in more claims than before. The load was there and it had to be absorbed. In earlier season it has been observed that twenty-two claims were considered tops for a day's work. Now the limit expanded: we offered twenty-five, twenty-eight claims. The store officials begged us to work evenings; they would give you dinner money, and a handsome bonus if you toiled until midnight. This extra pay was a heady inducement to many, and we had remained on the job doggedly often past the point of good sense. In our deed we were handicapped . . . you couldn't approach people in certain areas. Telephones still might operate up until nine o'clock . . . many customers could be interviewed and offer essential evidence. . . .

The strain began to tell upon everyone. Sales departments remained open through early evening hours, and when you had run all day it didn't seem fair to have to run into the night as well . . . many of us ran. Whips of necessity put fresh contusions on ankles long scarred by such application. We ached in bone and brain.

"I was talking with Callan today. You know, he's one of Mr. Russell's right-hand men. He said, 'Kid, you haven't seen a thing yet. Wait until the week *after* Christmas. It's pure hell where the adjustment bureau is concerned. Everybody in sales departments is worn out and uncooperative. They bite your head off when you go in to run down a claim.'

"And I said, 'Well, some of us might not have the opportunity to suffer. I've heard about those slips which appear in pay envelopes—'"

Irene wanted to know what Mr. Callan had said to that.

"He said, 'Don't be silly,' or some such remark. If I were to rely on his testimony alone, it would seem that I'm not slated for dismissal. But now I wish I were."

Irene and I sat in a dairy lunch, grabbing a quick bite on Friday the 24th, when I looked at her for a long moment and then said, "I just thought of something. We could fire ourselves."

Her fair steady gaze met mine, and tiny lines showed between her eyes. "You mean—just quit?"

"Why not quit tonight?"

"But— You told Mr. Farquhar you'd come on Monday the 10th—"

"And he was rather disappointed. He'd be glad to have me begin sooner. Suppose I start operations with the *Republican* on January 3rd instead of January 10th? What difference will it make in the long run to Mandels'? Or, in your case, to Carson's?"

She considered. "Actually I don't suppose it will make any real difference to the stores—"

"If I'm not to be fired, then someone may be sore because I'm quitting. The only person I care about is Mr. Russell himself, and I can explain my motives to him."

"But what about our money? Our salaries?"

"Carson's must follow the same policy which prevails at Mandels'. Any time an employee is desperate for money, he is privileged to go to the cashier's department and get a voucher which can be cashed for his entire salary, as due, up until that very day. You can't draw in advance for the day on which you apply. But anything up until that day."

Irene said, "It seems kind of daring. Wow!"

"Not where you and I are concerned. We'll just depart a week earlier—that's all there is to it. Agreed?"

She said, "I don't know why I should feel like an international spy, but I do. Wow. Agreed!"

We stopped at a Western Union office and sent a low-rate telegram to Farquhar. *Will report for work Monday January 3rd instead of 10th Merry Christmas Regards*. We scurried on to our stores in exalted spirits.

I got my saved-up claims out of hiding, and checked. Together with the ones done that morning, I had thirty-one to turn in. That represented a great day's accomplishment in any language. But it was only fair to work the day out if they would let me.

. . . First to the cashier, to inscribe a request for pay to date, and receive my money. If someone chose to hold out the wage for this extra day, I'd accept the loss with grace.

Then to Mr. Russell.

"Allow me to tell you first, sir, that I appreciate the thoughtfulness you've shown. But I'm just not department store material."

His ragged eyebrows crawled up. "Your manner suggests, lad, that you are quitting."

"I'd like your permission to do so."

"I dislike to give it."

"I can't quite understand why—"

"You may think I'm an old blether, but I'm not: it's the truth. I've inquired, and have learned that you've worked hard and done a good job. I became convinced that after the holiday season you might return to the correspondent's desk where you began. With knowledge gained through the tracing of claims—knowledge of the store and its customers which you've acquired in these months—you can be of true value to us. I'm hurt at the thought of saying goodbye."

I stared at him. "Mr. Russell, you've practically knocked me off my feet. I wouldn't have dreamt that you'd feel that way."

"Young man, I do feel that way. I've talked to various Buyers with whom you've done business, and others as well. Even your immediate superior, Mr. Frank—"

"Frank!" I exploded. "Doesn't he hate me? We tracers are convinced that he hates all of us!"

"You should be convinced of nothing of the kind. Frank says that you've been active and alert. Now, just why do you desire to leave?"

I told him briefly about the newspaper job . . . he kept shaking his head. "Ah, I feared it might end like this. But I

still think you'd be a good man in the store. If it doesn't work
out to your satisfaction, we'll be glad to take you back. I can
say no more than that. Oh yes," he added suddenly. "We like
the young man you brought to us."

He was speaking of George Butzen, one of the Graeme
Players, who had inquired about the possibilities at Mandels'.
George had been truck-driving for a large printing company,
and didn't like the work. I brought him to the store and introduced him to Mr. Russell, and he gave George a job.

"MacKinlay, you're bitten with this writing bug, and I trust
you'll bite it back. But if you don't manage to, and wish to
return—" He stood up and smiled and held out his stout
hand. "Now I've a million things to do, and no doubt you have
as well. I offer my regards, and please extend them to your
young bride. And thank you for bringing in George Butzen. I
hope he'll be with us for a long while."

He was. Years and years.

13.

. . . Only one other person above stairs to whom I wished to
say goodbye, and that was Tartini. The Returned Goods room
was truly a mess— Half-open crates heaped on high, and Verdi's
"*La donna è mobile*" waving out of the mess.

> *È sempre misero, chi a lei s'affida,*
> *Chi lei confida, ma cauto il core!*

We exchanged regards and holiday greetings, and parted.
Then I descended to the third subway. No splintered crates
there, but it was as much a madhouse as Tartini's domain.

Assuming the role of a faithful dog returning with quail, I
put my claims together and laid them before Mr. Frank.

He said distinctly, "What the hell is all this?" with dark eyes
glaring.

"I'm quitting. I'll work until five-thirty if you want me to. But here are the claims already settled."

By this time the room, rowdy as it had been, was hushed. Fellow tracers began a slow forward grouping movement. They wanted to hear the conversation.

"Why are you leaving? Are you going to another job?"

"Going to Cedar Rapids to work on a newspaper. It's more my kind of dish than working here. I don't think you'll be very sorry to see me go."

Frank's mouth thinned and he spoke with implied threat. "Pretty short notice, isn't it?"

"It's several hours' longer notice, Mr. Frank, than the management is giving to a thousand other employees this afternoon. How about all those little slips in the envelopes?"

His facial expression changed. "You know," and his voice was purring, "you might have to wait a while for your pay check. Giving short notice like this—"

"I shan't worry. I've already drawn all my pay until today. If the store wants to keep that, they're welcome to it."

That was just what the tracers hoped I would say, and by that there were eight or ten of them around us. They emitted a roar.

Even the grim Frank broke apart at the seams. He held up his hands, waved them violently, trying to quell the noise; but he was laughing.

"For God's sake! Sometimes I think you guys are way ahead of me!"

That was the first time he'd demonstrated such unqualified humanity since I came on the job . . . as if he'd played the role of a discreet fox who suddenly found himself outsmarted by a scrawny chicken.

He counted my claims. "Thirty-one," he said. "That's a good day's work in anybody's language. Yes, we can use you until the end of the afternoon, if you'll kindly settle a few more. And here—" He dug in this desk, got out a voucher, signed it.

"If you have any trouble picking up the balance—you may be able to use this."

So I went back to it all for the scant remaining time. Back to the escalators with their parade of tired gnomes, urgent young tracers or minor executives scrambling around the motionless figures—quite contrary to rule, but trying to get there fast, hurrying, hurrying. Back to mighty bells afloat, back to exhausted mothers, children, the now-less-than-dominant Buyers and assistant Buyers. I didn't see Tartini again, but once I was nearby and heard him singing. This time it was *Don Pasquale* . . . back to crowded delivery court, cold trucks mumbling, drivers and loaders snarling, or whooping in some rare instance. Even the store detectives looked exhausted as they lounged.

The bookkeeping department was a mess . . . rubber bands burst around sheaves of papers, the papers scattered on the floor, a few people were trying to pick them up.

A fat woman wailed, "But nobody's waited on me! I've been here at least a half hour, and you've taken care of other customers ahead of me. I don't like this kind of treatment."

I would describe it bitterly in my second published novel.

Department. Department. Maybe Twenty. Or Eighty-four, in the expensive stuff. . . . Little pitcher, laughing somewhere. Laughing savagely with a curved lip. A blue pitcher— she thinks it was blue— The shoulders and padded thighs get in the way. Excuse me. Pardon me, madam. I'm sorry; I can't tell you. *Noel, Noel!* I will find a floorman to direct you; he'll show you; he—

She thinks it was Wedgwood.

Where's Mr. King? Mr. King— Well, where's Miss Brice? Miss Brice, did you—? Please, just a minute; this won't take long. This claim; she says she bought it in this department. That is, she's pretty sure she—

Never. Huh? Oh, thanks. If you never had any pitchers that price, of course it wasn't purchased here.

Department. Department. Eighty-four. Excuse me. Woop —look out, little boy! . . . I'm sorry, madam. I didn't see him. I didn't—

Escalators. The store has a lot of slaves underneath,

naked slaves perspiring heavily. They turn cranks; endlessly
and endlessly, windlass, treadmill, round and round they go.
Emancipated slave; he sits at the bottom to watch anyone if
anyone gets hurt. But nobody ever gets hurt. Round and
round and up and up and— He wears a coat with gold but-
tons. It ought to make him happy.

   Big bell. It's paper, but it's crimson, too. If it rings you
can't hear it. The draught catches it and spins it slowly,
weightily from the long festoon . . . *certain poor shepherds
in fields where—*

Joining the gnomes again, going up and going down. I did
manage to settle three or four more claims, but that was all. . . .
Turned in my claims, said goodbye to the men who were
still there. Mr. Frank was gone away on business, the joint
was jumping again, it would be jumping all evening. Jumping
tomorrow too, for those weary worn souls and who would work
even on Christmas Day.

I got my hat and coat, and whatever else there was to take
from locker or desk— Didn't bother with any stationery this
time, didn't need to. The Cedar Rapids *Republican* would have
plenty of stationery.

A small figure awaited me inside the Madison Street entrance
of Carson's . . . figure in maroon coat with gray-squirrel around
the collar. The jaunty hat . . . was it the same one she'd worn
April 2nd?

We walked in weary bliss.

"Have any trouble, quitting?"

"Not in the least. Young Mr. Pirie happened to come to our
department, and I spoke to him first. He was so nice about it,
and facilitated everything. And—surprise—he offered Christmas
regards to us both."

I wanted to take a taxicab again. Irene said, "Are you crazy?
There's a bus right up ahead. If we get on at Washington, we can
ride around— No chance of getting on a northbound bus on State
Street."

So we rode around the little loop inside the big Loop, we were
tired, our hands clutched tightly all the way home.

We had no money to waste in sending out Christmas cards, and nowadays have come to the belief that a great deal of money and a larger treasure of effort are wasted by such indulgence. In belated crusade we quit sending Christmas cards when we had not yet been married forty years.

If we loved Dick and Tye, or Donald and Eleanor, it was hoped that better evidence might be presented than by this means. There seemed—and seems—little value in such exchange with an editor at Imitative Books, Inc., when you are no longer publishing pocket books with the Imitative house, and never met the editor in your life.

Yet we did indulge in such effort for a long time, and expended inestimable vigor in attempts to display ourselves as tasteful, artistic and original, when whatever Yule guilt we felt might have been better satisfied by sending a check to the Old Folks Home in Sarasota—and is, nowadays.

Still a few early evidences survive, and one might be worthy of reproduction. In 1926 we were not long enough of this world to be capable of disseminating such a message, but would have been forewarned and even reassured had someone given the words to us.

"My child, you will see many strange things. . . . You will watch the holly berries wither and freeze while the nettles are pressed tenderly. . . . The good deer will starve in icy thickets when the rat grows portly amid his corn. . . . You will see the inspired creator neglected and his smug imitators extolled. . . . Hero ignored and presumptuous coward feted richly: these you will observe. . . . The shyster shall dwell long in luxury; the diligent and dependable will fall early, and on the dole. . . . A kindly nation may shiver in terror of the iron harshness adopted by its neighbors. . . . Bright universe eclipsed, black tarn gilded by a permanent sun: you see your future so. . . . And yet in their season the candles will be lighted again, the cones smell pungent; men may sing with the tongues and throats of angels amid the saintliest frost. . . . There is time now for consideration of the noblest Fairy Tale of all, if one be willing to cry again, and believe: 'God Rest Ye Merry—' in the midnight clear."

$IV.$ CEDAR RAPIDS

1.

I had been let out of school . . . a dozen schools, all the parliamentary mercantile schools. Here was a typewriter on its scant desk in the newsroom, and my name and title on a card fastened against glass up above, caging us off from printers and operators in the back room. *Special Assignment Reporter.* In addition to this work I had a daily run including divisional railroad offices, YMCA headquarters, Iowa Masonic Library, public library, and a scattering of other sources.

Five days a week I ate a free lunch at one community club or another. I was supposed to interview important visitors who came to town, except for those in the sports or police fields, but occasionally was sent to overlap into those as well. My chief contribution each week—usually it ran to about two well-packed pages—was featured on Sunday. For the first time since my home town *Daily News* epoch I was subsisting by the typewriter itself —by activity of fingers, memory, and whatever perceptivity I had acquired . . . and, above all, whatever skills one might burnish in the management of words.

The affluent furniture-seller who'd made good escape across the Russian frontier in boyhood because Cossacks shot in the wrong direction . . . a rug-dealer, surviving brother of the notorious gunman and Federal agent, S. Glenn Young: he told of Young's outlandish skill with weapons, and how Ory Thomas shot him down because Young's .45 caught on a shirt seam when he drew it . . . Sir Harry Lauder came; he wanted to take a walk, and we took it; I asked him how he felt about Bobby Brollier and countless other Lauder-imitators who infested vaudeville and concert stages; he looked up with that gnomic grin and said, "Ah, lad, ye ken there's but *one* Harry Lauder!"

Mediums, fortune-tellers, ghost-horn blowers, they thrived in that largely Bohemian community crammed with Mareks, Cepaks, Palacks, Kostaks. Investigation of psychic phenomena? Utter nonsense, said wise M.K. Whereupon I proceeded to conjecture the practicing seers and seeresses to their doom. Like a thousand other wiseacre writers who came before and after, I dressed the entire psychic field in charlatanism. Our sophisticated newsroom resounded with laughter at each threatening telephone call. No one preened himself more smartly than this reporter.

(No one was more mortified and baffled than this reporter when, a generation later, he found himself up to his ears in *Poltergeister*, with an apparition thrown in for good measure.)

One morning I told Irene, "I ain't lingering at the hearthside, honey. Got a breakfast date downtown, and do you want to guess the guy I'm interviewing? None other than Mr. John L. Lewis!"

"Why, I didn't know you knew anything about labor relations and miners and things like that—"

"I don't. That's the reason I went back to the office late last night, to read some files, and kind of bone up on his activities. Now I'm ready for him!"

"Wonderful! Hope he buys you a nice breakfast."

The appointment had been arranged through editorial channels, and it was understood that Mr. Lewis was eager for publicity—actually craved it, in fact. When I called him from the lobby he spoke quickly and toughly, "Be right down," and was at my side in three minutes. I did not know what John L. Lewis looked like, but whatever preconceived notion I'd had was promptly sent out for repairs. (No, no *Life* or *Look* in those days . . . no meaty face and bushy eyebrows displayed persistently by the press . . . television was off somewhere in science fiction of peculiar eons to come, like Space Flight and Walking-on-the-Moon.) Mr. Lewis looked rather like a sleek customer who hung around the race tracks.

He ordered ham and eggs for us both, and he drank profoundly of black coffee. He was an honest man above all, and admitted freely that he had "played around too much last night" and was suffering from a hangover.

So to the business at hand.

"Mr. Lewis, I understand that you were born in Lucas, Iowa, which was named after the Territorial Governor Lucas. People might wonder whether you have been influenced in your career by the career of Governor Robert Lucas himself—"

"What the hell you talking about, kid? Oh, I guess someone might *say* I was born in Iowa; but if they do—see—it's just for publicity. No, hell, I was born in Ft. Wayne, Indiana."

Better try another tack. "Speaking of Indiana, Mr. Lewis, may I ask your opinion about the strike there? I mean—the most recent one, in southwest Indiana—"

"Kid, what I always say about strikes is— Well, it's a little like fighting, see? Man goes on strike, there's got to be a reason for it, see? Now, if a fighter wants to work close in— I mean, if the guy's got two brains in his head, it's something about the other guy's style, that he can take advantage of—"

"Mr. Lewis, when you were elected president—"

"*Me?* Elected president of *what?*"

"Of the United Mine Workers' Union. Did you—?"

"By God, kid, I ain't president of nothing. Get that? *Nothing*. Now, please ask me something which makes sense. Like about my boy, Bearcat Wright. They may think this other lightweight is a championship contender, see? Local opinion—the hell with that. He's a broken-down welterweight, that's what he is. My boy will carry him along—give the folks a little show, see, so they won't feel cheated out of their dough—but when it gets to the fifth round—maybe the sixth—you watch that left of Bearcat's. I tell you, just watch it. It's *dynamite*. That's the way he got nine out of his last eleven K.O.'s—"

Wrong Mr. John L. Lewis.

The *Republican* desk was a little disgruntled. But the ham and eggs, with fried potatoes, were savory.

2.

Jim Farquhar was a hired publisher. Our newspaper belonged to certain railway and power interests . . . Jim enjoyed the society of painters, writers, entertainers. He was a long-time friend of Chic Sale, whose *The Specialist* was still uncontributed to that particular earthy field of Americana. Farquhar put us up momentarily at the Hotel Montrose (rent paid by due bills held by the *Republican* for past publicity favors) but it was made plain that this hospitality could not continue indefinitely. We stayed long enough to observe Irene's birthday—was it her twelfth?—on January 8th, when she bought herself a new hat in celebration . . . shiny dark blue straw, brimful of spring flowers to enliven the downtown snowbanks.

We found quarters of our own. In many towns the east side is the bad side of town. In Cedar Rapids the east side was the good side; but there survived a few inexpensive lodging houses. We landed in one such hive and endured slamming doors, screaming babies, atrocious smells and recalcitrant plumbing for a single week, while searching anxiously for a better place. We found it on Second Avenue: a red brick pile owned by an elderly couple who rented out rooms in their mansion, mostly to Coe College students. Irene and I achieved a one-room kitchenette next to a large bath. When other tenants went to use the bath they'd fasten their side of the door leading to our room, and when they left they were supposed to unfasten it. We were to do the same in reverse: go in through our connecting door, lock the other outside door of the bathroom and, when departing, unlock the outside door again. This system was subject to vagaries of the human mind and the human body. Other tenants were eternally forgetting to unlock their side of our door; with chagrin I testify that sometimes we forgot to unlock the outside door leading into the hall. Aside from this complication, which resulted in a lot of beating on doors, we were proud of our two-jet gas-plate complete with its set of dishes, pots, pans, tableware and a cubicle tin oven. We bought modest amounts of bootleg alcohol and entertained a few fellow staff members and their wives. The tin oven was the subject of the evening. Irene attained immediate if limited fame with her first casseroles.

We saw the Whitemans whenever possible. Dick joined us on an occasional evening, but he was up to his ears in senior activities at Coe College. That scrambling small institution boasted an eager alumnus who had worn a path down to the *Republican* office, hastening with his college news notes. He'd graduated a year or two previously, and it was rumored that he was already at work overseas. Local admirers believed that William L. Shirer was someone to watch for.

The senior Whitemans were involved in a mingling of Christian Science, Masonic, and generally charitable activities. Still we were invited to their home probably more often than we deserved to be, and strolled blissfully back to Second Avenue in sated recollection of rare roast beef and fluffy lemon pies. Harry Whiteman took pride in my feature stories; solemnly he considered each new Sunday's effort to be better than the last. At weekly Conopus club luncheons he beamed from afar as I sat along with the *Gazette* reporter, making notes . . . forever I could hear his warm gentle voice reciting, *If you must drink, drink with me and I'll be glad to drink with you* . . . nearly half a century later I can hear it still, and embrace the memory like a religion.

Ours was a huge room. The double bed had been set between two south windows, and these looked out across a lawn onto the garden-clad funeral home next door. We could see the roof of a garage where an artist dwelt.

Whatever other benefits accrued from the Cedar Rapids experience, the beginnings of intimate friendship with this artist were luxuriance. We met him first in the Travel Inn where a few painters and newspaper people met regularly. He was there at lunch more often than not: a stubby man with high bald forehead and scrubby pink hair receding from the crown. He wore the

thick glasses of the forever myopic, and behind them his eyes
leaped like bright caged birds. His forearms were covered with
hair of the same tint that shone on his head, and they were thick
and muscular, suggestive of calm power and virility. . . . Virility in the sexual sense he did not admit or practice. He told me
in after years how the whole sexual problem was a closed book
to him, and why. It was a secret which I retain. People who did
not know him well, and read about him or met him casually during the term of his greatest achievement, whispered that he was a
homosexual. He was nothing of the kind. He was simply asexual
—withdrawn by inclination, habit and choice from such emolu-
ment.

His voice was sedate, studied; he employed it with deliberate
discretion, like a parson or professor whose utterances have long
been waited by his hearers.

The garage behind Dave Turner's funeral home had once been
a stable and haymow for horses which pulled the hearses and
ambulance. In our modern motoring age the lower floor was arranged for automotive equipment; but the space above was
rented out to the artist for living quarters, and a separate stair
ran up from an alley outside. By nature an artisan and inventor as
well as a painter, he had transformed the whole area into a com-
pact acquisition.

"Tiled floors," he said. "I did want to have tiled floors, and
saw them before my eyes in a pattern of black-and-gold. I didn't
know where such tiles could be procured, but I thought that one
of the local companies might bake some for me. Then came the
question of structure. I talked to Dave about this, and together
we examined the situation and got an architect's opinion. This
floor simply would not stand the weight—"

"But," the hapless visitor might exclaim, "you've *got* tiled
floors!"

"Not exactly. I have imaginary tiled floors."

"But they're all in squares, they're in a regular pattern, they're
of the colors you just said. Aren't these *tiles?*"

"They're just the original hardwood boards which were on the floor in the first place. I cut lines between the cracks, in order to make them look like squares."

"But how could you saw them?"

"To begin with, I couldn't. In order to make a groove in a straight line, it would be essential to have the piece torn out—"

"But how?"

"One day I was watching my mother as she chopped cabbage for cole slaw. She used one of those old-fashioned cabbage choppers, built like a half moon. So it occurred to me that if I had a saw like that— I went to a machine shop and had them make me such a saw, and I learned to file it and keep it very sharp. I'll show it to you . . . here it is. It looks like a big cabbage chopper, doesn't it? I could get down and cut those lines between the plank cracks, and then paint the squares accordingly."

In a realm of disappearing beds, cabalistic curtains which were pulled from nowhere but were adequate for purposes of privacy — A realm which included disappearing stoves, heaters, iceboxes — One would be reluctant to declare that the artist's greatest consummation was his invention of the cabbage-cutter saw. I do recall this: when he'd finished with the stint of indoor work, painting and plastering, he found that his old blue overalls were so stiff with acquisition of such materials that it would be difficult to wash them. So he plastered them inside the door of his liquor closet, under the retreating bar he had invented . . . when doors were pulled open, there were the overalls with their original pockets waiting neatly to accommodate bottle openers, ice picks, spoons.

From some warehouse of the Turners he acquired a glass-topped coffin lid of primitive design, and set this into his outside door. The glass was prepared with a dial, and arrows which could be turned in whatever direction he chose. According to designation on the glass, a visitor would learn that the artist was asleep, gone out of town, would return at any hour selected . . . was painting, was welcoming callers. So on, so on. Early in our friendship he showed us a trick of code according to this style. It meant that he was turning the public at large away from his door, but would be happy to receive intimates. The arrows were in this position more often than not.

A newspaper reporter's life is parceled into odd detail, and sometimes I would be in the home neighborhood at peculiar hours. It was gratifying to be welcomed by him, and to listen to the steady monologue with which he dispensed anecdote or opinion, or usually both mingled together.

His standards were exacting, determined. Requisitely he painted with sublimity in the face of popular opinion, popular belief and acceptance. His work had to suit him before it suited anyone else. I had been of the same inclination from the start of my writing days at sixteen, but sometimes feared that I was mistaken in this course. Years afterward I turned down a $700,000 Hollywood contract because I felt keenly that my way was right and another man's way—the wrong way. I would do this today or tomorrow did the same situation prevail.

Our artist taught his younger friends that there could be an invigoration, an almost holy stimulus in the mere bland doing of a deed which one believes to be the thing he must do. No explanations, no apologies. His was a mighty lesson in self-determination, and the only time he erred in later life was when he weakened and allowed himself to be persuaded into a contrary course, and lived to regret it . . . and lived also to break the structure apart, willingly and forcibly—sweep aside the pieces, begin again freshly and in his own way.

His sense of humor was prodigious. One night Dave Turner and his wife gave a costume party for the usual crowd of newspaper people, local muralists, would-be poets. Most of us were poor, and the mortician Turners well-to-do—very rich indeed, by our barren standards. Food and drinks were sumptuous, and we felt like momentary millionaires being entertained at some ornate spot on the Riviera . . . maybe Monte Carlo or Cannes. I think that none of us except the artist and perhaps the Turners had ever been to the Riviera or knew exactly what it might be . . . we had fun . . . oh royal good fun. One of the guests, a droll fellow named Leon Zeman—called Tony by the rest—appeared in a schoolteacher's long black frock and a wide-brimmed black hat. It was he who took charge of the Schnitzelbank.

> *Ist das nicht ein Gartenhaus?*
> *Ja, das ist ein Gartenhaus.*

This was the first time Irene and I had ever seen the rite performed, and we thought it overwhelming. So did the artist, who sang, chanted, roared along with the rest of us.

He came as an angel. He said that he had looked into a mirror, examined himself, and decided what he had best be in costume.

"You know, I guess I do look rather like an angel. So I decided to be one."

He was cherubic to perfection, down to his bare toes. He wore an old pink flannel nightgown of his mother's, and had constructed remarkable wings which hung semifolded from his shoulders. The crowning touch was his halo, supported by a single gilded stick going down to a harness strapped under the nightgown. The halo gleamed and shone, and so did his thick spectacles, dancing blue eyes, and rotund face . . . with that passive satisfaction which comes only to those who think hard, work hard, and accomplish much according to their own lights if not according to the lights of the world.

Our artist did accomplish much according to the lights of the world, but it was because he respected himself and his opinion and his skills first of all. It is grotesque to record that he died in 1942, two hours short of his fifty-first birthday. He deserved better than that, and so did the wide generations who admired and respected Grant Wood.

3.

A particularly devilish form of virus flu came to town, and it had Irene on its list. She was miserable for a while. Since July we'd endured a few colds or toothaches, but nothing like this. We could laugh about it, months later, but at the time the voice of

Infinity was tolling with gloomy accents. A different sort of inti-
macy befalls the untried and newly married in illness . . . the
poor things need assurance which nothing but the experience itself may give them. The first time I had to help Irene into the
bathroom and sustain her on the toilet, she wept, "Now I guess
you won't love me any more." That day a microscopic portion of
our Income was transmuted into Outgo in the shape of posies for
her bedside table.

She'd held a temporary job as hostess in the town's public art
gallery, and the people were sorry to lose her. As soon as Irene
was able to move, she went in to Chicago to visit her family.
Recuperation might be a lonely business in that one room, with
husband gone through the days and necessarily through some
evenings as well.

The Cedar Rapids *Republican* had been extant, under one
ownership or another, for over fifty-six years. In this season
we of the staff were feeling our oats. Our hated rival was the
other morning newspaper, the *Gazette,* owned or at least con-
trolled by a family named Marshall. When Jim Farquhar was
engaged to serve as publisher of the *Republican,* paramount
among his desires was: "Get the *Gazette.*" He'd drafted an
energetic little army, several of whom went on to journalistic
positions of repute. Our advertising lineage was leaping from
week to week, so was our circulation. In news and feature
fields we hamstrung the *Gazette* day after day. Hot feuds had
sprung up individually between *Gazette* reporters and *Republican* reporters, and the circumstances of these lost nothing
in the telling. But not a man in our jubilant herd could have
believed that, by the assembling and control of his skills, he
was working himself right out of a job.

Ten days after Irene's going to Chicago, the city editor said,
"I want to talk to you in private." Farquhar being absent from
the premises, I followed the city editor into Mr. Farquhar's office.
The door closed and we stood facing each other. He was Jean C.
Herrick, a slight young man with a high shiny forehead, thin hair,
and musing brown eyes.

(He would become important in the *Look* organization of the Cowles family until his retirement, when he went to live in England. But we were far from England, and *Look* Magazine had never been dreamed of.)

"Mack, when is Irene planning to return from Chicago?"

"This coming Friday."

"How's she feeling?"

"She's feeling great. We talked on the telephone last night, and she claimed she was eating like a horse. Her stepmother's fixing all her favorite things."

Jean studied me earnestly. He opened his mouth as if to speak, then closed his mouth again. He walked to the window and back.

"Mack, I'm breaking a rule in talking to you the way I'm talking now. But— Can I trust you?"

I chuckled, but this was a scary business. "How far?"

"Will you promise that you won't speak a word to anyone about—about what I'm going to tell you—until the thing comes out into the open?" He considered, then added, "Promise that you won't even speak a word to Irene?"

I mumbled that that was a hard thing to demand of me.

"Well, if you have to tell her, tell her. But swear her to secrecy, in turn. Promise?"

"Yes. I promise."

"All right. This paper is going to be sold—in fact it is sold already. No one will be told until next Saturday night. That was part of the stipulation. We wouldn't publish any more editions if we told them now. That's plain to see."

I sounded like a lame duck quacking about his own lameness. "Is it the *Gazette*?"

He nodded. "They've bought the *Republican* from the interests who own us."

"Who knows, besides yourself?"

"Well, the board knows—they made the deal. Jim Farquhar knows. I know, and Toffelmeyer, the managing editor, knows. I guess that's about the score."

I joined him at the window. Bright sunshine was a disgrace . . . should have been a tornado. "Jean, why are you telling *me,* and not the rest of the staff?"

"For this reason: Irene's gone to Chicago. And you came here from Chicago. You may have to go back there to get a job. I didn't want to see you bringing Irene out to Cedar Rapids, and then immediately transporting her back to Chicago again."

Mandel Brothers. Yes, Mr. Russell had tried to persuade me not to leave, but I would die before retreating to Mandels'. If by nature I'd loathed the process of mercantile endeavor before, I loathed it doubly now. I was alone when I came up out of that subway in Mandels' for the last time. There wasn't anyone to see me, so I wasn't grandstanding—merely gesturing to myself when I stood on the stairs, turned around, and spat at the territory beneath. (One might do that at twenty-two . . . later on he'd know better . . . just grin or shrug.)

Jean said, "I know how you feel, because I know how I feel. Rotten."

"You mean we'll be Out—just Out, like that? No advance notice, no advance salary?"

He nodded. "Wouldn't it be interesting if we had a newspaper Guild or something, to prevent things like this?"

Yes, it would be interesting. . . .

"Well. Are you going to bring Irene from Chicago?"

"Yes," I said explosively. "She could go to work for an art agency there—they've already offered her a job. But I won't go back to that damn store again."

"Got any idea about exactly what you'll do?"

"Not a notion."

He sighed. "Neither have I."

"Jean, when will the axe fall?"

"It will be just before our first edition of the Sunday paper hits the street, on Saturday night. They'll make an announcement on the front page. That's the way those things are usually handled, I guess. I never was part of one before."

It was impossible to thank him adequately for his thoughtful-

ness, then and there . . . I tried, but we were both rather choked
up . . . we've been friends through the years.

(Once upon a time, in Beverly Hills, Violet Saunders gave a
cocktail party, and we guests had access to a garden which lay
between the home of our hostess and the establishment next door.
"Who lives next door?" someone inquired. "Oh," said the hostess,
"those are the Herricks." I asked, "Not Jean Herrick?" "Yes,
that's the name. He represents *Look* on the West Coast, I believe." Irene was in the East, so I grabbed onto the nearest
available actress; she happened to be a beautiful one named
Aileen Pringle. Briefly I told her what I had in mind, and we
snuck out and concealed ourselves amid plantings directly beneath the Herrick windows. "What is the name of the man who
lives next door?" Miss Pringle projected clearly. I replied in firm
dramatic tones, "Herrick. Jean Herrick," and shadows appeared
promptly on the window curtains above. "Oh, isn't that the editor
with the lovely wife who used to be a dancer?" "Yes, that's Bonnie. But you should have seen his first wife. She was even more
beautiful." "What happened to his first wife? Did she die?" "Yes,
under rather peculiar circumstances. I don't know whether *this*
wife ever knew he had a first wife. Her body was found, rather
cut up, and buried in a place which no one else had access to,
except Herrick himself. But there wasn't enough evidence."
"Why didn't they bring him to trial? He might have been con-
victed!" "No," I explained, "in Cedar Rapids at that time, the
law was rather slack; people didn't do sufficient investigating.
Anyway, he had an important job on the local newspaper— You
know how those things go." "Yes, yes, it's the same here. And I
imagine," added Miss Pringle tartly, "that his present wife has
never even *heard* about the murder to this day." We squeezed
back out of the plantings, ran around through the Saunders'
place, and out the front door, to rush over and ring the bell at the
Herricks'. When the door flew open, it disclosed two Herricks
with jaws dropped a mile. Aileen and I burst into triumphant
yells. . . . Jean shook his head. "I should have known it was you,"
he said, and he and Bonnie went back with us to the party.)

4.

In that same private office Jim Farquhar affirmed what Jean had
told me. This time there was a hint of news on the bright side.

"I've decided what I'm going to do. I'm going out to Huntington Beach, California, and start a paper there. I think I know
where I can get the money to do it, but that doesn't mean I'll
have anything to throw around. I want to say this and this only to
you, so keep it under your hat. I can't afford to pay your way,
and Irene's way, out to the West Coast. If you can make it on
your own, and get there— I can promise you a job. I'd like to see
my own sons grow up in the newspaper business, but they're too
young to begin yet. Make it if you can."

"How soon would that be?"

"Say another month or so. There's a printing office already
there, and I can use that equipment to get started if I make the
deal. And I *think* I'm going to make it."

Already I'd walked or hitchhiked all over the Middle West
. . . had ridden on freight trains . . . the prospect of proceeding
across the Continent by such means was not unbeguiling. As for
Irene: her mother's family, the Lawrences, emigrated from England when the Colonies were young, and had known Indian
days in Massachusetts, Canada, Wisconsin progressively. One of
her collateral ancestors cried with his last breath, "Don't give up
the ship!" and I didn't believe that she would give up the brig or
sloop or frigate or whatever the hell we were traveling in. Question was: how soon would she be wholly recovered from the flu?
Those virus things took a while, even when you were sturdy and
young. . . . I began to think about Webster City. My grandparents had spent recent months in Corydon, the village where
my brother-in-law held one of his first pastorates. Mother was in
the town of Boone. Along with a printer and pressman from our
Daily News epoch, she was essaying the publication of a community magazine. The old home stood closed, but it would be

waiting for us in this time of stress. Neighbors had the key, and all I needed to do was to turn on water and electricity, and build a fire in the range.

By Herrick and again by Farquhar, I'd been sworn to secrecy: I'd promised not to *speak* to anyone about the situation. That might be interpreted rather loosely? I had just bought a new shirt and tie, and now regretted such extravagance. But here was a boy named Flannigan, a cub reporter recently come from Omaha, who was talking about a new suit, and on this very day.

"You know that place over on First Avenue where it says *Walk Up Twenty Steps and Save Twenty Bucks?* I just picked my suit out, and it's a dandy. It'll only cost twenty-two dollars and—"

I asked Flannigan, "Real busy?"

"Just doing some small items I picked up on my rounds—"

"Go down the back stairway," I muttered. "I'll meet you in the truck lot," and the youth followed me there.

"Flannigan, don't buy that suit. Can you still get your money back—your deposit?"

"Why, I guess I can. But you haven't seen the suit. It's a beauty. And I *need* a new suit; I'm practically all holes. Look at the cuffs on these trousers—"

"Flannigan, you're a good Roman Catholic. I appeal to you in the name of God. For God's sake, Flannigan, don't buy that suit!"

"But why not? Can't you give me a hint?"

"Can't tell you anything. But promise me this: you'll put off buying the suit until next Monday. If on next Monday you still want to buy it, go ahead."

He was miffed, and extremely puzzled, but he agreed.

No matter what jaunty ambitions I entertained of our frontier expedition to Huntington Beach, it seemed sensible to try everything near at hand first. I knew a number of editors and publishers in our region, either through some scrap of meeting or by reputation, and I must write to them all.

A couple of nights later I sat sole alone in the newsroom. I was applying to Harvey Ingham in Des Moines . . . I'd written editorials for him while still in high school. . . . Applying to editors in Davenport and a few other towns where my contributions had been accepted, or where people knew me because I'd helped Mother to represent the Des Moines *Register* and the I.N.S. as correspondent. I didn't tell any of them that the *Republican* had been sold: that would be breaking the oath. But I did say that I had been reliably informed that I would be at liberty the following week, and was searching for employment. They could draw their own conclusions.

At eleven o'clock I was still thudding away on the machine when three of the boys came in. They were our sports editor, and the man who handled our press wire, and another reporter. They'd attended a local fight or wrestling match—on Annie Oakleys, naturally—and someone offered them a drink or so along the line. They were in jovial mood, feeling no pain, and said that they had noticed lights in the newsroom at an hour when it was usually shut up tight. They wondered what was going on. "God. You must have a hot story—"

"Not so hot." I turned to appraise them. "Can't say a word to any of you, because I promised that I wouldn't speak about a certain subject. But you're three against one. I couldn't keep you from looking at this letter."

In nothing flat they crowded around to read the lines I had been typing. They, too, could draw their own conclusions, and did with agility.

Inevitably rumors began to circulate. If Farquhar and Herrick heard them, they said nothing. One might hazard a guess, also, that the *Gazette* was not above having a few leaks in its own organization. By the end of the week some people had heard tall tales and some people had not, and that was the way it stood.

In mellow sunset light of Friday, I put on my fresh finery, and strode to claim Irene at the railroad station. Very nearly did I feel like a leisurely young man about town. How elegant indeed! —the new shirt testified to my taste and pleasure: tiny red-and-blue squares, rimmed round with black in a checkered plaid effect . . . the new necktie itself . . . fifty cents it had cost, when usually I paid but a quarter . . . it too was red-and-blue in blobs, and looked something like a limp tobacco pouch squeezed down in the middle, with an adjustable strap to hold it under the collar. I had not yet learned how to tie a bow tie, had never worn a bow tie before . . . there was something gay about my socks, too, but I've forgotten just what.

Deferring to springtime weather, Irene wore a coat she had made herself. It was formed of black satin and adorned with left-over black monkey fur. (I never met a monkey garbed in that sort of pelage.) In an early novel I was to refer to such a coat as *sleazy;* but there was nothing sleazy about Irene's appearance when she stepped off the train. For my dough she could have emerged from the door of some *couturière's* salon in the Rue de la Paix. Beauty was there, and deftly applied makeup on top of it. But underneath quivered still a rather shaky little girl. No joke about that flu.

She'd experimented with a boyish bob before she became ill, but on viewing the unholy result she fell to wailing; I exploded with profanity; and after the resulting altercation we both wisely decided to say nothing more about it, and to hope that the hair would grow out with speed.

Saturday evening she spent with several newspaper wives, while I went down for the holocaust. It was a worthy accident of fate that a fire did not actually ensue. The experience of having one's chair jerked from under him, one's line-gauge ripped from his hand— It was not edifying. Mr. Farquhar ran like a rabbit, and no one saw him for days. He shouldn't have been blamed for this, but many critics did blame him nevertheless. Toffelmeyer and Herrick were there, standing to whatever guns they still possessed; the rest of us milled around, batting at rumors which by this time were flying like badminton birds.

About nine-thirty the managing editor of the *Gazette*—call him Raynard—walked in and climbed on a desk near the back room door. He was as wan as if he too were just getting over the flu, and seemed relieved to be bodyguarded by a couple of burly individuals from his own staff. He read aloud a formal announcement for all *Republican* employees—to say that, as of that date, the *Gazette* had purchased the paper, and their services were no longer required. There wasn't a word about any severance settlement or advance pay. No one received a dime over his ordinary salary payment. We were just Out, ninety-odd of us.

I stood by my own desk and looked through the glass into the back room. I was watching an old printer . . . he moved in silence, and his hands shook as he reached up to take his coat and hat, and put them on.

We heard mumbling and snarling . . . women from "Society & Clubs" were in tears. The managing editor of the *Gazette* returned to the newsroom and sat down to type out a story to be put on the press wire. The outside world would now know what had been done (if the outside world cared in the least, which most of it did not). It so happened that he picked the typewriter of our police reporter, whom we may call Bullitt—a gaunt short-tempered man gifted with the ability to talk up a storm of conflict in any given direction. He'd been off somewhere having a few drinks, perhaps with some city employees who were his cronies.

Bullitt halted at the entrance of the room, setting his eyes on the incredible spectacle of Raynard's appearance at his own desk. Then he shoved himself forward and stood behind the chair, lifting his hands. One and all we believed that when the hands came down they would go around Raynard's neck; but Bullitt made them into fists, and with futility he pounded the empty air.

He roared at the top of his lungs, "I never thought to see this!"

The two trouble-shooters moved closer and Raynard stole a glance over his shoulder. "Hello, Bullitt," and he went on typing.

Bullitt howled again. Some of our *Republican* folks walked him away to the wall, where he leaned with his head on folded arms.

That was when I started pulling drawers out of my desk and seizing copy therein. I had some half-written stories—in fact one feature story which was complete but hadn't yet been read by the editors and sent to be printed. I said something like, "Well, they're not going to get these," and proceeded to start tearing paper. In another moment everyone else was doing the same thing.

Raynard and his cohorts decided that they would be more popular over at the *Gazette* office, so they got out of there. Our shop resounded with considerable noise, noise from the back room too. We were informed later that linotype operators were stealing space mats out of the machines . . . I guess they were valuable and could be sold. You'd look around and see a type-writer on a desk, and look away, and then look back, and the typewriter would be gone. I didn't take my typewriter because I owned a rebuilt L. C. Smith which I had used for years and on which I doted; it was in our room on East Second Avenue and would go along with us to Webster City . . . in time it might be shipped out to Huntington Beach, if that's where we were to land. Newsroom and back room and offices turned into a sham-bles, a battleground, a city dump. You'd look at one corner and it would be in fair shape, and you'd look away, and when you turned again the drawers were out of the desk, and paper flying every which way. I saw one fellow calmly taking light bulbs out of their sockets.

Jean Herrick was going up to his mother's and stepfather's farm home, on the edge of a town named Humboldt. That wasn't far from Webster City, and he asked if Irene and I would come to visit in another week or so, and I said Yes. The Irish kid from Omaha threw his arms around me and thanked heaven about that new suit. *Walk Up Twenty Steps and Save Twenty Bucks.*

Our telegraph operator was the calmest of the lot. He said, "I'm not worried. I got rid of that deal about buying my house," and he winked and made faces and motions over the heads of the rest, and he was thanking me for letting him look over my shoulder. He'd gone to his landlord that other night, and can-celed a real estate proposition. But I wondered what he was going to do. He had a whole family—younguns and all—and I wondered where he would go, and never did learn. Now I can't even remember his name. *Mc*-something.

There wasn't much to remove from my own desk after I'd torn up the stories and scattered the fragments. I had a pipe or two, some favorite pencils . . . I fetched along a slab of copy paper . . . and my gilt reporter's badge from the police department. It's sticking up on my library wall today.

When I got home Irene was alone, reading in bed. She had a negligee of pure silk with a batik design, one which she had made herself, and it was in the purple-orchid category of color. She looked lovely in that. I locked the door and came over and sat on the edge of the bed. She smiled at me with those dreamy eyes of hers . . . I mean dreamy not in the slang sense, but in the pure lyric sense of the word, as expounded in the Oxford Dictionary. *Given or pertaining to reverie 1809.*

"Was it bad?"

"Kind of."

"Well, it's all over now."

"Yes, it is."

In bed, with lights out, I was thrashing around, and her voice came through gloom after another hour. "Darling, can't you go to sleep?"

"You know," I said, "I'd like to have a drink. Have we got anything?"

"We girls had just one apiece: that was all anybody wanted. It's gin that Marian brought along, it was her turn. There's a little left, over there in that small bottle in the cupboard."

I got up and fumbled around and found the gin. It was warm enough to have windows open. I looked through budding trees toward the rear of the Turner premises. Some activity there . . . lights on at the rear, and the ambulance moving into the garage. Someone had died and was brought there to be taken care of. Up above I could make out lights also, although drapes were drawn over Grant Wood's mullioned dormer windows. Probably Grant was working late . . . he often did when the mood was on him. Grant never let anything interfere with his ambition or with the principal piece of work at hand. I would remember long afterward how I congratulated him on the faces in *Daughters of Revolution.* "I've known D.A.R.'s who looked exactly like that. I'm sure that you painted Mrs. Chadley and Mrs. Bonn—"

"Maybe I did," and he beamed. "You see, I didn't use any models, actually."

"No models? You mean those women didn't sit for you, whoever they were?"

"No. What I did was to gather together every monthly or quarterly journal which I could get hold of, of ladies' organizations. D.A.R., Eastern Star, P.E.O.'s, Society of Colonial Dames, all such things. Those periodicals are generously sprinkled with photographs of the members, new officers of this department, that department. So I spent a while studying those faces, and then I put the magazines away, and just started in to paint."

I wondered whether Grant knew about the *Republican.* Maybe he too had heard some rumors, but he would not be fazed by it in the slightest, although it meant the departure of some of his friends. He would consider it to be disastrous only if we, the immediate victims, allowed it to become disastrous to us.

I put the empty glass aside and got into bed again. I'd heard Irene's regular breathing, I thought she was deeply asleep. But she wasn't, she was waiting for me.

She said, "I had the feeling that you've been lying here, thinking about something in particular."

"Yes. Perhaps that's the reason I couldn't sleep."

"Do you wish to tell me what you were thinking about?"

"I was thinking about a gentle old man down at the office. A printer. He was working as a printer's devil the day the first *Republican* was lifted off the press. That was over fifty-six years ago, in 1870. And he was there tonight, and I watched him as he listened to the announcement, and then he went over and got his hat and coat, and walked out. I was thinking about him, and those fifty-six years."

Irene said, "It's not solely tragedy. There's a strange beauty . . . I can see him as you describe him . . . little old man. But," she said more briskly, yet awarding advice rather than giving an order, "I think you've thought about him enough. It's time for you to go to sleep, so that you can be a happy healthy American author, and some time maybe you'll write something about the gentle old man."

I said, "Some time I will," and now I have.

V. *IRENE FEELS SWELL*

1.

The maples were my gods, and their highest branches switched and bent in wind, and the backs of leaves shone whitish against any stormy sky. In latest days of winter, holes were bored in each thick trunk, spouts of elderberry wood were hammered in. Sap dripped cool into tin buckets, it had a thin and woodsy taste, we called it sugar water, and we ate the icicles forming on those spouts when nights turned quickly cold again.

. . . There was the Baptist Church to which we were led each Sunday. Sun came through glass windows and stained the ladies' hats and faces with purples and pinks. We heard talk of Jehovah and Saul and Returning Unto Dust. We had a cat named Daisy, and she died and was buried in our garden; and Virginia and Mary Bale came racing home from Sunday School, and they dug up poor Daisy to see whether she had Gone to Dust, and No, she hadn't, oh dear, she hadn't Gone to Dust at all.

. . . We had a little calendar, and on it was a picture of an imp with horns and pointed ears . . . he was printed in the prettiest light blue. I asked Grandma what this imp might be, and she said, "I guess it's a picture of Satan." Satan I had heard about, and also he was called The Devil. I knew that he was dangerous and wicked. At church next Sunday a tall blond lady came out of a door behind the pulpit; she stood on the platform and sang a song high-pitched and screeching. I gazed fearfully at the tall lady, and listened with equal terror to the noises she made . . . her dress was blue—the identical color of the imp on the calendar—and I thought that she was Satan, or at least she was singing about Satan.

Down behind our house stretched a mighty cornfield. By midsummer the corn was grown to be a wilderness. I took my gun, cocked it, saw that the cork was set firmly in the barrel. Quietly as any hunter might stalk, I crept barefoot through grainy black soil with that thick jungle of corn extending overhead. Leaves scraped and rustled. Perhaps there were Indians prowling beyond, or bears . . . solemnly I shot three Indians and one mountain lion. Then I was hungry, and pulled broken cinnamon rolls from my pocket, and ate lunch.

Grandma had baked those cinnamon rolls, she baked all our bread and cakes and most of our cookies. I would come into the house; she'd say, "Grandma's got a surprise for you," and then Virginia would be beside me, tossing her curls and clamoring also for the treat. Hot, hot—fresh heavy bread glistening with the grease with which Grandma'd wiped it—and her sharp knife went deep through the end of the loaf, and then through the other end. Thus each of us had a heel, stiff with brown crust, and Grandma spread butter for us, and it melted and ran amid fluffy white flakes, it tasted of sunshine and dandelions.

. . . The Greenwood girls lived around the corner on Webster Street. There were three of them—ladies like my mother, or even older—and spinsters through many years. Aunt Martha had crinkly gilt hair and wore gilt-rimmed glasses; Aunt Esther had a cool voice and brown hair; Aunt Frankie was stunted and crippled, and smiled an eager smile. Seldom did she walk abroad; when she went she hobbled with two stout rolled-up umbrellas for canes . . . maybe it was infantile paralysis. But an older child insisted that Aunt Frankie had hurt herself while jumping rope too often when she was a girl, and this strange story Virginia and I believed.

Nearly opposite us stood the Gensman house, and in proper season there were violets growing over a grassy slope beside an old hitching post. Virginia traveled there to pick violets, and then screamed her way home, for she floundered upon a nest of yellow jackets among the flowers.

Grandma Gensman was a grim woman who rode a bicycle, and Grandpa Gensman had some fine Jersey cows. He loved those cows devotedly. In last sickness he rose at night and went wandering, as if hunting for his cows. Neighbors came searching with lanterns, and I tagged along after Grandpa McKinlay. We found Grandpa Gensman at last, lying in the road not far away, his eyes tight-shut, an extra cloth cap gripped in his hand. Thus I looked at death for the first time, and there seemed nothing frightening about it: only a pathetic peace. Men lifted Grandpa Gensman and carried him toward his house, and I walked behind with our lantern. It was dawn by this time, birds were beginning to carol in the elms.

. . . The town grew wider, it was filled with more people, the horizon broadened and warmed. . . . Kendall Young Library: it had a glass case hung with stained and feathery relics of Indians such as those who had galloped over the mild slopes where houses and lawns were now spread.

The main street boasted three whole blocks of brick pavement; and beyond roamed trains which went all the way to Chicago, it was said. In Chicago lived a distant critter called my father.

Not God, not the Father whom we addressed in prayer. Mother and Grandma read aloud from the Bible each morning, we had our private prayers as well.

"Our Father which art in Heaven—" I dreamed vaguely of the parent I had never seen . . . he was not Jesus or God . . . *my father which art in Chicago.*

At night I would pray for him. Mother knelt between us children, her face bent close to each in turn as she heard the pleas we had been taught to utter.

"Now I lay me down to sleep. I pray the Lord my soul to keep—"

She left out the part about, "If I should die before I wake," because she considered it might be disturbing to unripe minds. Instead we were trained to say, "God bless father and mother, dear sister [brother], Grandpa and Grandma," and I added on my own, "And every thing and everybody and every animal in this world," because my world was mainly good in those cramped little years, and I loved it well.

2.

Irene and I traveled from Cedar Rapids on the Northwestern railroad and reached Webster City in the evening. Willard Boughton, veteran local taxi-driver, carried us home, bags and baggage and typewriter. Arriving at 1718 Willson Avenue, we found Mother with her widest smile, crying "Welcome home!" She had come from Boone on the bus in order to greet us.

This was exactly what I had prophesied all along. Mother now cherished Irene as a daughter, when for long she had never expected—or hoped, probably—to own a second daughter. But once I demonstrated that I was deeply in love and resolved to marry, and did marry, there was no mistake about it. It is unlikely that she was deeply familiar with Theban legends or saw her son in the garb of Oedipus. Nevertheless since my infancy she had sought to be the dominating factor in my life, and rebuffs which ensued later made her only more determined. She was one of those individuals who thrive best when others are dependent upon them, and who grow heartsick and confused when the dependents, by whatever means, are removed from guidance or bounty.

For our sake she did not welcome the Cedar Rapids debacle—had not anticipated or desired it—but she glowed at serving as our hostess. Technically the house belonged to the grandparents; it had been bought by Grandpa McKinlay when I was a baby. Mother had lived there, we children had been reared there. Once we were separated from the menage by age and even a small degree of accomplishment, we still felt it to be our mutual

domicile. Effie Kantor was the principal sustaining force in the
family for a long time; but recently I had been able to pay taxes,
and also help provide a lean income on which the grandparents
subsisted.

None of us in that April identified these facts—or at least chose
to consider them and dwell upon them. This was my native den,
as it was Mother's. A generation of our life within those walls
had been pressed into the body of the structure. Unfortunately it
became a natural hazard of matrimony and proximity to an
elder, that Irene should feel left out when Mother was at hand.
This caused pain unavoidably. An overwhelming flow of reminiscence, of association with and deference to the past, swept
around the stranger. When we were by ourselves, Irene welcomed my rambling dissertations, even begged for them. But
when Mother came flooding along with hers, the newcomer was
stranded high and dry.

Considering the town at large, it was no longer the blossom-
scented garden of nursling days. Ambitious and assertive and
fiercely resolute, I'd accumulated fully as many enemies or weak
detractors as I had friends. Probably more.

I guessed what was being said in certain quarters, and what
would be said further.

"Well, I see the town poet's back among us again!"

"Guess he didn't do too well in Chicago, after all that hullabaloo in the papers."

"And appearing over the radio—on those 'Line Nights,' I guess
they call them—from WGN—"

"Then he went down to Cedar Rapids. That was supposed to
be a big job—"

"Yes, and now the paper's gone out of existence. So he's here
with his young wife, kind of hiding in the old McKinlay house."

"Wonder what he'll do now?"

"Oh, likely write some more poems. Guess he isn't going to
pay off the family debts with *those*."

If one knows a region and its people intimately, as in cer-
tainty I knew this one, he is aware of antagonism without having

the record played back to him. A verbal transcription was unnecessary, although some deleterious comments were overheard and reported by indignant friends. I had not advanced far enough—was not sufficiently secure—to feel pity rather than resentment. Vaguely I could recognize truth in any adage which stated that no person of importance ever grows up just across the street . . . important creators are off in a noteworthy chimera somewhere else. They never attended your school or ran in play across your lawn.

Still I had been bruised and disappointed enough—and already honored enough—to have my feet fastened hard upon the ground. I was in no way subdued, or embittered beyond the point of competency. It was preferable and wiser to ignore calumny, and accept encouragement whenever offered.

Mother fairly waltzed with fervor about her *Community Magazine* in Boone. The first issue was recently off the press, and they had distributed six thousand copies. Previously she yearned to found such a journal in her own town, but could find neither sufficient backing nor support. Fred Hahne, who had owned the *Daily News,* became discouraged when he failed in his first attempt to be elected mayor. A rural depression struck the Midwest years before there came any general economic collapse throughout the nation. Farms shrank pitifully in price when compared with the war years, earnings from farm products were down proportionately. Many small banks in Iowa had collapsed, and larger banks were being reorganized amid strain and toil. Financial throat-cutting was the order of the day.

A pressman and printer who once worked for Fred Hahne had moved to Boone to set up his own shop there. It was on his Kelly presses that *Community Magazine* was run off. The first issue comprised twenty pages inside glossy covers. Editorial content: Mother wrote zealously about Boone and its inhabitants, much as I had been doing with special assignment stuff on the *Republican.*

Albert Porter owned the presses, provided the paper, did the printing and stapling. He assumed necessary expenses for halftones which decorated the smooth stock, and could be used also in advertisements to an extent which rough newspaper stock might not offer. He paid the postage. It was possible that Mr. Porter thought of *Community Magazine* as being his own.

Nay, nay, never. It was Mother's. She wrote every word printed in it—solicited the advertisements, wrote them, wrote the articles. In this moment she was ardent in adventure. No one ever sparkled more flashingly than she in such condition. The valvular heart trouble which had plagued her when she was with me in Chicago, or visiting cousins, or staying with Virginia and her husband Jim Sours, down in Corydon? A bagatelle!—she never thought of it. She aspired to be the recording angel of her adopted Boone.

A retired post office employee who had once been a peace officer in the West . . . the young Italian workman, vastly decorated in the World War . . . a railroad conductor entranced by the heavens, who made himself into a meteorologist of proportion. Yes, yes!—he had saved his money, and bought an elaborate telescope! It was a treat to spend an evening with him!

The banker who gave seventeen acres of wooded land for a park— The little woman who ran the millinery shop, but who specialized in tending lost or wounded stray animals— Earl White, who ran the newsstand— Mr. Nutt, "the man who broke the price of glasses in Boone." He was a vigorous optometrist— Miss Goetzman, who conducted the boarding house where Mother lived— Such splendid people! Resourceful, able, captivating—

Never did it occur to my mother that she herself was the mirror in which, in turn, she viewed the newly met and newly won as friends and disciples . . . that she herself provided the silver and gloss which she was sure lay glinting in their natures.

I thought of John Kantor, upholstered with fakery. Ponderous, pompous, deep-spoken, Sephardic— She had always been fascinated by him, had gone back to him cheerfully time and again after he'd deserted her. She left him only because of obligation to her children: she could not keep coming home, and finding

furniture out in the street and her husband gone. Gone where?
—with warrants for his arrest snapping behind him. Still she
loved him with passion to the day of her death.

(And so, I found in later friendship, did another woman . . .
an actress and singer. The name? Sophie Tucker.)

My mother's buoyant confidence and trust and ecstatic acceptance had betrayed her before, would betray her again. But
in this springtime she was ardent, feeling pride and desire, and
compelling us to feel them along with her.

She had orders for me on Monday morning before I carried
her bag to the corner where she could catch the bus for Boone.
Storm windows . . . was it too early to take them off? Snow
might come in May, had come in May in our memory. But
there wouldn't be any more blizzards. If I took the windows off,
be sure to stack them carefully in the barn, where no one could
blunder against them, knock them down, break the panes.

Keep fittings in a salt sack tied to one of the frames, so appropriate screws would not be lost. . . .

"Now, Mack. When you get out the screens, put them in the
sun, wash them with the hose . . . when they're dry, look them
over carefully. See if you think they need paint. I was doubtful
about that last year but— Of course paint is expensive, but we
don't want the screens themselves to suffer, and it does help as a
preservative— See what you think. Do you have enough money
to buy paint, if needed? Oh look, son, there may be some paint
in the barn! Look in those paint cans that are sitting right inside
the room next to the old manger. There may be green paint
there. And you know how to wash the brushes in kerosene—"

Irene said gently, "I know how to wash brushes in kerosene,
Mother."

"Well, that's just fine! I'll leave it up to you. But don't put
on the screens yet, if you think weather conditions don't
justify it. And of course, should you paint them, let the paint
dry adequately before you put them on. Oh yes: about that
damper in the fireplace. Something fell off, two weeks ago when
I was last here; the ashes were hot and I couldn't find it.

When you clean out the ashes, look for it. I think it's a little hinge or something off the damper. Maybe you can put it back on yourself, although I know you lay no claim to being a household mechanic!"

Irene looked at Mother seriously. She said in sedate manner, "What are my instructions?"

Mother burst into laughter and flung her arms around her new daughter. "Your instructions are to remain as sweet and wonderful as you always are! And take good care of everything, and have a wonderful time together!"

The dyed felt hat with its rakish feather atop, the face wearing glow, eyes snapping brighter than any glow . . . thrice-remodeled spring coat, handsome tapering ankles showing above the how-many-times-brushed-and-refurbished shoes. She was trim, she was resilient, she was filled with imagination, alive to challenges before her. I took her down the hill—a trifle late, the bus was already in sight. When it halted I handed her aboard, the driver smiled and welcomed her. He knew her by this time, and so did some others on the bus. I handed up her bag and we all waved, and the bus went plowing south toward Huddlestun's Bridge.

I strolled up the easy hill of Ohio Street. I was thinking about Mother all the way, and wondering at her ability to do so much with so little.

"I had Dr. Julander for the three-color half-page ad, on the back page below the addresses, for the first April issue. But you realize we're going to distribute the May issue on the fourth Thursday of the preceding month! That will be April 28th, and Dr. Julander didn't take that same ad again. I got him, with the other three chiropractors in Boone, to take a double-spread black-and-white instead. That'll be on pages ten and eleven. The four of them: Dr. Julander, Dr. Anstrom, Dr. Struve, Dr. Achenbach— Achenbach! Isn't that a wonderful name for a chiropractor? People are always making jokes about it— But he's a charming man with a good sense of humor, he doesn't mind. Why, of course!—his sister Ada graduated from

high school in your class, didn't she? And then, to replace that
three-color job on the back half-page below the space for the
postage permit and address, I've got the Otis Lumber Company
in this May issue. If I can't get them for June, I'm almost certain
to get the Farmers' Cooperative Elevator and Livestock Company to take the same space. Three colors again—just like the
cover!"

A rustic journalistic heroine. The mere knowing of her was a
lesson in courage.

Those were good words to say above a grave, but they were a
lot better when recognized while the subject was still living.

At the house I found a hushed Irene, washing breakfast dishes.
There are many silences . . . during less than a year of marriage
I had learned to evaluate this one: the quietude of withdrawal
and disapproval. Of, if not of disapproval, discomfort.

We went through the *What's the matter? Nothing. What's
wrong? Nothing* routine for a while. Then it came clearly.

"It's just that I feel left out of things. Doubtless it's natural,
but I can't help feeling this way."

"What do you mean—left out of things? Mother's crazy about
you. Didn't you feel any response when she hugged you, and
told you to go on being as lovely as you are? That wasn't just
talk. She's incapable of saying things she doesn't believe."

Irene spoke hollowly, without echo. "I know you're right, and
I know that she meant it, and I do feel affectionate toward her.
And—appreciative. But it's just that— When she's here, you both
get to talking about the town and the people in it. You've got the
whole accumulation of your lives behind you—all the things
little and big that have come about— I can't *help* feeling ma-
rooned."

I accused her of being overly sensitive about this. Yet the more
one thought about it, the more one realized how correct she was
in her appraisal.

"Well," I conceded, "you're right about this: Mother is dominant. She has to be dominant. When she can't dominate a
situation or extend or carry the burden of conversation, she's

miserable. I've seen her in such condition. She was that way a year or so ago in Chicago, when she was with me. She's truly pathetic if she can't cry her enthusiasm from the rooftops of the world."

Irene didn't say anything. I walked out of the kitchen on one errand or another; but when I came back, she remained mute. Then she was taking her handkerchief from an apron pocket and touching her eyes. I went to her and said Please. She cuddled against me, and things were better after that . . . at least for a while.

That night I held forth.

"Dearie, you'll have to share my town and my past. I'm easily affected by experience, and what little experience befell me here I need to prattle about. Eternally I'll be talking about my childhood, and the Webster City I knew and felt and participated in."

(For a moment the young prophet knew what he was saying. Book after book . . . Clay City, Plattville, Shelldrake, Calumet, Hartfield, Lexington, Hickory . . . all wore the identical hide, housed the identical soul.)

"I guess if I live to be ninety I'll still be talking about it. It isn't all tenderhearted or childish-eyed, either. Some of it's tragic, some of it's funny as hell. You'll find out."

She offered the best reply any woman can give: a kiss. What I did not know was that our life would become more equable only when we had achieved sufficient common experience, sacred unto us personally. Impact of forty-six years could be reckoned in the range of megatons (a word from the far future). The paucity of forty-six hours or days or weeks would comparably bear the weight and force of ounces.

I brooded about Irene's and my brief common past, and about my own particular chaotic past which had immediately preceded. The notion was provocative. My private pack of hunting dogs went straying through streets and hallways of that bristling Chicago.

On Thursday the 28th I slid my typewriter into place between

the arms of a scratched Morris chair in the living room, and
sat behind the typewriter on its board.

She ground her cigarette into the steaming ash tray and
looked up, her eyes frankly level. "I wasen asking anybody
to take me out to eat. Abe'd take me, maybe. But I don'
want him to. He makes me sore. . . . Iss all right. You'd
think I was trying to pick you up, and I'm not."

Wise slammed the door, lifting his heavy brows as he
saw the others standing. "God, you're not going to leave all
this gin?" He shook the bottle into easy foam.

"Miss Ruska's taking me out to eat," said Javlyn. He
touched her elbow and quite gratifyingly she glided to the
door.

Wise foamed the liquor enticingly. His dark face was set
like a goblin mask in front of the cheap, yellow curtains
which shrouded the entrance to the tiny kitchen. "Taking
you out to eat? That's more than she ever did for me." His
lips still grinned but his voice was savage.

That was a portion of the first day's work on *Diversey*.
It would be my first published book, and the first book to be
issued by the firm of Coward-McCann, Inc. It would be the
first novel concerning Chicago gangs.

Other writers, including some copycats, came chortling afterward with *Scarface*, *Chicago*, *Little Caesar*, a dozen more.
Battalions of Chicago gangsters swaggered in print, on the stage,
before camera lenses.

I was just telling a story to which I was impelled, and which
I considered it bounden duty as a human chronicler, to recite.

My book would become crammed with structural faults, of
which the phonetic dialect was one. Novelists who have first
typified themselves as poets may march to the literary bar of
justice still clad in the glad-rags and poultices of their former
fantasy. Assuredly I led the van in this respect. Once I got
away from reporting the gambols of my principal characters,
there was an extravagant tendency to have *charioteers cracking
their reins through the whine of dizzy night* or to discover
lampreys gloating beneath their waiting lemon pools.

It might be possible for a bard to have a bad dream in Al Capone's back yard, but it wouldn't be a daily occurrence.

Nevertheless it could have been true that these very ludicrous qualities contributed to the credible significance of the book itself. Soon after my novel's appearance, Theodore Dreiser wrote a cogent article about Frank Norris's *McTeague*, which he regarded as the first modern American realistic novel of importance; and in this same breath he spoke of *Diversey* as an "honest transcript." The New York *Times* declared: "It rings true, and was worth writing." Nor would the *Saturday Review of Literature* cause suffering: "It is a first novel, and far better than most first novels. We are sure that we shall read few more stoutly realistic novels of gang warfare. . . . *Diversey* remains, in spite of annoying faults, a splendidly exciting portrait." Nor might any beginner take exception to the New York *Evening Post:* "As raw and rough and chaotic as Chicago, and with much of the city's terror and power. Mr. Kantor is someone to read and to watch for."

At that stage of the game I would not have become anyone to read and watch for, had it not been for the united devotion of Irene, my mother, and my sister Virginia and her husband Jim Sours.

The latter two came our way during the initial phases. A patriarch had died in a nearby village, and his family wanted Jim to preach the funeral sermon. In spite of shocking muddy conditions which prevailed in spring, the little town could be reached by graveled roads, so the Sourses came driving in their ancient Ford with its tattered top. They left the grandparents McKinlay still installed at Corydon, and fetched along their own son. He was an affable infant with round pink face; but I loathed small children. His presence did not imbue me with ambition to duplicate his being from our own stock.

(As I write these lines, he is president of Southern Oregon College, and still has a round pink face.)

The visit was on a weekend, Mother could come from Boone and join in. Irene prepared an excellent beef boil, and my

people were firm in their praise of her flavoring and her biscuits.
I could scarcely get down a mouthful . . . the manuscript, the
manuscript! I was dying to hold it in my hands—dying to read
aloud, to feel that renewal of strength which powers a writer,
and engages the machinery of his intellect and emotions, of his
whole body, in each heartbeat as he reads.

. . . My sister and brother-in-law knew less about such strata
of Chicago than I knew about their work in theology at Drake
University. As for Mother, she had lived with me for months in a
kitchenette apartment at 2829 Cambridge; thus she had stood in
the wings, as it were, when a few incidents which were fictionized
in the book actually took place.

Again, too, mine was a story of illicit love, and Mother disap-
proved of illicit love in any form. . . . There was profanity,
there was death. All in all, a portion of city life which pious
folk prayed did not actually exist. But in this book it was spread
in raw colors.

The exceptional factor about the evening was that my people
were so affected by the story that their objections, to the fact
or in opinion, were never even voiced.

I read on, wishing only that I had more to read to them.

". . . Where'll we eat, Conny?"

"Any place. Less go over to Dot's. Maybe she's got a steak
on ice." Conny had been a Catholic, once, and would need
a priest; Patch was a free-thinker, when he thought about
matters other than expensive criminal lawyers, a titian prostitute on Wilson avenue, and his fleet of trucks.

The Checker cab sulked closer.

"We'll go up on Lincoln to Ravenswood. Thass better at
night."

The green car ranged past with a spurt of speed. Their
last glance showed them a wide grin under a driver's cap—
they stared open-mouthed, which was unfortunate, as Conny
got it in the roof of his mouth and he would not be handsome in death.

Pam-pam-pam-pam-pam— The glass powdered over them;
the car swerved aimlessly toward the curb. "Uh-huh," sighed

Conny Welch as the Cab struck a young elm tree. And then he died.

Patch slumped lower beneath the steering gear, mumbling wearily. The Checker cab went fleeting to Halsted, took the turn on two wheels, and moaned north out of Patch's life.

When I'd finished, no one said anything for a time. Then my brother-in-law began to use the same words Pop Norris employed when I told him that Irene and I were married. He kept saying, "Oh my goodness, oh my goodness!" or "Goodness sake," or something like that.

My sister wiped her eyes, and went over and kissed Irene. That was typical of Virginia: give the credit where it belonged— to the woman who had helped to make the effort possible.

Mother held a little notebook, and was writing rapid figures. Jim Sours asked, "What are your plans?"

"We've got two choices now," I told him. "Before, we had only one. Irene's all over her flu pangs, and we'd be able to start out for California. I've still got a little money left—not much. I'm expecting a check from *Adventure*—"

"You mean you'd be willing to go, on that Farquhar newspaper deal?"

"Yes. He wrote and said for us to come whenever possible, and I could start work the day I got there."

"What's the other choice?"

Mother cried, "Oh, they don't know, you haven't told them. The man in Kansas—"

The man in Kansas had written to me immediately after the *Republican* was sold. His niece used to live in Cedar Rapids, and still subscribed to the newspaper. He'd read my feature articles each Sunday, and was pleased especially when I wrote about gunmen or pioneers. He had assembled notations concerning a long life spent in Garden City and Dodge City; he had known marshals and peace officers, and cowboy militants along with them. He wanted a book put together, and was

willing to pay to have it done. For us it would mean a trip
out to Kansas, and he'd have to pay for that as well.

Several questions remained to be answered. Did the old man
really have the money to invest? He wrote to me on flimsy
lined paper, scribbling in pencil, but that might mean nothing at
all. If he had money, how well might I be paid for my own
labors? We'd exchanged several letters . . . the old man seemed
eager, but reluctant to commit himself.

There it lay. California? Or possibly Kansas?

Virginia was short about the matter. "Irene mustn't undertake a
trip to California, going as you'll have to go."

Her sister-in-law became a trifle indignant at this verdict.
Why, she was all over her flu—didn't feel a germ in her body—
was able to go on long hikes. Only the previous Sunday, she
and I—with Amy and Milton Frank, a sister and brother who
lived nearby and worshiped the woodlands—had walked all
the way down to Church Hollow and Silvers Hollow, and back—

The family spoke in strophical dissent. "But that would mean
giving up the novel!"

"Not giving it up. No. It would mean putting it aside—"

Virginia cried, "You can't put aside anything as vital as this is
going to be!"

Mother told us all, "I've been making notes as I sat here. I
couldn't help beginning while you were still reading, because it
was so much in my mind. Children, I have been reworking my
own budget. I have found a way whereby I can send you four
dollars each week," and her big wild eyes came up to gleam with
pride.

"I'll tell you this," said Virginia. "We don't get too many
ten-dollar weddings. But every one we do get, we can send you
five dollars. Can't we?" she appealed to her husband.

Jim sounded much like a teen-ager whose voice was changing.
"We can send them five dollars whenever we have a *five*-dollar
wedding."

I told them all, "Our own wedding was only a three-dollar

one. Maybe the gods will punish us for that." And, to Mother, "You can't afford to send us four dollars each week."

"Oh yes I can!" She went over her figures again, she even read them aloud.

Irene and I walked for a long time before we went to bed that night. Alternately we were saying, "We can't let them do this." Yet the temptation hung as it was intended to hang.

Typically I included the cemetery in our wandering . . . always loved to go there when meditation was demanded. It seemed that I was drawing strength and more-than-imagined advice from people whose abandoned shapes rested beneath the grass. Even at this early age I had a lot of cronies there, because as a small boy I had so often sought the company of the elderly.

"Mind coming inside for a moment? In the cemetery?"

"Of course not."

"I wonder what they're saying, hon—"

"Can't you feel it?"

"I'm afraid so. We'll have to knuckle under. They're saying that one should do the Big Thing which he must do, first and foremost. And this is big, at least by our standards."

She said, "It's big by anybody's standards. You'll find that out next year. We can make it. I know we can."

"It'll mean night and day—"

"For you, poor lamb."

"For you too."

She said, "Well, I guess we've made up your mind."

We strolled down a graveled drive past the old soldiers' memorial plot.

"Charley's over there," I said, "down on that slope below. Charley Morean."

"If we were to ask his advice, I wonder what he'd say."

I told her. "Fourteen years old! I guess he'd say, 'I didn't really-truly mean to die. But, oh dear, I did.'"

Irene said, "You've got to tell about him, too, sometime."

I kept considering that sentence on the way home, and

finally burst out, "Oh, there is *so much* to tell about! And the
worst of it is that the more you live, the more there is to tell.
It's a life sentence, by God!"

She said blissfully, "Don't lag behind to fill your pipe. I'll
need to get up early, in order to fix breakfast for the family.
If I don't get up real early, Mother will be in the kitchen
before me. That won't do."

"No," I said. "It won't do at all. She's got to be able to go
back to Boone and work, so she can send us that four dollars a
week. God, Irene, what a courageous—"

Irene told me slowly, "Your mother is only proud, and utterly
delighted because she's able to help. That's the way she is . . .
I know it now. You know what? You're actually doing her a
kindness in letting her do it. And when the time comes when
she is dependent on *you*, instead of you're being dependent on
her— She'll turn her face to the wall, and die."

It happened that way, sooner than we ever thought it would.

3.

Winter's leaves and dead branches cluttered the lawn, and we
raked and burned. Irene adored the scent of leaf smoke, wood
smoke. We'd save the piles and heap them together in a se-
cluded spot where it was safe to make a bonfire. Then, when
shopping, we treated ourselves to a package of marshmallows.
We lounged at night on a blanket before boiling flames, and
watched and laughed and drew in deep breaths of the savory
scorch. I cut a couple of sticks, and we toasted marshmallows
after the embers burned down and were as childish as any
children might be; but happier than most children are.

It was affirmation of our delight in mutualism here identified
again, here impressed. I felt as I'd felt when standing before
the old property on Byron Street and observing the lawn
where a small Irene had roosted on her sled, bound up in
arctic clothing, staring at sunset light and hearty stars of a long-

ago winter, feeling herself to be a cold-weather Brownie, and disregarding any summons which came from a door beyond.

Here we were in a corner of the same garden where so often I'd bent my reluctant back and grubbed at tasks I hated. The apple tree beyond sheltered my more winsome years . . . a treasured green-glowing table lamp was awaiting us in the living room where my typewriter demanded its late evening stint. It roosted on a piece of shortened ironing-board which Grandpa had cut for me when I hunched, temporarily crippled, at the age of nineteen. *Come along,* said its implacable keys. *There's work to be done. All your life there'll be work to be done. You're a writer, and accursed accordingly. All . . . your . . . life.*

Maples, lilac bushes, the elderberry brake. These had been my portion, and would now be a substance of my wife—something to be reviewed to our progeny when the progeny came.

And would the progeny care a damn?

Only when they too grew older.

The vibration of merely being alive was ruling us, no matter what time I went to bed or we both went to bed—no matter whether Irene dozed near me before she went to bed or not, while I was still at the typewriter. We rose with verve when flesh-colored dawn came, or the smash of morning wind and rain against windows.

On a certain fair day we had risen early, breakfasted . . . I'd spent three or four hours on the book, and then went to the rear yard to clear some flower beds. Irene was busy in the kitchen.

She same running out to the back. "There's a very strange man at the front door. He wants to pray with us."

"He wants to what?"

"Pray. That's what he says."

I found, standing on the front step, an emaciated individual with a baldish head and straggling long locks combed over the bald place. He had a spandy new felt hat in one hand and a Bible in the other.

"I am your minister, the Reverend Mr. George McCorry."

"Well, hello. But I'm afraid you're not our minister. We ain't got none."

"I am minister to the world, though at the moment I happen to be the incoming pastor of the Church of the Pentecostal Nazarene."

I knew the Nazarenes, everyone knew them. Driven ebullient with religious enthusiasm, they screamed and ranted in a cramped wooden church down on the east side of town.

He repeated that he was going around having a word of prayer with folks, and wanted to have a word of prayer with us. I told him that truly we didn't wish to have a word of prayer. This rejection delighted him no end, and he set himself to persuading us both to pray with him: myself on the sidewalk, Irene on the screened porch.

> Obey them that have the rule over you, and submit your-selves: for they watch for your souls, as they must give ac-count, that they may do it with joy, and not with grief: for that is unprofitable for you.

Fortunately I recalled that a nearby resident, Mrs. Leah Gastin, was a stanch supporter of the Nazarenes and lived only a block and a half distant.

"I suppose that, new minister or not, you're already acquainted with Mrs. Gastin?"

"Sister Gastin! Ah, I know that she lives in this neighborhood. Tell me, which is her house?"

I pointed out the general direction, and Rev. McCorry said that he would pray for us even though we didn't want to pray with him. He set out at a stride for Sister Gastin's.

Irene regarded me saucily. "Is that a sample of your local clergy?"

"Honest to God, I never saw the man before in my life! He says he's new here and— Well, any time you're ready for a word of prayer, we can call him."

She needled me a little more about this during the noon

hours, and while we were lunching off bread and gravy and morels which we'd gathered the previous afternoon. If we only had steak to go with them— No worry about that at the moment. The mushrooms were angelic and we ate ourselves blind.

I was yawning, and Irene said that she knew someone who wanted to take a nap.

"Maybe you do too. Let me help you with the dishes."

"No, I'll wash them. You go and revise, and then we'll have our nap."

I didn't feel much like revision, but I did work a while, and then we went up the closed bent staircase. In our bedroom we drew down a strategic blind or two, and were soon committed to the esctasy of midday love-making. Contented briefly, we opened the outer door which gave out on a flat roof, and settled ourselves on the bed.

I was almost asleep when Irene, reaching over to adjust the window shade, suddenly froze with a gasp. I sat up and blinked. She pointed with shaking hand to the street. Her voice was thin, it rose in a bisyllabic shriek.

"What's *that?*"

There it was: a long-familiar vehicle, and one which I had not seen since 1925. Mrs. Estes owned that electric runabout for years: it looked rather like an antique buggy going off somewhere without any horses and without any top. After Mrs. Estes died, her daughter Mrs. King ran the car for a while, and then it was acquired by Aunt Lottie Crosley. Aunt Lottie was built like a little robin, and if you have never seen a buggy, high-wheeled, and without horses or top, going off somewhere with a robin as chauffeur, then you never did get to see Aunt Lottie Crosley on the road.

"Why, that's only Miss Charlotte Crosley in her car."

"Good God!" Irene mumbled something about, "I must indeed get accustomed to this town," and then we lay down again.

The languor of afternoon overcame us, we were drifting into drowsy comfort. . . .

A new sound penetrated. It was rather like a muted calliope

. . . lenient, humanized . . . no roaring of steam engine underneath . . . only the tender ecstasy of sound.

I recognized the once-popular tune, "Peggy O'Neil."

A gasp imploring beside me. "What's *that?*"

"The tune?"

"Yes, yes! What on earth—?"

"Oh, that's merely Al Martin. Pretty soon he'll come in view.
You see—" Managing to rouse a trifle. "People have lots of rugs
and carpets to be worked on, when they're cleaning house in
the spring. Just the way I whacked our parlor rug last Monday.
Al works with two beaters instead of one, and obviously someone's hired him today. So he carries two carpet-beaters, and he
swings them back and forth—"

I was wide awake by this time. "Let me tell you about Al.
I never have."

"All right," said Irene feebly, "but I don't think that I'll
ever really understand your town."

4.

Anecdotes of Al Martin included a scene in a tract called
the North Woods, but it was unnecessary to explain the North
Woods to Irene—she had been there with me already.

Our pleasantest forest edged the prairie north of town. Some
elderly women who lived somewhere in the East insisted on
keeping this timberland intact, the way it had been when they
were children. (Nowadays the woods have vanished and the
area is crammed with houses.) An invigorating stand of oaks,
hickories and locust trees were rooted there, with dense under-
brush around them. The region was laced by a couple of woodland roads which met and led to a farmhouse and fields
beyond. Otherwise there were only paths.

I worshiped the place and was intimate with every rod of
it: the clearing where wild iris used to grow, the single thin
stream, and a dry watercourse where once another creek had

trickled. My mother loved the woods as well as we boys did. Her passion was for birds as mine was for butterflies and moths.

In my early teens, contacts with Grandpa McKinlay became increasingly unpleasant. He was a silent and often surly man, distressed by financial losses, warped by accidents which had injured his body. I suppose that he, without honestly wishing to, resented me because "probably Mack will grow up to be just like his father." Grandpa despised John Kantor for a variety of reasons, all of them good.

Our basic lack of harmony showed itself perpetually. Grandpa no longer had a grain elevator to superintend; he worked at the sieve factory and didn't like his job. He had little hope for or confidence in me, and said accurately that I was sassy. I cannot recall that he ever beat me, even when I was tiny, but often he threatened to. He cut a thick strap into an ominous kind of paddle, and left it hanging on a nail in the summer kitchen; he said that this was strap medicine and that I would get a dose of it, next time I sinned.

One day we had a dreadful scene in which he tried to seize and punish me, but by this time I was too tough for him to handle. He retreated in fiery condition to the barn, and Grandma wept. She told Mother about it when she came home. Grandpa ate his supper in grim silence, and then sat down with the evening paper, speaking to no one.

Mother asked me to take a stroll with her to the public library.

"Oh, Scotland!" she cried as soon as we were out in the dark. "Lud, lud, lud!" Those exclamations were as close to profanity as Mother ever came. "I wish I could do something about it. That we could have a home of our own! But by this time I'm the chief support of the family . . . I can't keep up *two* houses."

I said gloomily that I wished I was old enough to do something about the situation.

"How I've longed!" she cried. "No one will ever know how I've longed! It's not fair to Grandma or Grandpa, our being

here. It was never fair to you children. Virginia ought to have
some place where she could entertain her friends without a lot
of old folks around, and young people are hard on old folks'
nerves. But there just hasn't been any other way."

Not until we were trudging homeward from the library after
nine o'clock, books under our arms, did the brilliant idea claim
her.

Her voice shivered with excitement. "We could get a tent!"

I thought about it. "You mean—out in the yard? That wouldn't
do much good." For a few summers we had pitched a tent in
the yard, full of nothing but beds, where we all slept in those
breathless August nights which exhaust the cornland.

"No. In the North Woods!"

"Could we get permission from the owners?"

"I'm confident that we could. Wesley Martin is their local
lawyer, and I've known Mr. Martin since I was a girl."

"Virginia doesn't like the woods the way we do. Virginia
wouldn't want to go."

"Virginia wouldn't need to go. She doesn't squabble with
Grandpa the way you do."

The Fort Dodge Tent and Awning Company, twenty miles
away, had a telephone call from us the moment they were
open for business next morning. I think the cost of rental on a
twelve-by-fourteen wall tent was seventy-five cents per week.

The tent was shipped by freight, and we engaged a rattly
truck to pick it up at the I.C. station and dump it down at a
designated spot. This was as deep into the little forest as any
vehicle could penetrate—a clearing among poplars and gooseberry bushes, with a view to the south across an open pasture
leading to the nearest farmhouse. Our tent would be in full view
of the Barham family all day, and thus a tramp or sneak-thief
might be observed if he came by. We couldn't think of any
way to lock up a tent.

A friend went with me that afternoon to help set the tent
up—my after-school employer gave me some time off, to get
situated—and late the next afternoon, a Saturday, I rode out in

the truck which carried our beds, chairs, kerosene stove, and boxes of food and clothing. Mother came hastening up the trail before six o'clock, unable to stay at her office a moment longer. Her face gleamed and her step was a girl's step (tall strong girl's).

My friends envied me, and all came to visit; on few evenings did we sit alone by our campfire. Mother's friends came, one by one or two by two, every night or so, bringing ice cream or steaks or "a dish to pass." When I went off to Scout camp Mother was never alone except for one memorable night.

She had a rifle loaded beside her, and she had our black and white collie-setter, named Rex. In the night Rex started to growl, he kept growling for a long time. Mother said that her scalp prickled, there in the damp blackness of the timber, but she slid her hand out until she found the rifle, and then she felt better. She was a moderately good shot with a .22, and the magazine was full of long-rifle cartridges. Rex finally stopped growling and whoever it was outside went away and didn't come back. It wasn't an animal, Rex never growled for animals. He pursued or attempted to pursue any or all of them, from gophers to Aberdeen Angus bulls, wow-wowing vociferously.

One lazy Sunday afternoon in June we luxuriated at peace before our tent door. Mother was seated in a little rocking chair admiring the activity of a pair of catbirds, and I was flat on my belly on a blanket, with insect pins and mounting board under my nose, working with the moths I had caught the night before. Rex yelped in a distant ravine, mining assiduously for a ground hog. When the ground hog mood struck him he would not leave the hole unless I whistled, and then he might come bounding and slobbering with his white ruff ruined.

Mother spoke my name in a low voice.

"What?"

"Don't look, don't turn your head. Just listen quietly. There's a man behind that gooseberry bush, over at the edge of the clearing behind you. He's just crawled up there through the brush."

"Who is it?"

"I don't know. I couldn't see him very well."

"What shall I do?"

"Get up and walk leisurely into the tent, as if you were going after something. Have you got any blanks?"

"No, but the rifle's loaded."

"Be sure you don't shoot *at* him. Just fire three or four shots quickly, over his head. It'll give him a scare."

I followed instructions, and inside the tent picked up and cocked the old Model 97 Winchester repeater, my pride and joy. It was a relic left in our home by the long-departed Doctor Von Krog to whom Mother had once been engaged.

I emerged suddenly from the tent door with the rifle half-aimed. I didn't want bullets streaming heedlessly through the woods, so I selected an oak tree a little behind the designated bush, and started pouring bullets into the oak. There was a tremendous scurrying and thrashing in the bushes. I stopped shooting, and the woods became silent.

We went over and examined the spot where our visitor had been lying. No clues, nothing but the weeds pressed down. But a few minutes later clue and solution came floating to us on the breeze. Far in the southern end of the timber rose a series of tormented yips. It sounded like a dog chasing a rabbit.

Mother and I looked at each other and burst into laughter. "Al Martin," we said.

His voice was unmistakable, we had heard it through most of our days. He was one of the several identified lunatics who roved amid Webster City life. It was typical of him to come sneaking and peeking. Possibly he could have been the intruder who caused Rex to growl in the night, but we thought it unlikely, since Al was paralyzed by the mere mention of Rex.

His dementia took only two forms which brought him into friction with the world: peeping into windows, and light-fingered thievery. But most definitely he feared a dog or a gun.

He lived with his mother on the west side of town. His

brother, a telephone pioneer with a streak of inventive genius, was long since gone to California. Ed Martin had been the owner of our early telephone system before it was sold to Bell. Away back before the First World War he experimented with a peculiar device of his own contriving. He called it a dial telephone. Local sapients snickered about this, and affirmed privately that Ed Martin must be nearly as crazy as his brother Al.

No one outside his family knew how old Al was. He never seemed to change through the years: a tan-faced animate with bright nervous eyes which glistened with that glassy impudence often seen among the demented.

Al owned peculiar passions. One was to be with young people; he admired the taller high school boys, and trotted in their wake. On a night before an important football game, he would stand on street corners and sing enthusiastically the songs he had composed in honor of his heroes. When pep meetings were held in the high school assembly room, Al would hover outside the building, yelling in chorus with the students.

He loved to do things with his voice. He could imitate horses, cats, cows, chickens; but his choicest feat was the imitation of a steam calliope. It was not uncommon, when a parade was held, to place a small structure on a cart, a wood-and-canvas frame with a stove therein and smoke pouring out of the stack from smoldering fuel. Screened thus from gaze of the crowd, Al Martin would ride at the end of the procession, fluting melodiously in a voice which could be heard blocks away.

Sometimes, when compulsive thievery did not yield him sufficient pocket money, Al would actually go to work. Usually his labors were light: he liked to go around and beg for old shoes, rubbers, scraps of metal. These he would sell to the junkman. But on occasion he could be persuaded to beat carpets, which he did with effectiveness. He pranced toward his task, two wire carpet-beaters gripped in his brown hands, his strange wordless hooting song breezing ahead of him. He swung the beaters in rhythm, and, persisting in this rhythm, he would soon have his carpet spread upon the grass. Thereon he would squat in a queer stiff-legged posture (both of his kneecaps had been broken when he "sawed himself off" when he was trimming a tree) and the carpet-beaters would pound in an alternate spanking, as if driven by machinery. In the core of his dust cloud he would sing or bray, hour after hour.

I wonder how many people in that town found the color in existence which Al Martin found. People said "Poor Al," if they were kindly, and "That damn fool," if they were not. Sometimes he was arrested for minor larcenies, which always dissolved his mother in misery. The old lady suffered, but not Al. He bounced out of vicissitude with a twinkling grin and a throaty growl.

W. J. Zitterell, local contractor, once secured a contract for a construction job in Kentucky. Mr. Zitterell called Mrs. Martin on the telephone. "Al is down here at my office. He's plaguing me to take him along on the job as water boy. Do you want him to go? I'd try to take good care of him, and it might keep him out of trouble."

Permission was granted, and Al journeyed riotously to Kentucky with Mr. Zitterell's crew—an unofficial court jester as well as water boy.

He had not been long on the job, however, before a telegram arrived from his boss, and neighbors came to lend their sympathy to the worried mother. Al had disappeared. Neither Mr. Zitterell nor any of the workmen knew why or where he had gone. He had vanished and that was all there was to it. He was thought to be without funds, but no amount of investigation brought any trace of him.

A fortnight elapsed, then a message came for Mrs. Martin. Al was safe and sound: he had turned up at his brother Ed's home in California. The brother said that he had bought Al a ticket to Webster City, given the ticket to the conductor, and put Al on the train with sufficient money in his pockets to buy food in the diner.

The day of his arrival came . . . no Al . . . another day . . . the traveler did not appear. Frantic long distance calls to California, and fruitless checking by the brother. Days went by. Weeks.

Early one morning neighbors ran out on their porches, and the grieving Mrs. Martin burst into blessed tears. *Hoot-toot-toot, hoot-toot-toot* . . . the calliope sound rose blithely under elms. Al was coming up the street. He was dressed in his usual attire: moderately shabby jacket and pants, moderately worn shoes, his little cap with its bill turned up. Over his shoulder he bore the branch of a lemon tree with several lemons attached, and lemons did not grow in Iowa. A further wonder: on examination, his pockets proved to contain more money than he had when he left California.

"Where have you been, Al?" he was asked a hundred times.

But he'd only wink one eye and jerk his head with a smacking of his lips.

Something impish and colorful would disappear from the pattern of the town with his passing. He may have aggravated or frightened some people, but if he ever harmed a soul I don't know who it was.

He comes to mind in strange and dwarfish beauty whenever I see a mass of deep-dyed violets. Such flowers grew thickly in a valley across the river from the baseball park, and on that slope Al Martin would crawl and pick through solitary hours . . . you'd meet him trotting along the street, and he would have a purple mound in each hand: violets, hundreds and hundreds of them, their slender stems crushed in substantial masses which even his hard hands could barely encircle.

Up to the telephone office he would go, and soon there issued delighted squeals from the room where girls sat before their switchboard. They welcomed the offering Al had brought.

They must, in turn, have represented to him some miracle which in his lunacy he would never be able to achieve. A few of the telephone girls were pretty, a few were not . . . there were rodent faces among them, overfat bodies, ugly mouths and fangs. But they were women—the only ones he ever dared approach—and so he came, chirping and twinkling, putting his treasure before them; and some of us wondered what his illusions might have been while he hunted in the violet beds, flattening the heart-shaped leaves he crept upon.

5.

Irene and I headed for Chicago early one tinted morning.

Jean Herrick had indeed driven us to Humboldt for a three-day visit which was all a joy—farm life and farm fare and canoeing—but otherwise I'd worked on the novel consistently. Even with briefest exposure to the magazine field, I was beginning to think in the months-ahead terms of a professional. Surrounded with viridity of spring, I had written a poetic sketch about autumn, "The Wheaten Dance," and quickly sold it to Swanson of *College Humor* for thirty dollars. The check gave us courage. When we left Chicago in the middle of the winter, I hadn't consciously considered writing a modern Chicago novel, although the notion was probably crawling around in my subconscious. The beginning of *Diversey* emphasized that I must refresh myself in the city scene.

There were scores of references which needed to be cleaned and sharpened for capable presentation. When you stood at the intersection of Broadway and Diversey, just how far down the street, looking toward the east, could you see? What shape did this building assume . . . that one? How far would the sound of traffic on Sheridan Road penetrate to the west? Little things, trivial things grown suddenly monumental, scores of them. I was bound to approach the task as if this were a historical novel in which every element of fiction should find its logical setting amid faithful reconstruction of an existing landscape. Loyally must sounds and sights be reproduced.

Nor would we need to crowd in with Irene's family at their apartment. Dick and Shelby Little had urged us to join them whenever we could manage it.

I sent a hasty note to R.H.L. and told him we would soon be

on the road. I called Mother in Boone and told her what we
were going to do. She felt normal trepidation about Irene's risk-
ing her neck in a picaresque sortie, but didn't attempt to dissuade us. The trip could and should be made. The very adventure implied was a brandy.

We dug around in chests and closets to see what could be
found in the way of clothes . . . here was a pair of Army breeches
I had acquired years before, still in good condition. Flannel
shirts . . . a pair of puttees, then another pair. I taught Irene
how to wrap the puttees . . . another pair of trousers from Boy
Scout days, they fitted her perfectly. We both had felt hats.
Here was a stained European knapsack left by Dr. Von Krog;
I had used it through years of hiking and camping. I discovered the same pup tent in which my friends the Richardson
boys and I had slept during an exploration of the Boone and
Des Moines River valleys.

Irene learned how to roll blankets: I would carry those and
the tent as well. There was another knapsack for her, filled with
clothing, toilet articles, miscellaneous stuff.

We started out along the graveled highway, with sun edging
up out of willow groves ahead, and had a magnificent sense of
being on our way among prairie bluebirds. Untrammeled, unheard, we were soon harmonizing on "Remember the times we've
had, dear?" at the top of our lungs. Irene had seen *Topsy and
Eva* when the Duncan Sisters first presented that song. (We
knew not that nearly a third of a century in the future, Rosetta
and Vivian Duncan would be reviving "Rememb'ring" in our
own living room . . . but they would, they would. What were
thirty years? A millennium. Even a day was a long thing.)

Past the town limits a mighty truck slowed to a stop. The
driver looked out and grinned—big fellow with Scandinavian
face and jaunty humor about him.

"Where you kids going?"

"Chicago."

"I ain't going there, but I'm driving all the way to Waterloo.
Get in."

Well-kept gravel persisted across our county and across Hardin
and Grundy counties beyond. The truck growled at a slow but
steady pace, the driver regaled us with exploits of his children
at home in Fort Dodge. . . . Sven was the brightest scholar in his
class, Leila a born zoo-keeper, what with kittens and rabbits and
a real live baby alligator . . . Andy was a born hell-raiser for
sure.

Between eight and nine o'clock we reached a loading platform
beside the Rath Packing Company.

"This is the end of the road for me. I've got two thousand
pounds of lard and fifteen hundred pounds of bacon. Got to get
rid of it." The driver opened up the rear of the truck.

"Don't they give you a crew to help unload?"

"Got to do it myself. Won't take long."

I installed Irene with our packs at the other end of the platform, and figuratively spat on my hands. Two thousand pounds
of lard in tin buckets, the fifteen hundred pounds of bacon
wrapped in slippery packages: a ton and three quarters. It would
have frightened the daylights out of a cholesterol-avoider, but
we had never heard of cholesterol, and neither had anyone else.
I boasted around a hundred and forty pounds of weight distributed over my skeletal carcass. I won't say I did the lion's
share of the work—just a lion cub's share. When we had the
cargo transferred to the receiving room inside, the driver and I
shook hands rather slimily.

"Thanks a lot, kid."

"And thanks for the ride."

I found an old rag and wiped my hands and forearms, then
claimed our baggage, and Irene and I started east along the
street away from Rath's.

Irene's voice was shaking. "Darling. Did you look at yourself?"

"Oh, I guess I did get a little on me."

"A little *on* you! The whole lower part of your shirt in front,
the upper part of your trousers—"

"Well, I guess I did get a little—"

"You're *solid white pork grease*."

"Have we got any soap?"

"Of course, but not that kind of soap. When we come to a grocery store—"

We bought a bar of Fels Naptha. Another long walk, and then we were out in the country again with a creek over to the right. We moved across a field and into shade of willow trees. I took off my clothes and, knee-deep in the creek, started in on the job. Irene worked on shore. We found sand, sand would help. Water was cold, the soap strong, the sand abrasive. Still, it wasn't exactly a French hand-laundering result which we achieved.

Nobody came near except some cattle strolling by to stare contemptuously.

Irene said, "They act as if they know we've been at Rath's."

"Hell with em. I wasn't unloading beef. I was unloading pork."

Irene spread the garments in sunshine beyond the willows. I shook my head. "We ought to be on the road."

"There's nothing to do about it, dear, but wait. You've got to have those things dry enough so you can wear them without catching cold."

Irene had fetched sandwiches and cookies for our first meal. But she wouldn't let me dress for another couple of hours. Then we packed up and went on, myself still soggy, but declaring loudly that the clothes were practically dry now.

We were offered two rides, and accepted eagerly. But by late afternoon we had reached the termination of gravel, and stepped into a sea of mud. We were tired. We sat on roadside grass and spread out a road map.

"Where are we now?"

I showed her.

"Oh, Chicago is so very *far* from Webster City!"

"Something like three hundred and eighty-six miles by rail."

"And it will be farther by road?"

"I'm afraid so."

Irene touched the map. "Look, that next town. There."

"Yes?"

Call the town Ashford.

"That's Ashford?"

"Sure is."

"Well, isn't that where Lucy and Part are living?"

"Why, yes. Guy Partridge used to work in the Ashford news-paper office, before he went to Cedar Rapids."

"Don't you remember? Part and Lucy urged us to come to Ashford and visit them if we possibly could—"

I was a little doubtful. "Aren't they living with her folks, now that he's lost his job?"

"Lucy told me all about it. They've lived with her mother before. It's a big house, old fashioned. She said they had lots of room."

We recalled the Partridges fondly—especially fondly in this muddy moment. Threatening clouds were heaping above soaked farmland in the west. Blackness of the marshy road was direful.

In high school agricultural classes we midland dwellers had been instructed that our native soil should be termed "Wisconsin drift"; but in our opinion—during rainy seasons and following snow-melting—we held it to be formed by a copious mixture of putty, coal dust, mucilage and molasses. Over some of the worst spots wooden trestles had been built, strips of a size to accommo-date wheels of a car or truck. Those low places marked where ancient sloughs had stretched, once teeming with cattails and blackbirds.

"There's another car mired down ahead—"

We counted seventeen cars stuck in the mud before we reached Ashford. Irene dug into her knapsack and brought out a tiny address book. Many of us on the *Republican* had exchanged information when we parted. Here was the Partridges' address, in care of Byerton.

"That was Lucy's name before she was married. It's her mother's house."

6.

Our quarters that night consisted of a lofty front parlor which had been transformed into a bedroom. We snuggled in a huge four-poster bed, and growled when we didn't feel like wailing. Everyone else in the household, including the Partridges' two tiny children, slept upstairs. The muted aspirate of our whispering could not penetrate to upper regions.

Irene mourned, "I'm ready to cry."

"Crying won't do any good."

"When will you realize that when I say, 'I'm ready to cry,' I almost never *do* cry? Oh, gad. We shouldn't have come."

"Course not. But it's too late to do anything about it now."

"If only we'd pitched our tent out in the woods somewhere—"

"You saw the woods. They're wet, fairly seething with ooze. We wouldn't be very comfortable when that water soaked up through our blankets."

"Couldn't we have put the tent *under* us?"

"Huh. Just listen to that rain. It started in again almost an hour ago."

"Oh, this is too terrible! Lucy said they were going to be living with her mother. She didn't say anything about those two old-maid sisters."

"Hell, honey. You'd be an old maid too, if I hadn't married you out of sheer charity."

"It's not the fact that they're old maids. It's the *way* they *are*."

"Sure. They resent our coming, but they also resent the fact that Part and Lucy and the two little kids are here. They're mad at Part because he lost his job. He couldn't help losing his job any more than I could. The *Republican* was sold overnight, and there were ninety-odd other people out of work on an instant, besides Partridge and Kantor."

"But how could they look so dreadfully at us? They seemed

to count every bite we put into our mouths! Not Mrs. Byerton—
she's sweet. But those—*harpies*—"

"They're gainfully employed, and Part is not, so they're putting
the food on the table. They don't own this bed or the ceiling
above our heads, thank God. Those belong to Mrs. Byerton, and
she's welcomed us as warmly as any woman could. But—"

"Mightn't we pack up now, and just go off in the rain? Wouldn't
have much to pack . . . we didn't undo the blankets or the tent
or . . ."

"If you want to be really dramatic about it, we can leave a
note and say, 'Thanks so much for the evening meal, and for
making us feel at home, but we feel that we must be getting on
our way.' They'd know we were crazy then. They may just
think we're crazy now, but then they'll *know* it."

"Darling. What will we do if it keeps raining tomorrow?"

"I don't know. We'll have to figure out something. Part's doing
the best he can—you know that—and we can't say or do anything
to embarrass him or Lucy. He's a good linotype operator. The
local weekly newspaper editor likes him, and gives him whatever jobs he can with copy to set. But Part can't earn much that
way. He's trying to get another job. He's applied in every direction: Dubuque, Des Moines, St. Louis, Minneapolis, Sioux City."

"But those *Sisters!*"

They were much older than Lucy. Right now I'll bet two bits
that neither of them ever married. I hope the town of Ashford
was fresh out of masochists. One was a school teacher, un-
doubtedly hated by her pupils, and one a bookkeeper in some
local bank—long since replaced by a computer, we trust.

When we greeted them next morning, First Sister said, "You're
going to get wet today." Second Sister said, "How long'll you
be with us?"

Irene helped give breakfast to the infants in their high chairs,
while Lucy prepared food for the rest of us. A side street past the
house was unpaved . . . Part and I stood at the window, watching cars and trucks wallowing through the bog, heavy tire chains

clanking, mud swishing up in streams behind them. One truck
was stuck in a vast puddle halfway down the block.

We ate eggs and bacon which Lucy had prepared in old
farm style—eggs basted, slabs of bacon curling and brown.

First Sister asked Second Sister: "Will you have another egg,
Arita?"

Second Sister to First Sister: "I guess so. If there *are* any
more left."

When the spinsters went off to work, I heard them in the
front hall asking their mother, "Will *they* still be here when we
come home for dinner this noon?"

Poor Mrs. Byerton, faltering in reply: "Why yes, girls. If it's
still raining, I don't see how they can leave."

Thank heaven my wife didn't hear that.

Part told me that we could find the latest forecast downtown.
"The State weather bureau sends a telegram every morning to
the newspaper office, and they put it in a frame by the door so
everyone can see. Maybe you'll get some favorable news."

He and I sloshed away to the business district. I read the
forecast while Partridge was inside the office, trying to find out
if there was any work coming up for him that day. There
wasn't.

"Cloudy with precipitation continuing and possible thunder-
storms in northeast portion of State." Which we were in.

I told Part that I'd treat him to some pool. We went into the
pool hall and played forty cents worth of rotation. I felt like a
spendthrift, but we were in affliction.

"Part, where are the freight yards for the Illinois Central?"

"Out on the west side of town."

"Well, the I.C. hasn't been stuck in the mud yet, has it?"

He knew what was in my mind. "Let's see how much gas I've
still got in the old buggy."

I told him that I could pay for a little gas if he needed more.
We went and took a look.

"I've got plenty—still a quarter tank full. We'll go and see what the situation is. The road's paved—this long street which runs west beside the tracks. We can get there without any difficulty."

We drove out, far past water tanks and lumberyards. There were several sidings along there . . . boxcars and gondolas waiting to be picked up.

"The afternoon train'll get some of these. But the railroad detective has a pretty sharp eye. He's always around here, day and night, so obviously you'll have to wait for the eastbound evening freight. See—there's a good place right past those coal sheds. I can park there tonight, you'll be under cover of the sheds if it's still raining."

Back at the Byerton house, we didn't say anything about our survey of the railroad situation. Part related bits of gossip which he'd picked up at the newspaper office and pool hall.

"They say there's at least two dozen vehicles stuck between here and the county line, east of town. Several families were trapped in their cars overnight, and one woman started to have a baby. They got help from a farmhouse, though, and carried her over there, so she had the baby safely in bed, with a nice old lady for midwife. Dr. Schuman walked out there this morning, and he said both mother and baby are in fine shape. Maybe they wouldn't have been, if they were still in that car."

Lucy was doing the children's laundry, and Irene insisted on helping. The Sisters came home for the midday meal. Mrs. Byerton fried some catfish which Part had caught a couple of days earlier, and she also baked hot corn bread, and Irene mixed cabbage salad. It was a glorious meal, with outside torrents still pouring down . . . or perhaps they were pouring *up* by this time.

Second Sister to First Sister: "Will you have another helping of fish, Grace?"

Grace to Arita: "Why, yes. If there *is* any more."

I thought this was particularly mean of them, since Part had caught those fish his own self, and it hadn't cost the Sisters a dime. We finished up with canned peaches which Mrs. Byerton put up in jars the previous year. The peaches were excellent. The Sisters remarked that there were very few of those quart jars left.

Part and I were allowed to wipe dishes after the Crones had gone back to work. No more rotation pool could be afforded; we played checkers for a couple of hours. We tried to inveigle our wives into a game of Five Hundred, but Irene demurred.

"I'm still a little weary from the trip yesterday. I'd like to take a nap."

Part said, "I'm going to take a nap right here on the sofa." He proceeded to stretch himself out forthwith, and I went to join Irene in the front bedroom. I found her with white face and wet eyes. The children had napped earlier and, on arising unsupervised, had been very busy. The object of their attention was Irene's knapsack which lay beside the boarded-up fireplace. The special object of attention was her one and only box of face powder: Houbigant's, as I recall, which she had been given on her birthday. Some of the powder heaped in a pile on the rug, the rest was spread all the way to the door.

I couldn't help exclaiming weakly, "The Sisters!"

Irene giggled through her tears. "Don't be absurd. It was Naomi or little Guy."

"Some of it can be spooned up. I'll go get a spoon."

"Bring the carpet sweeper too."

We cleaned the mess, and were able to salvage a small amount of powder. My bride had news for me when we finished.

"We're never going to have any children!"

7.

Well before the evening meal began (can't remember what on earth it was) I had revealed my plan to Irene. "Are you afraid to try it?"

"You've done it before?"

"A little bit."

"Then I'm not afraid. Anything's better than staying here."

About three quarters of an hour after the dishes were done, Part held up his wrist and tapped his watch, offering me a signal over the heads of the others. I went to the front room and removed our baggage to the porch, and came back to say goodbye.

Mrs. Byerton didn't quite understand what was up. "You're not leaving now, in all this rain?"

"Oh yes. We've got to get along."

We thanked her profusely for her hospitality, and the dear woman kissed us both.

The Sisters were openmouthed and goggling. "They're leaving *now?* Why, they can't get any rides on the *road!* It's a *morass!*"

Part said, "Come on, folks, let's go." To the Sisters, "They're traveling by train."

"By train? The evening passenger train doesn't come through for *hours and hours!*"

I told them, "We're going by freight."

"Freight? You mean you're going to hop on a *freight train?* Why, that's against the *law!*"

"Oh, no," I said sagely, "we'll be shipped regularly. I'll fix a couple of tags and fasten them on our clothes. Tags directing us to Chicago, and saying, *FOB Ashford, Iowa.* That way we'll be a regular shipment, see?"

Guy Partridge carried us away through the downpour. He tried to stop between pools of water when we reached the coal sheds west of town. The freight train was early, already halted on the track.

Part said, "I'd better drive out of here right away, so we won't attract attention." He and I shook hands, and he kissed Irene goodbye. "Let us know. Send a penny postcard," and then he was gone.

It came over me with a rush: he knew how we felt, why we were going; he'd observed the attitude of his sisters-in-law, even though he said nothing about it, couldn't say anything about it. He was trapped. He was robed in the traditional stringy misery of the young man out of a job, young man with a wife and children on his hands, young man forced to take shelter in a manner he deplored. The wanderer returned to what constituted a home town . . . and having people talk about him behind his back, or sometimes not even behind his back. Had he owned a sunny menage, he would have entertained his friends honorably. There would have been pride and pleasantry in the occupation, but now there was no pride, and we'd barely attempted to have joy. I couldn't guess at what sort of job he might find, or where, and he couldn't guess either. In that moment I felt far more impressive grief for him than I did for ourselves. We had the venture immediately before us and around us; he had none, couldn't have. He and his wife were the target of family scoffing, a factious patronage amounting to scorn. We had suffered it only in transit and were not beleaguered by parenthood.

I wondered if in some miraculous way Irene might recognize the pain in which Partridge was riding now, as his creaking old car splashed through pavement floodings on the way home.

No, of course she couldn't sense it. She was a woman, never to be aware of the lack of fulfillment which a man might feel.

Her hand came through the dripping darkness and joined with mine. "Golly," she said, "I feel so sorry for Lucy. And especially for Part."

8.

If there were any freight yard detectives a-prowl we didn't see them. Nor was there anyone else hiding in momentary shelter of the coal sheds . . . I explored to make sure. Then, leaving Irene and our bags, I ran across to the line of cars. First one was locked and sealed, second the same. The third was an open gondola.

Fourth car . . . yes, a boxcar. The door was slid half open. I looked up. A man leaned there against the frame: long-haired old tramp with a spooky beard, and a slouch hat pulled down over his eyes.

"Howdy, young fellow."

"Hello—"

"Bad night."

"Yes, it is. Are you alone in that car?"

"Sure am."

"Let me make certain," and I climbed up beside him. Inside the car I struck a match and searched around. He was right . . . no one else crouching there, no other hoboes. There were only a few newspapers and piles of shavings which had been used for packing material.

The old man chuckled along after me. "What's the matter? You ain't scared, are you?"

"No," I said, "but I needed to make sure. I've got a woman with me."

"A *woman?*"

"My wife."

The line of freight cars lurched under impact of an engine far down the track, and we were almost thrown off our feet.

"Better get her," he warned. "They may be pulling out in another minute or so—"

I dropped to the ground, raced over to the coal shed, and brought along Irene and the knapsacks. The old man was by the door, extending a hand to help Irene up. We boosted her into the freight car and I shoved in the bags, then climbed in myself. The whole train was crashing and quivering again. Irene landed headlong in a pile of shavings. The old man said that wouldn't do, and found some fresh newspapers.

"I been saving these. I didn't know what for, but they'll be nice for your wife." He showed her how to spread them across the pile. "Then, if you get feeling kind of cool, you can pull these others over you."

She said later that she had no idea that a freight train could bang and crash so much. "They seemed to be putting on cars at one end and taking them off at the other, didn't they?"

I assumed that the tramp knew what was going on, but we didn't know, and at the moment didn't much care. At least we were gone from the Sisters, and were out of the rain, and had an affable soul for company. I told Irene that I could open up the blanket roll if she wished.

"That'll make too much disorder. We might have to get out of here in a hurry, mightn't we? Anyway I'm perfectly warm now, and didn't get very wet."

I owned one weapon: a Marble hunting knife with a short sharp blade. I fumbled around and found it in a pocket of the German knapsack, and fastened the sheath on my belt. Certainly I had never stabbed anyone; I hoped I wouldn't have to begin a stabbing career on this trip; but there was always the danger that other people might also board the same boxcar. The knife did give me confidence. I spoke nothing about these worries to Irene. Let it be a lark of gayest proportions, and we were fortunate to have this gentleman along with us. He and I sat down together and talked.

"I'll bet you've seen a lot of country, sir."

"Boy, have I seen country! Seen all forty-eight States, from end to end. I used to be a printer and—"

I asked him if he had ever worked in Webster City, and said that I had more or less grown up in a newspaper office there.

"Then you know about us tramp printers?"

"Certainly. They used to set up copy when they were just fooling around. I've got a card with 'When the Baby Wets the Bed,' printed for me by a tramp printer—"

"Eugene Field!" he exclaimed in glee. "I used to set that myself. And 'The Passing of the Backhouse' by James Whitcomb Riley. Oh, I've set a lot of type! Say, did you have another printing office in your town?"

"Sure did."

"Did they send you over there to borrow some type lice?"

"Sure did. And a left-handed line gauge!"

He crowed, "Hah-yah, boy!" and shook hands with gusto.

Irene found the plight a trifle less savory than we. When finally the impact and shoving ceased and the train jerked into forward motion, she sat tense amid her papers and shavings. Repeatedly I went over to reassure her; she offered no complaint, she only wondered whether other wayfarers might enter the car at the next stop . . . maybe railroad detectives? I told her about my knife, and let her feel the hilt. But that was the worst thing I could have done. It gave her the notion of knives.

Belatedly she became accustomed to crunch and battering of freight cars, and was able to stretch out and go to sleep when I came to lie beside her. She had a dream. It encompassed the idea of our tramp printer degenerating into a murderer, and creeping toward her with a freshly whetted blade . . . pure nightmare. She'd wake, and realize that it had been a dream—that we were in the boxcar, and I was there with her, and she would turn and clutch me, and seek assurance. But then she'd go to sleep and entertain the same illusions again. Once more the old man would be edging on his vile errand, once more she would hear herself shrieking in illusion, even though I never heard her utter a sound.

With my grasp cemented on the hilt of my knife, I went to sleep, warning myself to rouse at any stop in case other wayfarers got into the car. Actually that was unlikely . . . the printer and I had shoved the door shut, once we got started.

When I dreamed, it was to see our companion trespassing through endless elegant vistas. Forty-eight States, he had said. Thus I saw him in all of them, in far reaches which we had never visited, but might become familiar with some day if we were fortunate. I saw him in Maine, saw him in New Mexico, Mississippi. Deserts and cactus and high pine woods swept past the car in which he reigned. Busy trout leaped in mountain streams beneath the bridges. He fared well among palmettos of Florida and grainlands of the Dakotas, he became a *Minnesinger* who rode high and away.

Through turmoil of metal and couplings my imagining turned ecstatic. Irene and I would go to those far places too, but not in a boxcar. I must delve, learn, and tell all stories to all peoples, for her sake and my own, and for the sake of the peoples as well. We would accept luxury of private quarters in fast trains at home and abroad, and taste whatever graces might be found therein. "Make your book to be the best you possibly can," I ordered as I slept, and said the same thing in counsel when I had awakened and was once more in consciousness. We must achieve, never yielding to dismay in the effort.

9.

The Chicago excursion, inauspicious in its initial phases, was triumphant in result. Beyond the pleasure of being with the jaunty companions whom we felt Dick and Shelby Little to be, I quickly found answers to minor problems relating to the Diversey neighborhood which had vexed me previously. Also I was able to examine newspaper files concerning the activity of bootlegging organizations which began to bloom and boom in Chicago a few years previously. I had owned an uncomfortable firsthand acquaintance with some of this savagery in 1925. But it was essential to go back for what an historian might term cross references. Veteran of big and little wars as he was, R.H.L. summed it up in the word *reconnaissance*. Not until years later, when I made my own study of high altitude bombardment in two later wars, did I realize how apt his statement was. Photo-recco—or photo-recce, if you will—is part and parcel of any such program if the task is to be performed properly. That applies whether you're dealing with a novel or with five-hundred-pound General Purpose bombs.

Low on cash, we dared not linger in the city too long. Whenever possible we walked distances in order to save the nickels or dimes which might have been expended for surface fare. The last night we spent with the Layne family, and Irene's stepmother Jessie cooked us a fabulous farewell dinner. Also she endowed us with a slab of salami as big as a man's forearm, and an immense loaf of home-baked rye bread, to be munched on the trip.

Irene's father wished to advance us money for the return to Iowa—at least in a day coach; but we were stubborn, mainly because we didn't know when we would be able to repay the loan. He too was close run, although according to different standards than ours. It was a Sunday when we left, and the family swooned in a variety of attitudes, out on the sun porch, to see us marching west on Wilson Avenue, once more in our traveling togs and carrying our packs.

Salami and the bread and the bottle of mustard to go with them were a benison. A day later we rode imposingly through the streets of Rockford, perched high atop three slabs of Indiana limestone on an open truck, with Irene making sandwiches for us and the truck driver.

The driver said that he was sorry to lose us when it came to the parting. "You're quite a pair," and we preened ourselves at his opinion.

"You find so much to laugh at. But I suppose one of these times you'll be getting married, and then you'll laugh on the other side of your faces."

"But we are married. We told you so."

"No, I think you're just covering up. Maybe you've both run away from home or something. You just couldn't be married. You have too much fun."

Nevertheless Irene bore certain bruises from the trip, and would bear them long. I swore that these events must not be repeated. It was too hazardous, and I must refuse to expose her to such experience in the future. The memory of the boxcar assailed her again one night when we lay in our tent in a patch of woodland. Before daylight a wagon drove out of a nearby farmyard and across the ridges on some rural errand. Half-waking, half-sleeping, Irene heard the rumble of wheels, and dreamed once more of knives and similar menaces . . . perhaps the farmer was as dangerous as she had feared our fellow tramp might be? Perhaps he was coming closer and closer to wreak his worst? And there were other perils on the way which she noted, and which besieged her in recollection, though resolutely she tried to hide them from me.

But the events, despite their aftermath of unpleasant emotional debris, were to become valuable in recollection. In our homely little record of strivings and yearnings, we might be excused the affectation of royalty. The queen who accompanied her husband to ancient wars, and slept in his pavilion, and heard the tone of bronze on bronze and steel on steel— She had a clearer idea of the battle than she would have had if she'd stayed home.

10.

"Anything happen yet?"

"No, nothing."

"Maybe you made a mistake on your calendar?"

"No, I didn't. I've checked the dates meticulously all along. I was due three days ago."

"Well, hell. Don't be worried, you're just a little late, that's all. Remember? Last December you were several days late."

"Yes, but I had a cold then. Frequently a girl is delayed when she has something like that—or at least I've been, occasionally. But there isn't anything like that now, to ascribe it to."

At first we felt hopeless, and in some way empty and leadened down, whenever we thought of it. No Pills had ever been fabricated in those days; other people might have heard of diaphragms but we had not. We used some peculiar little brownish cones, purchased over the counter at a drug store, and had used them ever since we became intimate.

The plaint was: we didn't do anything differently than we'd done before. We didn't slip up, we didn't try It without any cones . . . or had we taken a chance, after all? Couldn't remember.

This must be merely a trick of nature. Irene couldn't be pregnant, she simply couldn't. We dwelt in utter poverty, and people in utter poverty shouldn't have babies. Or did they have them anyway? Ugly pictures of Dickensian slums, with scrawny nurslings wailing in starvation, came to view.

On the night of our engagement, well over a year before, I had delivered an arrogant statement. "Just want you to know this: I don't want us to have any babies."

And there had been Irene's remark when the Partridge young-uns raided her powder. "We're never going to have any children!"

Faced by this threat we found ample opportunity to lift our eyebrows, shudder, make cryptic utterance in the presence of others—there were so few others—and snicker together.

So few others indeed. But a patient couple named Hall lived in the next block, and I brandished the novel before them on every possible occasion. Lorene Quackenbush Hall had served a sentence as little-girl-sitter with my sister the afternoon I was born, and thus affirmed an intimate interest in my strivings.

Amid echoing pioneer influence of our community, many neighbors and friends were endeared by the common titles of elder days: grandpa, grandma, aunt, uncle, in general conformation and confirmation. A few were nearer to Mother than certain natural-born sisters might have been, and close to her children resultantly. . . . Aunt Grace Sheldon was a prize.

Gracie Howard and Effie McKinlay had become as bosom twins when they were girls, and so they remained. Grace was plump and mellow, with a soothing voice and pure gentility of nature . . . married to a lean man who was soberly going down-hill in the grocery business. We called him Uncle Jack, and many people considered him remote and withdrawn into static bitterness. But with intimates he still displayed spritely humor, and he liked to play pinochle, and—God love him—he loved to have me read aloud.

Aunt Grace welcomed my spouse to her bosom as if Irene were a favorite doll whom Grace had lost in youth and now miraculously reclaimed. Strangely, too, their voices sounded very much alike . . . gentle, soothing, rewarding.

In private Irene said that she might be only half pregnant.

"I don't see how I could be fully pregnant, after all those cones. They have some kind of chemical in them to destroy the cells, or we couldn't have used them so successfully from the start. If I should have a baby now, it might be all sort of moth-eaten around the edges."

Gruesomely we conjured the specter of a baby gnawed by drugs which had failed to prevent its being. Like many others—probably since the dawn of time—we provided a name for the unknown and barely-to-be-recognized-or-imagined foetus. We called her, him or it, Calliope.

"Oh, no, we mustn't. It's reminiscent of Al Martin."

"Might be all the more appropriate. It could have happened that afternoon when you first heard Al prancing down the street, making his Peggy O'Neil sounds."

"No, it couldn't have occurred that afternoon, because—"

"Why not?"

"The timing would be all off."

"Are you sure?"

"I'm not sure about anything," she said tremulously.

Where did the mystic union begin? Where and when? There in the old house, or out in devout woodland? Over on Huddlestun's Hill, perhaps, or an evening when the frogs of spring were conversing? We had gone there and built a fire and cooked our supper. Then we let the fire die down, and afterward, in moonlight—

Out in the garden, by another fire? Perhaps in the Littles' apartment in Chicago? "If we have a child, we'll have to name it Shelby or Dick."

Nothing happened. . . . We told Mother, and she rolled up her Kilkenny eyes. "Oh, wait a while. Probably everything will be all right."

Irene talked to Aunt Grace Sheldon. Aunt Grace said flatly, "I think it would be very nice, and I just hope that you do have a baby."

"How *could* we?"

"Well, wait a while. Perhaps there's nothing to be upset about."

The first processes of death often go unidentified, misinterpreted, joked about. So with the first processes of life itself.

Our family doctor, E. E. Richardson, father of my boyhood pal Robert, no longer lived in Webster City. The next month Irene went to another doctor selected through the advice of friends. He was a buffoon who made local capital out of his natural and sometimes assumed drawling geniality. On examination, he declared that Irene was pregnant and no mistake about it. When we spoke of Calliope and the cones, he had a few jokes to tell us on allied subjects.

In a later age I grew understandably without appreciation of this man's humors. He classified one dangerous cardiac case as "just a little indigestion," and the beginnings of osteomyelitis in another patient as "just a little inflammatory rheumatism." But we were compelled to accept his verdict at the time.

(I entertained even graver doubts of his powers as a prophet in a year far beyond that. It was when I came back from my first tour overseas in the winter of 1943–44. The movie made from my story *Happy Land* was given its premiere in Webster City and a score of other Iowa theaters the same night. I was called upon to speak in my home town, and the next evening in Des Moines. Friends entertained us and some fellow townsmen at a buffet supper, and Dr. Cordiality was present. He drawled out a question. "Mack, when is the war going to end?" I opined that I couldn't tell him; and neither, I reckoned, could anyone else. "Oh yes," he said, "it's quite plain to see. The war will be over next spring—probably about April." That made it the spring of 1944. I replied that I hoped the Japs and Germans knew about his date. "Don't talk to me about Germans," said the worthy medico. "I was overseas in the First World War, and I know what cowards the Germans really are." I thought of Jerry fighters diving at us through their own flak. "Not the ones we met up with, Doctor.")

I asked Irene what her inner reaction had been on that en-

gagement night when I declared that we mustn't have any
children.

She smiled. "I wanted to have children—someday. Certainly
I enjoy normal maternal impulse. And I grew up in a good-sized
family."

"But what did you *think*, when I said that?"

"I thought to myself, 'I'll probably get him over that silly
idea.'"

"But, God damn it! I can't abide the patter of tiny hoofs or
the angel choir of childish voices! It's partly Mother's fault.
She's mad for little ones, and has always been flinging them at
me. A couple of years ago, when she was with me in Chicago,
Janie Bale Morris was always coming down to our kitchenette
and bringing little Mack with her. I didn't like the looks of
him, didn't like the sounds he made, or like his actions. He was
always saying, 'Boy want bipe,' and carrying my pipes around,
and I'd have to search the wastebaskets after he left. Or he'd
get up and hammer on my typewriter as if it were an anvil.
I don't mean that there was anything particularly demented
about that one little boy. I suppose he was just average for his
size and sex and general condition. I suppose they're *all* average.
But that doesn't mean that I *want* any!"

Irene said cozily, "Then, when Calliope is born, we'll just
have to teach him or her to stay away from your pipes and
typewriter."

Very nearly with horror I discovered, and instantly, that the
threat of parenthood has its own stimulations. I worked till all
hours that night, and on the typewriter. And I smoked pipes
too—although it wasn't yet necessary to warn any infant away
from them. In some witching hour before dawn I clambered
up the stair, and Irene roused a little when I came into the
bedroom.

"It's awfully late," she murmured. "How did you get along?"

"I did thirty-four hundred words tonight!"

"You did? How is it? Have you read it through again?"

"Just got through reading it over. It's swell!"

When I got into bed she took my hand and drew it over to acquaint her flesh with my fingers.

"I wonder when I'll first feel Life?" she whispered. "This is exciting. Once I woke up and lay for a while thinking about it . . . then I went back to sleep again."

I considered our mortal puniness in the world at large: my own lack of a job and regular income, our need for a home of our own—I didn't yet have a private chicken shed or a kennel to put my wife and descendant in.

"Hon," I asked, "how do you really feel?"

She breathed out the word with elation. "Swell!"

VI. *TENDER. AND COLD*

1.

I finished *Diversey* in a seemingly momentous night of late August. If there'd been any liquor handy I would have taken the most generous drink ever contrived by quivering human paws, but the booze cupboard was bare.

> . . . Those who were ready to die, and those who were ready to drink gin, and ready to love, and ready to build with ingots or typewriter ribbons. All soaring outside his window; prying at his mind while he went to sleep.
> Josephine Ruska turned the corner at Cambridge and Diversey sometime after twelve o'clock. It was a cold night and few people were walking out; there was no one coming from the Henderson or going there, and the building loomed harshly at her with no light in any of its windows. Remembering that Wise and Spence Sailor had died in front of it, she felt childishly nervous. . . . Her eyes watching the bright toes of her shoes beat evenly against the concrete, and never knowing until she got there whether she'd turn in, or keep on going north.

Already I'd gained considerable ground in retyping the manuscript—double-spaced, on white paper. Now I flew at the thing with a kind of brindled canine energy. I'd never learned any proper system of typing (then or since). I used one finger on my left hand and two fingers on my right hand like many newspaper people. Those three fingers took an awful beating, especially the index finger of the right hand. It was increasingly sore and swollen, and finally split open alongside the nail. I contrived a little pad or sock of gauze and tape, and went ahead with the typing. Blood would ooze through, and this was disconcerting, but I was fresh out of secretaries at the moment.

Determination demanded that I lug the manuscript to Chicago and deliver it personally to H. N. Swanson, editor of *College Humor*. Why on earth I thought *Diversey* would be a milestone as a *College Humor* serial, the Lord only knows; but I did think so. Why on earth Swanson didn't have enough editorial acumen to buy the book and present it— That too will never be known. He and I discussed it several times in later years, and there ensued mutual headshaking. Certainly it wasn't their type of serial. Their serials consisted mainly of haughty James-Montgomery-Flagg and Arthur-William-Brown-drawn snoblings who assembled at Long Island country clubs. Still Swanson agreed with me eventually that the rawness and naïveté of *Diversey* might have been greeted with enthusiasm by the magazine-reading public.

In hearty imagination it seemed that if I appeared at the office fresh and ebullient, manuscript in hand—I had notion that editorial judgment might yield to my enthusiasm.

Irene's rough-and-tough traveling days were over for the nonce. She must remain in Iowa, and we greeted this awareness with wails and gnashings. But at least I was traveling by rail. A genial gentleman named Harry Carson, married to Aunt Grace's niece, provided me with a stock pass. That meant that I could ride in the caboose of a freight train, accompanying two carloads of hogs which were being shipped to market. I was told that I didn't have to do anything to the hogs—just give them my good wishes.

Technically I was a stock-car tender, but had no idea how to proceed with any duties. Bills of lading were in my pocket, and those must be delivered to proper authorities at the termination of the journey.

Harriet Ashbrook, the first publicity representative for Coward-McCann, contrived the story a few months later that I worked my way to Chicago "on a stock train, with the manuscript of *Diversey* wrapped in an extra shirt." That tale still appears in print in several of those books of biographical sketches which are written about authors with no assistance from the authors. Stuff and nonsense. I had a suitcase: it was good and solid, if made of woven material. And I had at least *three* extra shirts, and they reposed in that suitcase along with the manuscript.

Several times en route I went along with other shippers or attendants to "look after" my hogs. I didn't have the slightest notion of what might be entailed, but since the men said that they were going to "look after" their own stock, be it beeves or pork on the hoof, I believed that I should make such gesture.

On one occasion some kind of barricade put up to keep the hogs properly encompassed had fallen down, and a few of the beasts were in danger of being trampled. Several generous souls, discerning that I knew nothing about the situation involved, came and helped me to put the boards up again. I was rather timid about hogs anyway and, with small-town rearing among the pig breeders of our neighborhood, knew certain people who had been mangled by boars.

(One victim, Mr. Cutler, had to have his leg amputated in his own kitchen. The lost member was duly buried in a meadow, and for years Mr. Cutler resisted successfully the incursion of a new highway across his fields because of human interment therein.)

These critters squealed and champed in terrifying fashion. I felt that personal honor was at stake, and made a great show of leaping in merrily amid the mob. They were cooperative if noisy, and only tried to get out of my way. We got the little barricade back in place and the shipment was well behaved from then on in.

The journey occupied some twenty-four hours or perhaps twenty-two. Anyway it was dark when we got to the Yards. I heard talk about a fabulous inn where the shippers, or men accompanying shipments, always went for juicy steaks in celebration. Definitely I did not belong to the juicy steak contingent. I turned my papers over to bored and extremely minor officials, the hogs were counted and receipted, and I took my precious suitcase and hurried to the nearest streetcar line. Dick and Shelby Little were vacationing elsewhere, so of necessity I went to the Laynes'. And to bed in Irene's former quarters, after I'd taken a very necessary bath. It seemed strange, lying in her bed, thinking of her far removed, hundreds of miles away. I was wondering how she rested in that remote Iowa, and how much she truly feared the future. Was it righteous for either of us to give way to any fear at all? And . . . sleep, sleep.

Next morning in his office Swanson tossed my manuscript into the air, and caught it, and cried, "It seems about the right weight. But I'm still not sure that you can write a novel." He was merely having fun, but my bruised disposition was so sensitive that I felt he must be jeering, even this far in advance. A horrible truth was apparent: he would never buy *Diversey* for his magazine. I wished that I hadn't fetched it, I prayed only that he would give it a quick reading. I submitted also a couple of small sketches, and then ran earnestly around town and saw what other editors there were to see. Not many.

One was a stalwart Navy veteran who rejoiced in the name of Ewart Hetherington Ross, but had been given the nickname Bud for reasons which must have been eminently acceptable. I'd known him slightly when he was in the editorial chair of *Outdoor America*, official publication of the Izaak Walton League. There I'd contributed occasional verse and short prose, for free, in the interests of the conservation cause. Bud was now editing a trade journal called *Water Motoring*. I pricked up my ears when he said that he'd be able to use a limited amount of fiction.

"You know, something to do with outboard motors. I don't have a big budget. But maybe you could do something like that for me at a modest price."

I faltered in response, "But, Bud, I don't know anything about outboard motors."

"Well, I'll send you some literature—" They used that word for advertising broadsides even then.

I had a little fun on the last night. Sat with Snowshoe Al Bromley in his brother's apartment and listened to the Dempsey-

Tunney fight on the radio, and heard the Long Count, and wondered about it along with the rest of humanity.

The stock-car arrangement included a return trip to Iowa via day coach, and I was on the train next morning, sleeping a good share of the time. I reached Webster City in the evening. Irene was already in bed, reading, when I got home. That light in the bedroom was one of the most reassuring beacons I might ever see. She came down in her queenly batik robe to let me in, and we sat with crackers and milk while I regaled her with every detail of the Chicago venture.

I told her frankly that Swanson would never buy *Diversey* for *College Humor,* but she merely shrugged that off.

"Some publisher will want it soon. I'm utterly confident."

So was I, or said that I was. But our faith was tried severely when the manuscript was returned by mail a few days later, after Swanson had decided in the negative.

Promptly I mailed it to Lida McCord, a New York agent who'd had the handling of my first-written novel two years before. That was called *—And Angels,* and it is a matter for shudders when one considers that it came close to seeing print. It was designated as one of the runners-up in a contest mentioned earlier, won by Martha Ostenso with *The Wild Geese.* Lida McCord had the handling of this manuscript in the meantime, so I sent *Diversey* to her and asked that she return *—And Angels.*

Almost immediately ensued the astonishment and revelry occasioned by my first short story sale of consequence. *The Biggest Liar in Eagle Falls* was purchased by the revived *McClure's* Magazine. The incident has been related in detail elsewhere and there's no point in going into it again. But that hundred-dollar check set the stars askew in their courses . . . bread, manna, ambrosia and nectar. It accentuated beyond doubt the glittering fact that somewhere there existed magazine editors who might appreciate my wares.

Best of all, we were justified in seeking another place to dwell. My grandparents had returned to their home, and living harmoniously with them was an impossibility. They were elderly, tired, frail; our presence was sheer imposition and nothing else. Of course they made us welcome and tried to share contentment. Grandpa sat and read newspapers or lodge magazines most of the time. But my grandmother, sweet and patient to the point of deity in daily life, could not understand why I must be left alone when I was working. A dozen times a day the living room door would fly open and she would appear to report that Kitty had just caught an English sparrow, or that she was almost certain that Amy Frank wore a new fall hat when she walked past the house on her way downtown.

The check from *McClure's* meant that I could pay the family grocery bill, and that the young couple might sensibly go in search of quarters of their own. We pranced to the task.

A small house, and the furniture to stock it? That was beyond our means, and we never even considered such a course. We sought a furnished apartment which might be procurable at a price less than the cheap Chicago standard of fifteen dollars per week. But such abode in a county seat town usually meant a dreary couple of rooms on Main Street, upstairs over the hardware store or shoe emporium. Ventilation was achieved by a series of skylights, and the rooms bore the faint stench of previous tenants who had not cleaned up very well.

A few glimpses of such interiors and Irene was sunk in gloom. I knew the town better than she, and still held hopes.

"Let's forget the business district. What we need is something in a private house."

"Perhaps," she faltered, "it would be worth while to advertise?"

"Let's just go on looking, and tell people what we want, and maybe somebody will hear of something."

The first afternoon we did indeed learn of lodgings for rent, and right on Willson Avenue. No one was home when we first appeared, but a note on the door said for prospective tenants to return in the evening.

We went back after supper that night, and our blood chilled. This was the first time that we together had ever encountered

the emanation of pure evil from a fellow human. . . . Make up a
name for the man and call him Wipperly. There is no such name
in the modern New York telephone directory, and perhaps no
such name anywhere. He was devil-browed, with bulbous gray
eyes and a sniveling manner of speech. He went with us every
step of the way on a tour of the rooms available, and Irene
declared that the flesh crawled off her body when she had to
stand near him. My own reaction was nearly as violent. We
couldn't get out of the place fast enough.

"If that's what it means to live in furnished rooms in a
house—!"

"Cheer up, pet. Must be something better, somewhere. Just
have to keep looking."

We forced ourselves to entertain hope, but had a sorry time
getting to sleep that night.

(Years later we experienced the same vile issuance . . . in
houses which stood empty at the moment, but with taint still
apparent. In Westfield, New Jersey, we walked into a handsome
residence, accompanied by a talkative lady real estate agent.
In the front hall we stopped, then turned around and marched
out again. . . . "But you haven't seen the house!" . . . "Sorry.
We couldn't live there." "But—" "We just couldn't." Same thing
occurred later in Beverly Hills on a more elaborate scale.)

Boldly we agreed that if there were impressions of evil so
apparent, there must be genial welcoming forces at work as
well.

Next day came a telephone call from the widowed Minnie
Arthur, mother of Herbert.

"I heard that you folks are looking for an apartment—"

"Indeed we are, Mrs. Arthur!"

"Did you know that the old lady next door has some rooms
for rent? She's got a separate little apartment. But you know
she's kind of queer."

Whatever knowledge I had of Mrs. J. W. Letts had been
gained when I was nine, ten, eleven. In such occasion there is
small necessity or even probability of a noisy boy and an

opinionated old dame establishing mutual rapport. When our militia, dripping with bandoleers and bolo knives, invaded her premises, Mrs. Letts marched us out again. But I knew that her rambling house offered sanctuary to several school teachers who lived with her season after season. One of them, whom I especially admired, spoke often of Mrs. Letts with tenderness and affection.

Hastily we walked through town to call on her. It was a bright autumn day, but Mrs. Letts knew that snows were to come. She had dragged out the winter's storm windows, without which few householders in that time and climate felt serene in imagining blasts to come. She had secured a tall stepladder, and stood in a loose rusty jacket which had belonged to her husband who'd died many years before. Also she wore one of his ancient felt hats crushed down on her head. There was a sauntering musing aspect in her attitude.

"Well, well, you're Mack Kantor, aren't you? Guess you know me: I used to chase you kids out of the yard."

"Mrs. Letts, this is my wife Irene. Please don't chase either one of us today. We hear you have an apartment for rent."

She measured us with calm gaze, and smiled and nodded to Irene. "Thought you lived with your grandparents. Folks said you were living up there."

"The truth is we'd like to be by ourselves."

"Well, it's not very fancy. I fixed it up for somebody a couple of years ago, but now they're gone."

The rooms were at the rear of the house, with a separate entrance which would be private to us. An old porch had been transformed into a kitchen with a gas stove. Irene announced later that her heart went out to the place the moment she walked through the door. It was tiny, but immaculate and peaceful . . . sun came through windows with love. A black cat lay in one of the chairs and stretched in genial welcome when we came in.

"Does Kitty go with the apartment?"

"That's my Thomas, and he's got quite a history. You like cats?"

"We both love em."

"Here. This door leads to the private toilet and lavatory. You'd have to share the bathtub next door with me. The teachers have got their own facilities upstairs."

When I asked about the price of rental, she measured me cannily.

"Let's see. I heard you were writing a book—"

"I've finished it, and it's being submitted now."

"Working at anything else?"

"There's nothing here in town. I tried the local newspaper when we first came—the *Freeman-Journal*—but they don't need anybody."

"Let me see, now. You saw what I was doing?"

"Yes. You were fooling around with some storm windows."

"Like to fool around with em yourself?"

"Not very well. But let's go and take a look."

She said, "They need more than a look. They need to be scrubbed, and so do the windowpanes underneath. How are you at scrubbing windows?"

"I've washed quite a few."

"The way I like?"

"What's the way you like, Mrs. Letts?"

"Here, I'll make up a kettle full. We'll see how you do."

She filled a big saucepan with water and poured in a generous contribution of household ammonia.

"Not spirits," she said, "just plain good old ammonia. Always does a better job. Now here's a couple of clean rags. Climb up there on that ladder, and let's see how you do."

Irene played with the cat, examined shrubbery, re-examined the apartment while I worked on the ladder. Mrs. Letts's eye was on me every minute, and it was a shrewd eye. She was by no means a woman given to excessive praise—nor, on the other hand, to my surprise, excessive censure. "Use a little more elbow grease. I like to have the panes shiny and nice."

I worked on those windows the better part of an hour. She

produced essential tools and screws . . . I had them cleaned, on that side of the house, and the storm windows in place.

"Come inside," she said, "and I'll let you taste Mother Letts's new corn relish. It's late in the season, but I found a few small ears that were reasonably soft, out in the garden. I ground em up. You like to work in the garden?"

"No!"

"Well, you don't have to take my head off about it. Had any experience in taking care of a furnace?"

"Certainly, ma'am."

We tasted the relish she had made, and definitely with relish. Then she ushered me to the basement to demonstrate the furnace which was not yet in operation, but would need to be in the near future if weather ran true to form. It was the familiar hot-air structure with which I'd grown up: long runs of asbestos-covered piping going off to all sections of the sprawling menage.

"I burn soft coal, bituminous coal. It's easier to handle in a thing like this. But the clinkers get awful bad."

I knew clinkers, I'd grown up with them too. At an early age I'd learned to pry the massive molten racks loose from grates which they would ruin if left in place.

"Those big cans are for putting the ashes in. I like a place kept neat, not with a lot of junk sprawled around. Every so often the cans can be dragged up that little back stairway and left outside, and men come round and empty em. Actually the furnace holds fire very well, and doesn't require too much care except in extreme weather. I like the fire stirred and coal put on about five in the morning, so's the house'll be nice and warm for my roomers when they get up. Well," she said, "that's the size of it. The couple who were living in these quarters—actually I had the thing rebuilt to suit em— He used to take care of the furnace too, and that helped a good deal. But he got transferred to Illinois—"

Back upstairs again, Mrs. Letts went into her own rooms to answer the telephone while Irene and I whispered together.

"Of course it's poorly furnished—"

"Not so badly. It looks meager, but we can brighten it up."

"That bed in the corner— It's just springs with a mattress on top, set up on chunks of wood—"

"I tried it, and it's very comfortable."

"She says the fireplace doesn't work—"

"I know. But see these windows! The light would be good for your typing in that corner over there—"

Our hostess came out and asked, "Well, how do you like Mother Letts's abode?"

"We like it fine, ma'am. Now there's some questions to be asked."

"Of course," she said, "and answers to be given."

She possessed a jaunty let-the-chips-fall-where-they-may manner of approach, but you knew when she was dead serious and when she wasn't. She sighed, and said that she had hoped to rent the small quarters for twelve dollars per week. It turned out that the couple who had preceded us couldn't pay that much—they could pay ten. Then the man was offered better-salaried work elsewhere—

"I decided that I should get the same ten dollars a week again. But I'll make you a proposition: if you can do chores around the place—at least there won't be any gardening this season, except mowing and raking—fix the windows, take care of the furnace, take out the ashes—I'll offer the apartment to you for seven dollars per week. That's a dollar a day. I doubt you can do better than that anywhere," and we doubted it too.

"Mother Letts," we asked, employing this endearing term which she had dangled rather in the manner of bait, "when can we move in?"

"It's all ready. Soon as you can make it."

"Tomorrow?" In rapture.

"Course you can, if you can get your stuff moved."

It was merely a question of having Willard Boughton bring his light truck instead of his taxi to ferry us down there—suitcases, typewriter, Morris chair and all. Grandma, worried but blissful at our departure, offered any small articles we might

need, in order to have the new quarters arranged in home-like
manner. Grandpa said, with jollity rare for him when dealing
with the present, "Well, I understand you're going to be a fireman too!" He'd fired a factory furnace, among other jobs in elder
years.

Irene was delighted at the idea of cooking on commercial gas.
No gas main ran into our immediate neck of the woods on
Willson Avenue, and we relied upon a coal range in winter and
a kerosene stove in summer. My fresh young housekeeper had
managed miracles, but this was like the manufactured gas of
girlhood days in Chicago. She kept turning it on and off, blissfully, just to see the reassuring glow.

Tommy, the black tomcat, welcomed us into his family circle.
When we arrived we found him stretched out on our bed with
paws tucked under his chest. He was to be a comforting companion when weather became frigid and I made my trips to the
furnace. In icy mornings when I opened the door from our own
chill region and started down that warm stairway, Tommy
would buzz and reach out from his bed-box on a wide shelf
beside the steps.

This October was still summerish, though leaves sprinkled
in profusion. Days were counted dreamily, filled with smoke of
vanished Indian fires. It was a prideful season in which to be
alive and young and working.

(Irene thought so too, until the doctor informed her that she
must wear a maternity corset. She acquired one of those mon-
strosities and tried to fix it to suit, while I attempted to aid with
the lacings. Finally in frenzy she hurled the object across the
room and burst into tears . . . we owned baffling moments as
well as bright.)

2.

There are islands in existence, or perhaps promontories or penin-
sulas, from which we watch the driftings which extend beyond
us. We are ruled by steady application of toil, and consummate

enjoying of the simple and the good. Taste of food, twitter of household adventure, the steady exploration of humanities which come our way— In such state Irene and I were affirmed.

Autumn was unseasonably warm and dry and prolonged. In earlier weeks Irene was still not grown too large in pregnancy to preclude our long walks among the woods. We watched leaves turn, and gasped in pleasure at the splintering rosy bouquets which the oaks became. Heavy bundles of fruit on sumac shone red as well, then died and dried through various stages of brown until they were great dark birds perched heavily among the tiny boughs.

"Calliope will love the woods," we said in faithful accurate prophecy.

My typewriter challenged on its chair board. I wrote thirteen stories during the autumn and early winter . . . in time eleven of those would appear in print, but considerably later. I sold only one during the time we were there. It was called "Oarsman," and went to Bud Ross for forty dollars.

I knew next to nothing about markets where my product should be offered. I submitted continually to impressive big magazines, seldom to little ones. The process of merchandising a young writer's wares is something quite apart from the act of producing them. This he must learn through experience, and he dares not let bitterness of protracted failure rule him. He must make the stories to be as good as he can, that is all; and then learn a totally different craft in the business of marketing.

I try to think of raw and rainy days—there must have been some—but in general pageant the autumn flowed, warm and beneficent. Haze drifted over the woodland in legendary swathe. We carried a blanket with us for picnic lunches, and yielded to the light sounds of birds and animals which still moved feeding there, and we built kinship among them.

Sometimes on Sunday afternoons Aunt Grace would call and say that she and Uncle Jack were going to drive to the country: did we want to go? Always we wanted to go. We brought home butternuts and black walnuts, big gunny sacks full, and I spread

our share on a shed roof to dry, and when colder weather came
we would share again with Mother Letts. Our relationship with
this woman prospered: we joined in drollery and affection. She
had a colossal store of community anecdotes—some even on the
ribald side—and these trivialities we accepted with glee.

A boyhood chum named Edgar Atkinson lived with his beautiful German wife less than two blocks distant. They had tiny
girl twins. Irene grew big-eyed and shuddering at the mere idea
of twins, and was constantly appealing to me on the subject,
and searching both our categories of ancestry where twins
seemed numbered in eminent profusion. Edgar's mother was a
widow of considerable means, but she loathed the idea of his
marriage to Martha, principally because the girl was Catholic.
These young people dwelt in a kind of mother-inflicted penury,
in a flat which didn't seem as attractive as our own. Nevertheless
they had an affable landlady who was able to sit with the babies
once in a while. When we all felt sufficiently daring to achieve
the expense, we went to the movies together and even on rarer
occasions visited a Greek ice cream parlor afterward.

Sunday noons we usually went to my grandparents', where
Mother would come from Boone for a day and a night. This relationship prospered gently as it could not do when we were
compelled to live together. There is dignity in such separation,
and we had achieved it, even with that necessitous demand of
the seven dollars a week rent which must be paid at all costs.

This island in the sea of our contingency might have been
habited by grim and demanding shapes. It was not. Bright
days flowed with gentility. The past became dramatic and
full-fleshed in a stream of reminiscence.

Grandma said, "I don't know just which month it was, but it was
a season when Papa didn't have much to do down at the mill.
It was before grists were coming in, or after. So he came up
the hill and said to me, 'Evvy, I'm going to take a nap in the
hammock.' It was tied out in the yard between two trees, a little
distance from our house. I went on with my housework, just
doing things in the kitchen, and then I happened to look out in

front. Papa was sound asleep in the hammock, and a man was
coming down the hill. I didn't have a notion who that man
might be; we knew all the neighbors for miles around. He was
tattered-looking, like a tramp, and I remember he had a beard
and rather matted hair. The thing was that he was carrying an
axe in his hands, and walking slow, just holding that axe and
walking along. Then he spied Papa in the hammock. He changed
his whole manner the moment he saw your grandfather asleep
there. He stopped, stood real still, and stared at the hammock.
I could scarcely catch my breath. The man turned aside
and started toward Papa, walking more slowly than before, and
lifting that axe a little as he moved. My brother Uncle Jo was
down at the mill. There wasn't anybody else around, and Effie
was sound asleep in her basket there in the kitchen. I knew I
couldn't go out and grapple with that man, I wasn't strong
enough. My heart was in my mouth . . . I guess I had what
you'd call an inspiration. There was a wooden pail near the
door, and I snatched up that pail. I threw open the outer door,
and yelled across the yard at the top of my lungs, 'Adam
McKinlay, you get up out of that hammock and come in here
and get me a pail of water!' Your Grandpa sat up, astonished
within an inch of his life. As for the man— He just stood a
minute, then turned away and started walking down the hill
toward the mill, more rapidly than before. I went out and stood
on the step, and Papa sat there in the hammock, fairly stupefied,
and we both watched the man go. He crossed the bridge
beyond the mill and turned into the woods. Soon as he could,
your Grandpa went to the mill and called Uncle Jo and another
neighbor or two who were hanging around. The mill was always
a place to sit and gossip. . . . They armed themselves, and
went across the bridge and started looking for that man. They
didn't find him, but pretty soon they came across the axe. It was
stuck in the stump of a tree which had been cut down before.
Just the axe, stuck deep in the stump. They had a job prying it
out. The stranger was nowhere to be seen. No one knew where
he'd gone or where he'd come from. We never did know."

Grandpa said, "The last panther? I saw him, and I think he was really after me, but kind of afraid to attack. It was when your mother was still a baby, and Grandma was feeling poorly that night. We had singing school up at the Pleasant Hill school house. Every couple of weeks the singing master would come around, and practically all us folks in the neighborhood joined in. We used to like to sing. Well, Grandma was home with the baby, and I was at singing school, and it was a real chilly night. I started home alone past the last house: the Uncle Jimmy Adams place. You know where it is, on the corner of the Bone's Mill road where it joins the main road north and south. There wasn't another house between that place and ours, and the woods were thick in between. It was late on this evening, too, because we'd got to working over some parts at the school, on new songs, and everybody stayed past the usual time. Nobody else was going my way—I was the only one going west. I kept feeling awful peculiar, I didn't know why. I kept looking around behind me, and then pretty soon I saw the panther. It was a big one, and it was following me. I quickened up my pace, and went faster, and the thing went faster too. Then it got in the woods beside me, I could hear it going through the leaves. Finally it let out a yell—loudest yell it seemed I'd ever heard. That did it: I lit out and run like I'd never run before. I went down that hill so fast it's a wonder I didn't go head over heels and break my neck. The thing was keeping pace with me, or really was a little way ahead; because the last time I saw it, it dashed square across the road, right in front. Then came the lights of the house, and in another moment I was safe inside. Your Grandma said she was scared to death about that man with the axe. Well, so was I at the time. But this was a different kind of scariness. With that panther and all."

Mother said, "Gypsies were the bane of my life. Schoolmates were always talking about them and telling how they'd kidnap little children and carry them away—dye their skins to make them seem brown, and maybe trade them off for other children later on somewhere. Every sort of wild tale about gypsies! On this

day we children were coming home from school, and suddenly
we looked ahead, and there it was: a gypsy caravan. Several
gaily painted wagons, but of course all rather tattered and dirty-
looking, and some men riding on horseback. They were coming
along in a regular parade. We children didn't wait for anything,
we crawled under the fence and went tearing into the woods.
I remember one little girl named Lucy, and she was so frightened
that she couldn't go with us at first . . . we had more or less
to drag her along. She closed her eyes as tightly as she could and
just trotted in a circle, wringing her hands and jumping up and
down. It's odd, every time I hear the name Lucy now, after
all these years, I get a quick impression of that little girl, trotting in an insane circle, wringing her hands. . . . We got safely
away in the woods, and the gypsies passed by. The older boys
said, 'I guess they're gone now,' and we came out of the woods
and started down the road. Then we looked back, and the
caravan was just going out of sight along the road to the west.
Then it stopped, all the horses and wagons. One man turned
around on his horse and started galloping directly toward us. Of
course what we thought was that they had seen us belatedly, and
now the man was coming to capture us. This time we burst into
the woods again and ran like little demons, hard as we could
go. Oh yes, Lucy was along with us too. I guess she was over her
first fright, and she legged it as fast as the rest. My Uncle Rufe
was separated from his wife at the time, and living in a cabin
where he had a smithy—you know, a blacksmith forge to put
metal tires on wheels and all that sort of thing, and do the
regular horse-shoeing too. I can remember how Uncle Rufe
looked, standing in his big blacksmith's apron, there at the forge,
and grinning at us, saying, 'Are you *sure* the gypsies are after
you?' But we wouldn't go home until somebody escorted us. We
wouldn't leave, we were too badly terrified. . . . Why did the
gypsy man ride toward us? Lord knows: perhaps they thought
they'd dropped something out of one of the wagons. Anyway he
did start toward us, and galloping, and that was all we waited

to see. Doubtless gypsies haunted all our dreams for a long time after that; I know they haunted mine."

Mrs. Letts said, "You say you stopped by the Burgesses' house to borrow a magazine? Did you see that dang Honeybunch? . . . She was there, big as life? My heavens, to think two people could make that kind of fuss over a big old Persian cat, the way they do over Honeybunch. Well, they haven't got any children, so I suppose it fills some sort of need. You know, Honeybunch is a kind of remote ancestor of my Thomas. I think I told you about that: how, when I said as much to Mrs. Burgess, she crows angrily at me and says, *Very distant!* Yes, I did tell you about that. Well, let me tell you another one. When they first had Honeybunch, years ago, Mrs. Burgess decided also that she needed a maid. She got one from the country, from down in the southern end of the county. The girl was a kind of Scandinavian. Mrs. Burgess set down and told her everything she wanted done around the place, and she said also that she and Mr. Burgess liked to take their meals alone, and she hoped the girl wouldn't mind eating in the kitchen. The girl says, 'All right,' in her peculiar accent. As I said, maybe she was Swedish. Well then. And this is all true: the girl told it herself, told it to everybody she saw. She said that she fixed up the first night's supper —or dinner, as the Burgesses called it—everything just right, just the way Mrs. Burgess told her to do. She had that nice supper all fixed up, and then she started in to serve it. And guess what she found? She walked into the dining room and there Ed Burgess and Mrs. Burgess were setting at table, nice as you please, waiting for their meal, and there was Honeybunch between em. That dang cat was all set up in a high chair, and she had a pretty pink-and-white bib around her neck, and she was waiting too. The girl went back to the kitchen and upstairs, and started to pack her suitcase. I guess she called up on the phone for someone to come and fetch her. She was maybe Norwegian, and talked kind of queer. Mrs. Burgess says, 'Why, aren't you going to give us our meal?' and the girl said in her accent, 'No, ma'am, ay don't mind eating by myself in the kitchen, but ay ain't going to wait on no cat.' So she just got out of there, just walked out. I think maybe she was a Dane. Mrs. Burgess let her go, she had to. They haven't got any maid nowadays, but they've still got Honeybunch."

3.

Weather remained tender through the end of October. I could remember Halloweens as a boy when our hands became so cold that we needed gloves as we chased about in our hell-raising . . . . sometimes some of us actually did wear gloves. It could snow on Halloween, I'd seen snow come that early. . . . This year it was like a July night. I went out in darkness with a couple of farmer friends—we'd all been boyhood chums—and spent most of the night wading in the Boone River. We had our trousers off and tennis shoes on, and prowled through warm water with fish spears in our hands. Probably it was against the law to use the spears, but we weren't looking for game fish: we were looking for carp, and we found a few. I brought home a nice one . . . ten pounds if it weighed an ounce.

Next day Mrs. Letts showed Irene how to cut the fish into chunks after I had scaled it, and cook the chunks. You had to be careful in preparing the meat, because carp were so full of small bones. We went up to Aunt Grace's that evening, and spent hours—all four of us, Grace and Jack and Irene and I— picking out the clean white meat. Then recipes . . . Aunt Grace had an ancient cookbook which mentioned carp. The meat was to be pressed into tiny balls, and accompanied by a sauce. There was enough for friends and neighbors to have a share.

After sleeping I'd come back to life that day, and had written a short story while Irene was busy in the kitchen. I was dying to read this aloud. When we'd finished our long chore, Aunt Grace beamed at Irene, knowing the cravings of pregnant girls, and asked, "Irene, maybe you're a little hungry?"

"Oh, *God!*"

It was a feast, with apple and nut salad, and thin deviled egg sandwiches. I read my story and was praised as I desired to be. I would send it first to *Liberty,* to be rejected promptly, then to *McClure's.* (They did keep it a little longer, and wrote a letter when they sent it back, and said they were sorry.) I would sell it months later under circumstances even more demanding than those of the present . . . sell it to *Real Detective Tales,* which was about my speed then in magazine writing, though I could not recognize this.

The driver came back, stumbling under an inert shape he had hoisted across his shoulder. "Where—I—gonna—put him?"

"Lay him on the floor. Put that pillow under his dome. There. Lissen, grandma, you get in there beside him."

The shaking old creature crept into the rear compartment of the ambulance, and the driver stood staring down at Plestina, who still held the pistol clenched in his fist.

"Drag this cot inside the gate. Under that tree. . . . There. I'll be all right. I'll be—all right—"

The attendant licked his dry lips before speaking. "I'm gonna send somebody back from a farm down the road. . . . You're cock-eyed with dope, if you wanta know it. Charley ain't so bad hurt; cracked his head and laid him out cold. This is the only ambulance in Montessa. I can't get back for you before daylight—"

"On your way," gritted Benny, in a tone that was jerking with pain, "on your way, brother. That old lady's in a hurry."

Some customer had brought a gift of *Peistengl* to Uncle Jack at the grocery store, and we sipped this cogent rhubarb wine as we ate the last of our salad and sandwiches. Irene and I took our portion of the carp meatballs in our basket and strolled the five blocks to home. Most leaves were down now, they lay across the sidewalk, and our feet rustled amiably as we walked, and we said how warm it was, and breathed the limpid air, and marveled at persistence of summer. . . . Ah, ice would come again, and snow deeper than we had seen for long.

We felt that combined tenderness of the homely and trivial, without which it is awkward to live, and with which there is a prospering even in stringent hours.

4.

The blizzard began its song in an evening of early December. First there'd be wind straining fierce. Rumors said, "Always coming down from the northwest," if you were in a place to entertain rumors, which we weren't at Mrs. Letts's. She entertained *roomers*. Ha.

I heard the moan, and got up and watched pebbled snow beginning to twist among trees and buildings, and remembered other menaces. There had been one in March of 1923 which the few surviving ancients designated as the worst storm since 1857. That was when they were skinny youths: the year of the Spirit Lake Massacre.

An interurban line ran between Fort Dodge and Webster City, and in 1923 the snow drifted over the trolley wires. Sort of deep.

Like a bunny I put my nose out of doors. The cold snapped at me, but I remembered the old homily about Too Cold to Snow; at least there wouldn't be any of that forty-below-zero stuff while precipitation was coming down . . . only afterward? I rebanked the fire in the furnace, and scooted back to bed.

Under blasts of wind our apartment quivered, and I played with fancies wherein this built-on structure was wrenched loose from the main body of the house. . . . At time of dawn no true shreds of daylight appeared—only a lightening of gloom. At first you thought you were imagining it . . . had to check with pictures on the wall, with patterns of wallpaper, and observe how objects indistinct became vaguely lighter again.

This was a school day, and those teachers upstairs would need to travel. Irene slept blissfully through my gettings-up and comings-back to bed again. I crept out, listening to the shudder and hissing and occasional crash of a falling branch from a tree. I didn't have any boots. There were some high galoshes left from earlier days and with some kind of sense I had brought those down from my grandparents' place. I put on three sweaters and wound my throat with a wool scarf.

Thomas the black cat reached out and spatted me cozily from his box near the step when I sought the snow shovel. I had used it only a couple of times before . . . snow was skimpy until now. Thank God it was a good shovel; Mrs. Letts bought soundly of household devices. This was metal, with a sharp rim—not one of those wretched wooden things ready to fall apart in freezing and thawing.

I went through the Letts house, unlocked the front door, cleared off the porch. West side was drifted, east side bare. Then the steps. The normal beginning of a blizzard pattern was in effect: snow drifted against obstructions or alongside them in swales and swirls, but areas to the southeast were clear. I scraped off steps, little front walk, main sidewalk before the house. There was a partially barren spot at one side, caused by shelter again, and this I made use of as an access to the street, but blinked at seeing the street itself.

Back through the house again. I cleared off steps outside our kitchen . . . one big drift already, reaching over from the Arthur property next door. I broke through this, and achieved a path of sorts to the alley entrance of the yard. I'd need to go that way to stores and post office—

What about mail? Certain trains might have come in during the night, but there'd be none today. Mail: the benefit awaiting, the illusion. The trust that sometimes there might be acceptances in those envelopes instead of manuscripts returned—

In our quarters I found that my breath had frozen on my glasses . . . there were tiny panes of ice over the spectacles themselves.

Irene called, "Is it storming as terribly as I think?"

"It's a blizzard, hon."

"I want to get up and see!"

"You stay there in bed, and I'll bring you some hot tea."

We both loved tea in the early morning, often preferring it to coffee. And we had oranges; we'd bought them, fresh come from California, at Uncle Jack's store. I selected a big orange and squeezed the juice for Irene, and fed her her breakfast in bed. When sated with morels during the previous spring we'd tried drying them, but we didn't know much about drying mushrooms. Some of these shreds Irene had put to soak the night before, and now they appeared reasonably soft after simmering. I mixed them with scrambled eggs. They were pretty tough . . . it was a job chewing them, but at least the fantastic morel taste crept through. Grandma had deeded us a loaf of homemade bread . . . slices toasted brown, with the light grease of margarine steaming. It was exciting to be young and hungry—to eat—to hear snapping and hissing and howling outside.

Mrs. Letts tapped at the door from the bathtub room which she shared with us. She poked her face into the kitchen. She was bundled up, with a pink shawl over her head.

"You didn't go out of doors? You shouldn't have gone!"

"Just pushed my nose out the front door. Looks to me like a brownie's been at work. Well, if that willing brownie intends to keep up his good deeds, he'd better get busy again. It's filling in."

Once again I renewed shoveling efforts, though the drifts were growing difficult to deal with. I was able to make headway only because of previous efforts. Again I cleared a path to the curb, but doubted that it would do much good. Up the street to the west a vast ridge was forming. It was unlikely that cars would be in use . . . some high-wheeled trucks?

I went back to the north and cleared the path to the alley again, but it did seem rather silly. In this better light, nearby householders appeared . . . faintly sounded some shoveling in other regions. Most folks merely came out with their implements, looked around sadly, retreated.

The community seemed strangely silent round about. No buzzing of automobile traffic . . . I listened, straining ears with that
slightly open mouth which is natural and productive to him
who would hear. No rail traffic, no distant whistles.

Back inside, I visited Mrs. Letts's telephone.

"Six-nine-seven." That number had been awarded to the
McKinlays when the first line was strung.

And the circuits were still open. Grandma answered cheerfully. "My, isn't this a *storm?*" It reminded her of pioneer
times. . . . No, I didn't need to come to the house—they had
everything necessary for comfort. Frank Bonebright had fetched
eggs and milk the day before, and she'd baked that week, she'd
had an order sent up from Alkire's grocery. The furnace was
working fine—

I thought of Mother in Boone, and wondered whether the
storm had struck there as well. Probably. These things started
up in the Dakotas, swept down across the northwest corner of
Iowa, and often dispersed themselves before crossing into Missouri and Illinois. Often, not always. We were in the blizzard belt.

The milkman came stamping up the path. Cream had already
frozen in the bottles: it was curled up and out like ivory, with
little paper caps pasted across the top.

"Doubt I'll be able to get around tomorrow. You want extra
bottles?"

. . . I saw our landlady in delivering the milk. "Are you
warm enough in here?"

"Just fine. It held well through the night."

"But there are some clinkers underneath. I didn't want to
disturb the fire last night, because a storm was coming on. But
this is a real one. It'll continue for days, and I ought to draw
out those clinkers and build up a new fire now. Then it can
hold, and you won't be worried about your grates."

She made a face. "When you put those clinkers in cans in the
basement, the whole house'll be full of gas. It smells horrible,
and I don't think it's good for people to breathe it. Probably
full of carbon monoxide."

"Nope. I'm going to tote the clinkers out and dump em in the snow."

It was a nauseous task, one I'd always hated. Breaking the fire apart, pushing coals to the back and sides in order to salvage as much of the actual fire as possible. Then, levering with the long bent poker, prying from the bottom until huge red-hot slabs were torn from their hold on the grates and pushed upward, to glow and spatter their sparks . . . the business of balancing them out, prizing the masses through the front compartment where a metal bushel basket was waiting. Already I'd opened the outer cellar door at the rear. Then trundling the laden basket up the steps and out, for the blue-black slabs to steam and sizzle in a bank of snow. There were only two clinkers on the main grate—or at least one which broke into two parts— but they were mighty and noxious. Snow would cool them and they'd turn hard as iron. Then closing the sloping cellar door at the back, fastening its bar into place, going down with that gaseous reek still around me; raking coals into place again, building up fresh blaze.

There is pride in dealing with the elemental puzzle of fire itself. A beneficial atavism is contained therein, and in final triumph I felt it keenly.

5.

Mrs. Letts published an edict: no more outside shoveling.

"But it's the only way to operate—"

"Why?"

"In order to keep things open."

"You don't have to keep em open. The teachers all got to school, but they didn't stay, and they're back home again. People were fetching em in trucks. Schools are closed, and won't reopen as long as this storm keeps up. No use wasting wind and limb in a futile cause."

Still I was determined to visit the business district. It was only three short blocks away, and the post office even nearer. Irene and I had our hearts set on a soup bone and a bit of extra beef to go with it. Our landlady gave me two or three small commissions to fulfill, and I immersed myself in sweaters and scarfs and went plunging away. It was difficult to breathe while struggling through the drifts. Cars parked in front of nearby residences or in their driveways already emerged as mere snow-swept mounds, wind wrenching long trails around them.

I floundered to the post office, knowing that whatever mail had accumulated would be the last for a while. There were three of my own typed return envelopes in the box. Two were heavy with manuscripts, but one seemed remarkably thin, and this I tore open eagerly. It contained a brief note of acceptance from *The Bookman,* and a five-dollar check for a humorous sketch I had submitted. That would take care of the necessary groceries and a lot more. Also appeared a circular from Denver, Colorado, asking if I wished to take a course in learning how to write. It was fun to crumple that up and ball it into the wastebasket.

. . . Wallowed to grocery store and meat market. They were both open, though a number of other stores didn't seem to be. A few cars parked on Second Street before the storm now resembled fabled Eskimo huts built out of snow and ice. There was no joking about a storm like this. People tried to make light of it, as they often do when natural disasters befall.

(The same thing happens in warfare. Some folks are bound and determined to do and say comical things when the going is at its worst. Bless them all.)

Jimmy MacDonald was a native Scotsman devoted to cobbling activities. There might not be many fresh customers coming today, but he had a backlog of repair work to look after. I saw him in his shop, characteristic puffed cheeks as red as cranberries, and he waved with a shoe in hand. He must have brought his lunch that day, or perhaps he ate something at the Greeks'. No one in his right mind would have attempted to go home for a midday meal. Jimmy did go home at the end of the day. He fought his way through drifts, and dropped dead in his own dining room.

There were other deaths, some close to us, some farther away. Four miles northwest of town twelve-year-old Juanita Goehring and her elder brother attempted to drive home from their dutiful school effort, but the car stuck in a bank of snow. The young people tried to fight their way to a neighboring house. Little Juanita grew so tired that she sank down, while her brother struggled ahead. *Go to sleep* the voices of the blizzard's gods whispered in the girl's ears. *Juanita, you're weary. . . . Go . . . to . . . sleep.* And so— She did.

6.

I presented Irene with precious meat and bone as if it were a portion of a saber-toothed tiger for which I'd struggled through wildernesses. Just as proudly I delivered to Mrs. Letts the items she'd wanted.

She cocked her head on one side. "You know what everyone's going to be saying now. They'll say, 'I haven't seen anything like this since—' Each of em will name a different year. They'll say 1923, and 1904, and 1896, and I don't know what all."

By this time telephones had quit functioning—at least ours had. We couldn't reach anyone we attempted to call. Irene told me to stop worrying about Grandma and Grandpa. "They were fine early this morning. They've got coal and they're got food. And," she added wisely, "they've been through more blizzards than you have. So quit fussing." Good advice.

In fact I didn't get to south Willson Avenue until well into the next day, and then it was only by riding on a snowplow part of the way. The grandparents were snug. Although loose snow still blew wildly, no fresh fall seemed imminent. Another day or two, and daring drivers would be traveling again.

I returned through broken drifts, and found Irene stamping

happily about the little kitchen, her eyes glinting with excitement.

"The most wonderful thing has happened," she cried. "I've
made a great decision! You know we couldn't decide what we
might give for Christmas to Grace and Jack and Martha and
Edgar and all— Now I know what we can do. I'm going to
make candy, right here on the gas stove. I've been looking over
some old recipes, and new ones cut out of a magazine. It won't
be expensive; just requires attentive work. We've got all those
wonderful nuts from autumn—"

"I can pick em out for you," I volunteered.

"At least you can crack them. And then really— All it requires
is just the expense of sugar and chocolate and a few flavorings,
and corn syrup on some of the recipes. We'll look around for
leftover little boxes. I can pack the candies carefully, and make
a real attractive display. Won't that be marvelous?"

I stood and looked at her. Sunny hair, the smiling face, the
slim figure bunched and swollen with child-carrying . . . small
feet wrapped in old galoshes against the cold. I wanted to burst
into tears, but I didn't.

That moment kept coming back to me again and again through
the years.

Winds twirled for days after the snowfall had ceased. Our
candy-maker held valiantly to her newly appointed task. There
was no basement under that little kitchen, which had been a
porch in previous seasons. Sub-zero cold rose high, it came
through thin boards, through linoleum above them, and I'd hear
Irene stamping as she walked about. I'd fetch her back into the
one large room of the apartment—push her down on the bed,
take off her overshoes and make her put on one pair, two pairs,
of wool socks which I had used for winter wanderings in the long
ago. Then the galoshes again—

"Why, darling. It really isn't *that* cold out there," but it was.

The candy tasted better than anything ever contrived by
Fanny Farmer or Fannie May. I wasn't permitted to eat much

of it. Every now and then I'd steal a piece, claiming that it was necessary that each new batch be sampled. Sometimes Irene would sing as she worked and, if I weren't typing, sometimes we'd both be singing.

7.

My hundred-dollar story appeared in the December issue of *McClure's*, and we held high session, poring over the illustrations by L. F. Wilford. (He and I would live a few miles apart in the Sarasota region in years to come, and know each other in casual meetings through the decades, and never discover our mutual sharing in this museum piece until we were both grown old.)

The magazine boasted a full-color cover by John Held, Jr., on which a redheaded boy in lilac Oxford-bag pants was kissing a pert blonde amid gentle snowflakes. I had ingratiated myself into the Big Time of the moment and no mistake. The editors were daring the temper of this excessively advanced age. "What Place Should a Magazine Give to Sex?" they demanded, while readers caught their assorted breath. Scores of noted individuals offered opinion on the subject: George Bernard Shaw, John Erskine, Arnold Bennett, Owen Wister, Kathleen Norris, Irvin S. Cobb, Ben Ames Williams, George Ade, Dorothy Canfield Fisher—big names of the age. Even my own insignificant appellation appeared far down the list of those who had voted resoundingly in Sex's favor.

"If Every Married Woman Had a Trained Nurse for a Sister" she'd use Zonite. So said a full-page ad. "Venida Hair Nets Make Useful Gifts"—so said another. George White declared himself in favor of Lucky Strike cigarettes, but Fatimas were in there pitching too. The pages dripped with Jed Harris, Bobby Jones, Percival Christopher Wren, Manuel Komroff, Elsie Robinson. This would be a fine world to be successful in.

VII. DARLING DADDY

1.

Mother spoke to me soberly on Saturday evening. "Will you do something I want you to do?"

"Course I will."

"I want you to send a copy of this magazine to your father."

"Oh, for God's—!" Ire rose at mention of the man.

"I'm asking that you do this for my sake."

"What would he care about a frontier-small-town story like mine?"

"It's a certain triumph—call it a milestone if you like—in your life. I want him to be aware of it."

"Mother, I don't know his address, I haven't got an idea where he is. I was told that he'd left London—"

"You can address him at the Mount Royal Hotel in Montreal."

"How on earth do you know that?"

"I had a letter not too long ago from your Aunt Besse, his brother Herman's wife. You know we've always been fond of each other, and I hear from her occasionally. She mentioned that John was in Canada, doing very well in the mining business."

I tried to growl, "Probably peddling some phony stock," but the hurt look on her face halted me as I uttered the words. "O.K. If that's what you want me to do, I'll do it." On Monday I sent off the magazine with bad grace, but at least I sent it.

Next week Mrs. Letts summoned me to the telephone one morning about nine o'clock. "It's long distance—"

Good Lord, good Lord!—perhaps Lida McCord in New York
—Perhaps my novel— Perhaps—

Then, receiver clamped against my ear, I heard an excessively
deep voice all too familiar.

"How are you, my son?"

"Oh. Hello, Dad."

"I appreciated very much the magazine which you have sent
to me. It is a beautiful beautiful story. A Webster City postmark
appeared on the envelope which wrapped the magazine. My
secretary called your grandmother, and the call was relayed to
this number where I have reached you now."

"Thanks. I'm glad you liked it."

"What are you doing back in Webster City? I thought that
you might still be in Chicago."

"No, sir, I've been in Iowa all year."

"Are you employed at present?"

"Well, I'm trying to write, as always. I finished a novel recently, and it's being submitted in New York."

"That is very good news. But I have other news for you
which might be better. My son, I am offering you a job."

What did he want me to do? Break the Blue Sky Law, as he
had sundered it commonly? I laughed, and said something about
my not being any financial genius . . . afraid that I wouldn't be
interested.

"You should be interested. The work for which I want you is a
writing assignment."

"Writing?"

He told me that he was a director and chief fiscal agent for a
copper-gold-mining organization. They had wonderful wonderful properties in northern Quebec.

"This is no fly-by-night company: many of the officers are
men in high repute. One of my associates is a member of the
legislative assembly. Another is a cousin of the Duke of Argyle.
This is a vast and powerful firm. For some time I have been
considering the thought of having special publicity written for
our mine. On reading your story and on reading other works

of your own—never mind how I came across them, but I did—I
have come to the conclusion that you can instill a certain amount
of humanity and appeal in publicity which some people might
not be able to do. How does that sound to you?"

I told him that any change might have serious consequences
just now. My wife was pregnant . . . I had to be assured that
any sudden move on our part might not prove disastrous. The
baby was due in another few weeks. A journey to Montreal
might be more expensive than would be justified.

"I am prepared to meet all necessary expenses."

In frankness I said that I wouldn't consider going unless we
had return tickets.

There came a sigh, and so long a silence that I thought we
had been disconnected. Then he asked, "Is that stipulation essential to your plans?"

Determinedly I said it was. "I would make the same stipulation, in any case, to any firm or individual who summoned me
to work in Montreal. It's a long journey, and to another
country."

"Very well, my son. If that is requisite to your peace of mind,
all I can say is, 'It shall be done.' I shall send you the necessary
funds immediately. Give my love to your beautiful mother—"

Etc., etc., etc.

2.

When I was thirteen, soon after the death of Charley Morean,
our family was summoned to Chicago in piecemeal fashion.
Virginia and Mother went first; I was left in Webster City, and
resented it. Not because I longed to see my father . . . I did
not wish to see him at all. He seemed a remote if imposing
bully who had made Mother unhappy and had disgraced us
flagrantly.

But I held fascinating recollections of the one time I'd visited
Chicago at the age of seven. I remembered the resounding clang

of streetcars which shot green fire from their trolleys at night—
the garish electric signs on State Street—the chocolate cream
puffs in our hotel dining room.

Not since I was eight had my father sent us any money, nor
had he written letters to us. Then, in the spring of 1917, about
the same month war began with Germany, Mother wrote to
him, asking financial help. Prices were going sky-high; Virginia
and I were in our teens and it cost a great deal to feed us,
clothe us, pay our dentist's bills, and buy school books. (After
my parents were divorced when I was a baby, John Kantor had
been required by law to pay a monthly sum to my mother. Only
a fraction of this amount was ever paid.)

When his reply came, and Mother displayed the letter, I
yelled my head off. How could she do such a thing without
consulting me? I didn't want any money from that—that old—
If it cost too much to take care of us, I would quit school then
and there, and work all day in order to help out.

I had an independent spirit, but was not very wise. Probably
I couldn't have earned over six dollars per week if I worked all
day. Furthermore, Mother was richly entitled to any funds
which she might receive.

His letter was like all the letters he ever sent—then, or before,
or later. It was impossible for the man to unbend or laugh at
himself. One time I wrote in another book that he sounded
like a Masonic burial service. I take back that statement now.
It is an insult to the Masons.

He promised to send twenty-five dollars per month, each, to
Virginia and myself, as an "allowance"; the first checks were
enclosed. Of course we turned the checks over to Mother, but it
gave me a chance to drop a careless hint now and then to other
boys that I was receiving an allowance from my father. The
boys looked doubtful, and I couldn't really blame them. If I had
all that money, why was I always so hard up?

In that year John Kantor was working for the Moose Lodge
in Chicago headquarters of the organization. He was in charge of
getting new members on a national scale. In addition he was

mixed up in Chicago politics and real estate. A later newspaper report stated that at this time he received a salary of sixty thousand dollars per year as a "real estate expert" for the city.

He loved to live expensively—choice cigars, tailored suits, diamonds, suppers at luxurious restaurants. He scarcely ever drank liquor of any kind; rarely would he order a bottle of beer. I think he feared that liquor might cause him to lose the deep-voiced dignity in which he elected to be swathed.

But he gorged himself on rare fruits, oysters, cold cuts, thick steaks. At thirty-eight he was growing fat, despite his height—well over six feet—and the excellent physique which Nature had given him. He would seldom walk a block if he could ride. He had no interest in sports—certainly no interest in warfare, even when vital interests of his country were involved. He was nineteen when the Spanish-American War occurred, thirty-eight when we entered World War I, amply able to take part in either fracas, the little one or the big one.

He never went within a stone's throw of a recruiting office. If he had gone, the listening world would have heard about it. With unction.

. . . Virginia and Mother were sent for first. The suggestion was that matters could be "talked over" and perhaps some plans prepared for the education of us children. Mother made arrangements to leave the weekly *Herald;* someone else would do her work for Senator Chase while she was gone.

Within another week came a telegram, early in the morning: "Have Mack take noon Illinois Central train today to Chicago. Wear Boy Scout suit. Daddy will meet him." This was from Mother. The Scout uniform was advised because it would make it simpler for my father to pick me out of the crowd at the Twelfth Street station late that night.

Money had accompanied the telegram—enough for my ticket, and for me to have supper in the dining car. There was a great rushing around all morning; Grandma packed an old woven suitcase with my dress-up suit, shirts, handkerchiefs, underwear. I had some new merit badges which had not yet been sewn on the sleeve of my uniform, and she was stitching those on for me at the last moment. Before eleven o'clock I rushed away to the noon train, lugging my suitcase and a shoebox of lunch. Rex had to be shut in the cellar so he wouldn't follow, and the last thing I saw was Grandma leaning out of the open screen door, waving madly, with the muffled yips of poor Rex rising behind her.

Grandma's lunch was a triumph: deviled eggs, cold boiled beef sandwiches, the wad of cinnamon-flavored homemade pickles oozing in a roll of bread paper. There was milk in an old fruit jar, and only a little of it spilled . . . I munched the dessert of apple and cookies. I was something of a man at last —with fresh and horrid tragedy recently behind me, and a confused and doubtful future. How long would the war last? I would be fourteen next winter, and several local boys not much older than that had run away to the Navy already. If the war lasted—

A beaming conductor had collected my ticket, glanced at my khaki uniform, and boomed out jovially, "Well, well, for a minute I thought we had another soldier aboard!" I felt my face growing hot, but I was happy.

Wealth of cornfields and oatlands, towns where unfamiliar boys and girls ran in errands or play—towns with strange names: Cedar Falls, Independence, Manchester. The sweeping rivers (I knew my map, and here were the Cedar River, the Wapsipinicon). A shriveled man came through the coaches, bearing a square basket filled with oranges, pop, tiny packets of candy and nuts. I bought a chocolate-almond bar and munched blissfully.

A station sign in the afternoon: *Epworth.* Grandpa McKinlay's father had been mayor of that town for years; I never saw my great-grandfather—he died when I was a baby. But I pressed my face against the sooty windowpane, staring at houses of Epworth, wondering which had been his.

(Six years later I went on a hiking trip with a friend. With our knapsacks we strolled through this same village of Epworth in the dusk, a trifle footsore. Darkness gathered as we stumbled along north of town, hunting for a place to camp. At length

we found a smooth dry patch beside the dirt road . . . grass
was thick and matted, a good soft spot to spread our blankets.
We rested peacefully, and in the dawn I went strolling. Here
was the town cemetery, twenty steps away on the other side
of the cartpath. The first gravestone I saw bore the name
William McKinlay. Thus we had slept through the night, the
dead and the living, my great-grandfather and I, a few rods
apart—one as unknowing as the other.)

The diner with its heavy silvery pots and dishes . . . I
ate one of my favorites: cold ham and potato salad. I ate every
scrap of the serving, and gravely replied to questions of the
waiter who asked about my merit badges. The Mississippi was
long since crossed, and our mighty engine pulled its line of
crowded cars through northern Illinois. I thought of Rex, back
in Webster City . . . hoped that Grandpa would pet him before he went to sleep. I thought of Charley Morean, and stifled
in the thought.

For a time I dozed, then was awake with electric excitement.
Chicago—these must be the suburbs. Smells of gas and coke,
odor of the stockyards swept into our car. Wheels crashed across
switches, there were warning lamps, whistles, ringings, bangings
. . . blue lights in night-working factories. We grated under train
sheds. This was the old Twelfth Street station at Park Row.
I climbed out, dragging my suitcase.

Distinctly I had carried the picture of my father, whether I
felt drawn to him or not. Here he was—kinky-haired, meaty-
faced—dressed immaculately in a dark green suit and wearing
a hat with a snap-brim. He looked like a visiting Oriental sultan
or grand vizier out of the *Arabian Nights,* but garbed with more
modern richness than any of the Webster City bankers.

He kissed me. I had been reared in a school of manners
wherein men did not kiss men (as indeed they often do abroad,
and properly). I felt that I was a man, and shrank from the
contact. The oily smell of Havana cigars hung around him. I
was no smoker then, and did not like the odor.

"My son." Daddy (oh, yes, I must speak of him and to him

so) indicated a blond young man standing behind him. "This is Anderson. My chauffeur."

I murmured an embarrassed How-do-do. I did not know what one should say to a Chicago chauffeur. Only one family in Webster City had a servant thus called, and he was a light-colored man named Middleton, and he mowed the Atkinsons' grass and helped in their kitchen, and we boys called him Chick.

Later I discovered that this chauffeur business was merely more of my father's pretense. Anderson was a private taxicab owner who drove his own car, and who rented out his services to individuals from time to time. Not until the next year did Daddy acquire an automobile and chauffeur of his own.

We whirled away in the red open car, to the apartment of Kantor relatives out in Rogers Park, where Mother and Virginia were waiting. Mother did not seem happy—I thought she looked strained and tired. We talked until late and then, with Anderson still at the wheel, were conveyed back to the La Salle Hotel. I slid into bed exhausted, feeling that I was across a dozen oceans from Grandma and Rex and our maple trees . . . feeling empty and perplexed, impressed with the strange talk and attitude of folks who were certainly blood relatives, and yet whose way of life I did not know and would never wish to know.

Nothing was settled, that trip, about the future of Virginia and myself. There were a lot of Ifs and Possibilities and Perhapses—some hollow promises were given, and Mother returned to Iowa a few days later. Virginia and I went to our Uncle Herman's home, where I slept on the living room couch.

Our father took us shopping. I begged for long pants, but was allowed only a suit with short pants, and a flat gray hat which the storekeeper declared was just the thing. I wore that hat once after going back to Iowa, and the very dogs ran into the street in hysterics.

But a precious parcel I would carry along also, and this was not to be sneezed at. It contained an insect mounting-board, slim black insect pins, and a factory-made butterfly net. More than these articles too: three Riker mounts, packed with cotton, shining with glass fronts, and containing tropical butterflies and moths.

"What would you like your Daddy to buy you for a present?" This before an audience of admiring Moose.

I mumbled, "Nothing. You've given me a lot of new clothes and things—"

"Surely there is some other little trinket which you would like to own. How would you like some golden cuff links? Perhaps a beautiful jeweled stickpin for your new neckties?"

Stammering, I told him that I would like a real butterfly net —not one which I had made myself out of wire and broomstick handle and an old curtain. Thus I came into possession of the net and other equipment. The tropical insects were Daddy's own idea, a special gift. He was not excited about butterflies or any other form of natural wonders; but these were brilliant—jet and cobalt and glaring gold—and as gaudy things he appreciated them.

Before Daddy wearied of our company he questioned me for a long time about the drowning of Charley. I was reluctant to talk about it, but under his persuasion I got the whole story out. He took his cigar from his lips, blew a smoke ring or two, and shook his mighty head.

"Too bad, my son. You did wrong. You did not know the proper thing to do."

(The accent of his native Sweden still clung to him; it was hard for him to master the *th*; rather he said, "De proper t'ing to do." But any attempt to render his exact manner of speech phonetically might be grotesque.)

I whispered, "Yes, I did. We had lifesaving and everything in the Scouts. He was just too big and strong—"

Again the headshake. "Do you wish me to show you the proper thing to do?"

I nodded weakly.

"Always—*always* when you approach a drowning person—"

He had never approached a drowning person in his life.

"If they give you any trouble, you must strike them in the face. Like this." He made a gladiator's fist out of his plump hand. "Knock them out."

After that, during the week or ten days which followed, he would flaunt the torturing tale before a group of his business friends, among whom he often hauled me along to luncheon.

"Son."

"Yes, Daddy."

"Tell these gentlemen—tell Mr. Finder and Mr. Davis and Mr. Conn—tell them about the drowning of Charley Morean."

Again silver lights would burst in my brain, and my tongue would seal against the roof of my mouth. Dully I'd gasp, "I—just don't want to—"

Daddy would flash a look of contempt from his handsome brown eyes. Then, settling himself in his chair, he would turn to the others, beginning the tale to suit himself. "Boys, my son had a very very dear friend, out in the rustic village where he lives. Charley Morean was his dearest friend—"

Charley was not. Herbert was.

"One day a few weeks ago, the children went swimming in the old swimming hole—"

At this point he might recite lines from "The Old Swimmin' Hole" by James Whitcomb Riley.

His voice would go resounding with its organ tones, spelling forth a false version of the whole occurrence. "My son attempted to go to the aid of his chum, but Mack had not been properly instructed in—"

The thick lash of his voice would whip my spirit.

Sometime later came the summons. "Son." He gazed impassively through cigar smoke. "Show these gentlemen—Mr. Conn and Mr. Finder and Mr. Davis—the lesson which I have taught you. Show them what you will do the next time you encounter a drowning person."

Weakly I managed to clench my fingers, lift my fist . . . strength went out of me, and my hand fell back in my lap.

Through a straining lifetime I have been unfortunate enough

to encounter a number of cruel men. We all must, one time
or another. Still, looking back critically through the light of
years, I think that in such hours my father was one of the
cruelest men who lived.

3.

That December night at Mrs. Letts's I did my best to speak in
extenuation of my father, but my best wasn't very damn good.
Memory was laden with the recollection of compounded debts
and discrepancies.

Irene and I lay restless and unable to sleep. I told her at
last, "Well, there's just this about it: we'll wait and see whether
the money comes."

"You mean that he might not send money to us, after these
promises?"

"You can't tell what the man might do."

"But you agreed to go—"

"I had little choice in the matter. Yes, I did agree to go. I
haven't an idea what the work might be. But if we go, you're
bound to secure competent medical attention when the baby is
born . . . proper hospitalization. At the best, we'll have a comfortable place to live, and no immediate financial worries. That's
at the *best*."

"But at the worst?"

"I stipulated that we must have return tickets: round trip.
I told him that I wouldn't go under any other circumstances,
and he agreed. So now we'll just see if money comes. If it does
come, we'll join in another adventure."

Next morning I sloshed between melting snowbanks to the
Western Union office. I knew the young manager well: his name
was Gordon Eaker, we'd gone double-dating together when he
first came to town and I was still there on the newspaper, in
1924. I gave him Mrs. Letts's telephone number, and said that
a sum of money might be arriving, telegraphed from Montreal.

I was flabbergasted when I received a telephone call a few hours later from Gordon. Funds had been sent, together with a typical message . . . paeans of fatherly love, and the hope that we were on the verge of profound professional association.

> . . . Adequate expression of my feeling of parental obliga-
> tion accompanies this message in the shape of cash for the
> journey. I would appreciate it if you would secure a draw-
> ing room so that your dear wife may have every comfort.
> Also I am including the amount of your return fare for which
> you expressed a desire although in no way do I hold this to
> be essential. . . .

I carried the Western Union check to the Farmers Bank which flourished then on Saturday, its busiest day of the week. This seemed like an appalling amount of cash, but we had an appalling journey before us. I went to the Illinois Central station and ordered tickets to Chicago, and thence to Montreal. No drawing room . . . we had to think of that return journey. One lower berth for the two of us to Chicago, and the same from Chicago to Montreal. If we departed from Iowa on Friday the 23rd— the next Friday, that would be—we could spend Christmas Day with Irene's people in Chicago, and go on to Montreal on Monday, arriving there on Tuesday the 27th.

He had not thought to include anything extra for tips, taxis, meals. The expressed preference that we arrive in a drawing room was typical . . . I winced at encountering this same familiarity of gaudiness again.

The agent hoped that he would be able to have our passage arranged by the following Monday, as considerable telegraphing would be involved.

Of course I was unaccustomed to expenditures on any scale such as this, but the green-and-gold bills in my wallet were a comfort to be examined and approved.

Irene asked, "If you're so suspicious about the whole matter, why are we going at all?"

"Because this is a circumstance in which I have no choice. The miracle could always take place."

"Miracle—?"

"The fact that his talents might now be expended in honest fashion with an honest company. I'm not going to sit down now and be constantly reviewing the past—that is, I'll try not to. We must try to think that this experiment is right, and will be something we can cope with."

Good solid luck cooperated with us and Mrs. Letts as well. A new pressman had been engaged by the local newspaper, and this young man and his wife were searching desperately for a place to live. They rejoiced in the opportunity afforded, and cried that furnace and similar odd duties were more of a stimulation than a deterrent. Mother Letts gave guarded approval at the first meeting, and they hustled in, bags in hand, while we were still strapping our suitcases.

We left for Chicago on Friday night the 23rd, and Saturday and Sunday became a quick blur in which Dick Little, Shelby and the Laynes intermingled in felicitation amid faded ornaments and fresh holly. We cried Hello and Goodbye in the same spangled breath, and Irene's candies were worshiped by all. Monday we boarded a train for Montreal.

4.

We held an exciting sense of venturing into the mysterious and unknown, even though that realm would be dominated by a man concerning whom I entertained suspicion and doubt.

Still we were in youth when we could appreciate an adventure for its own fair sake, and not because of any dedication or obligation involved. We were going to the east . . . far into the northeast, and we had never been there. Going to Canada and the wintry Province of Quebec—sacred to snow-pasted hills, ski-jumpers, horses loaded with tuneful bells, and gaudy-sashed skiers treading the streets. We doted on postcard joys, thought them to be imaginary, never realized that such pageantry would become common before our eyes.

Somewhere in areas above and beyond, a bountiful hoard called the Gold-Copper Trove lurked beneath wilderness ground. And I was scheduled to write publicity for this mine.

"But you don't know anything about gold and copper and mines!"

"I know I don't, but I've been reading a little. You know I went to the library several afternoons, there in Webster City. I've been reading about Canadian mining, as much as I could find about that region. There's a thing called the pre-Cambrian shield in upper Quebec. As for copper, its production more than doubled in value in a recent period of only eight years—"

"But suppose that the whole situation is hideous and—"

I said, "I've got our return tickets in my pocket."

She snuggled closer. "That makes me feel better."

Earnestly we sought to people a vague landscape of the immediate future and find the spectacle good. I'd hunted up Canadian maps and vacation folders at the Chicago railroad station, and we pored over those . . . magic designations, the French ruling all. Irene had fetched along her high school French books, and when she wasn't dozing she studied them avidly.

In bright Michigan afternoon sunshine we watched skaters. They colored like redbirds and bluebirds and green birds on the sharp white ice, and we chuckled over Hans and Gretel Brinker of childhood reading, when Mary Mapes Dodge was become our guiding goddess. Momentarily we felt ourselves bypassing a fabled Holland rather than the Holland in that very state.

Irene returned to little girlhood, with gaze grown meditative.

"Honey—"

"What?"

"This is invigorating."

I agreed fervently, and went off to the smoking compartment to fill my pipe and sit in induced but blissful reverie.

As when traveling from Iowa to Chicago, I planned to spend most of the night in that compartment, so Irene could enjoy the luxury of an otherwise uninhabited lower berth. Mightily I was stirred at the notion of seeing Toronto for the first time, even in shrouding darkness. No, I had never visited Toronto, but had written about that city in my first attempted novel, —*And Angels*. The youthful hero was visiting in Toronto when the Great War began in 1914, and he enlisted in a local unit, the Forty-eighth Highlanders. To achieve authenticity I had delved deeply into lore of the latter regiment (little knowing that I would write about it again in years to come). I did not expect to see the Forty-eighth Highlanders marching forth, nobly kilted and following their pipers. But just the notion of Toronto . . .

Irene had done complete credit to her own appetite, and to the appetite of a greedy Calliope, in the diner at dusk. But starvation pangs of expectant girls are something to marvel at. Our early dozings were broken, and so doubtless were those of nearby inhabitants of other berths, by my constant wanderings back and forth—to see whether Irene felt all right—whether she wanted to whisper—whether she wanted to be reassured—

Before we reached Toronto she was famished.

"Do you suppose maybe the porter could bring me a sandwich, if it wouldn't cost too much? Maybe a sandwich and a glass of milk?"

"I'll go see."

Eventually I found our own porter in the next car, orating to a compatriot.

"Is the diner still open?"

"No, sir, it's all closed up. It'll be taken off in Toronto."

"Is there any kind of cafe car, or anything like that?"

"Yes, they's a club car. But they ain't serving no more—least I don't think so—"

He went exploring, but returned with grim news that the cafe car food closet was locked up for the night.

"Isn't there any way I could get hold of a sandwich?"

"No, sir, can't think of no way."

I bore these tidings to my spouse, who writhed and groaned like a traditional Starving Armenian deprived of her bowl. "Oh, gad!" And then, "Did you say that we are approaching Toronto? Well, mightn't there be something open in the station itself? You know—maybe you could get a Hershey bar or—"

"I'll get a musk ox, kid, if it's there," and I took coat and scarf and went back into the club car. Switches marking the railroad yards were beginning to flicker past.

When the train halted I was down frosty steps the moment the flagman had opened the nearest exit. The station itself shone far down the right-of-way; but directly across a series of spur tracks, on the opposite side of a principal road, blazed bulbs on an alluring sign. LUNCH.

"How long'll we be here?"

The flagman looked at his watch. "Exactly eight minutes."

"Then I'd have time to run over to that little lunchroom and grab something? Grab a sandwich to bring back to the train—"

He looked at his watch again. "Easily."

I went off racing. Little more than two minutes elapsed—two and a half at the most—before I stood in that lunchroom, spectacles steaming white from the cold outside. A waiter was busy serving people at a bar farther back, but nearby on a counter I saw magic: big piles of sandwiches, each wrapped in oiled paper; and a pyramid of glass milk bottles, pint size, obviously provided for people who were in desperate hurry.

I crowed something to the man at the rear, and he beckoned me on. I grabbed two of the sandwiches, one bottle of milk, and thrust them into my topcoat pockets. I threw down a dollar bill on the counter . . . perhaps that was not enough? I reached for loose change, threw down another half dollar. Surely a dollar and a half would be more than ample recompense for two sandwiches and one of those milk bottles when you considered prices in dining cars. My heavens, you'd pay a dollar and a quarter for a full meal.

I yelled, "A dollar and a half?" and the man waved his hand again. Then I was spinning out beyond the street, across spur after spur of tracks. The train sat comfortably. I was just opposite the rear observation car, and on its hind open platform stood a group of overcoated men.

They began to retreat. The train was moving, and it hadn't even been six minutes yet. I broke into a sprint . . . moving, yes, but slowly at first.

The men saw me coming and looked down in amazement as I threw my hands up and around bars on the little fence which edged the observation platform. My heels were dragging . . . there must be a supreme effort, I must pull myself up. Truly there was no danger of falling beneath the wheels, for the wheels were ahead of me. But—Irene going on to Montreal and to all that portended there—going alone—and how and when would I follow? I swung against the barrier, and there came exclamations, and kind strong hands reaching down. Somebody grabbed the collar of my coat, it went up over my head. Another hand was laid on. The train was moving speedily now. Faster, faster, with clicking and rumbling.

"All together!" somebody cried, and then, with a combination of my own strain and effort, and with the hands dragging at my coat, I was up against the fence and could swing my leg over.

Voices upbraided. "Young man, you were crazy to try that!"

I managed to say, "Yes." I saw their faces, and it seemed that some faces were very white. I don't know what color my own face was. I sobbed out, "Thanks. Thanks a lot. He said it would be eight minutes but—" Then I was gone into the car, feeling automatically for the milk bottle. Thank God it hadn't been broken in the struggle.

I staggered through the train until magic numerals of our own Pullman appeared. There I stopped on the platform and caught my breath . . . didn't want Irene to see me gaping and shuddering. There was a little frost and snow on my coat, and I brushed the fragments off, then opened the car door and went on to our berth.

Irene was sitting up anxiously. She had pushed the blind aside and was looking out.

"They didn't stay very long," she said, "and I was fearful

that maybe you'd been left behind. I had an awful feeling for a
moment. Did— Did you get the Hershey bar?"

"Better than that," and I produced sandwiches.

In rapture she cried, "Ohhh—!" and could scarcely wait to get
the paper off the first sandwich.

I bragged, "If there'd been time I would have put some mustard on it."

With her mouth blissfully full, she looked up at me, the lovely
eyes beaming like those of a child who has been promised
a fabled dainty and finally gets it. "Why, it's *got* a little mustard
on it. And butter, too! It's a *wonderful* sandwich."

"And here's milk," I said proudly. "Just wait a minute and I'll
go and get a paper cup from the washroom."

"Don't bother," she mumbled. "I think Calliope was very
hungry too. Calliope was kicking merrily. Oh, it's all so *good!*"

I took the cap off the milk bottle, and she drank deeply
and then looked up in radiance again.

"How luxurious! To have a sumptuous midnight lunch in my
berth!"

5.

Desperately I had wanted to march into this enterprise on
the right foot, and in characteristic form stepped off on the
wrong one.

My father strolled to meet us on the Windsor Station
platform, and he wore a great astrakhan turban. His overcoat
was cumbersome, with ornamental frogs down the front. He
was meaty, monolithic; and the gaze of his syrupy eyes swept
over and around us as if to say, *You are mean things, weak
things, shabby things, but I pity you, and shall bend from my
immensity in order to give you surcease.*

I said, "Irene, this is my father. Dad . . . Irene."

Irene told me later, "First of all I remember the way he
kissed me. I couldn't stand it. It was as if—"

"As if what?"

"As if he were awarding a dime to a beggar," she said slowly.

Irene's winter coat was in its third season. It still might have been considered as presentable in meager society, but scarcely anything for a modiste to rave about. As for myself—

"Son—"

"Yes, Dad."

"You had best go back to your Pullman before they take the train away. You have forgotten something."

"Forgotten?"

"You have forgotten your hat."

"No, sir, I haven't. I don't wear a hat."

"You don't wear a *hat?*"

This was a rather childish affectation which I had picked up from my friend Don Farran and practiced the year before. Don insisted that it was healthier not to wear a hat at all . . . I had grown accustomed to the same rigor. "Oh, if there's a blizzard, I just wind a scarf around my ears."

"My son, this is Montreal, and you will need to wear a hat. All men wear hats in winter. I think that you might even be arrested without one."

He added, a few minutes later, while a spruce chauffeur was stowing our luggage in the trunk of a limousine, "Also you will need to buy a heavy overcoat."

My coat was one purchased from Minnie Arthur. Herbert had abandoned it, and his mother offered it to me for five dollars. My own old overcoat was fallen apart at the conclusion of the Cedar Rapids episode, and I gave the rags away. This was a topcoat of gray tweed, and appeared as rather handsome . . . if you didn't examine the sleeve cuffs too intently.

"Winters here in Montreal are something with which you have never contended. You must go shopping for an overcoat and hat."

"Dad, we've got some other luggage. It was checked on

our tickets and is in the baggage car. I've got my typewriter
and some bags."

"You will give the checks to the porter at the hotel, and he
will arrange to have them brought to you."

Motor traffic blurred. Sleigh traffic, jingle bells, tall constables
at the intersections, people scurrying in bright scarves, men
in mackinaws, jingle-jingle, a pink-and-green showshoe team
a-striding in the street, others clad in different colors marching
ahead.

"They are assembling," my father said, "for a procession.
It will be a colorful colorful spectacle, and you should witness
it," and then we halted at the Mount Royal Hotel, only a few
blocks away from the station. Peel Street? I think so.

> Do ye ken John Peel in his coat so gay,
> Do ye ken John Peel at the break of day,
> Do ye ken John Peel when he's far, far away
> With his hounds and his horn in the morning?

It was a long time ago historically. Young veterans of the First
World War were still marrying girl brides and having new
babies. There was no Commonwealth of British Nations. George
the Fifth was King, and this was the Dominion of Canada.

"You are now entering the lobby of the most beautiful hotel
in the British Empire. . . ."

We swam past gilt, marble, inlaid woodwork, flowers. Bright-
uniformed men had come out to take our luggage. Here exuded
luxury, servility, general bewilderment. Here presided Mr. Cardy,
the resident manager, and he came to greet us. We were not
accustomed to being greeted by resident managers or any other
sort of hoteliers. But we were the son and daughter-in-law of a
potentate; we were not presented to Mr. Cardy, he was presented to *us*. He was saying things about making our stay
comfortable, and being glad to have us on his premises.

"Here is the porter, my son. He will take your baggage checks
and see that the shipment is delivered to you promptly."

. . . Elevator (lift?) carved out of gold and adorned with gems. We rode and marched in phalanx.

"You will observe, Monsieur Cardy, that my son wears no hat. It is an affectation of his. He will soon learn that Iowa is a tropic land compared to the Province of Quebec."

March, march, march . . . keys did not merely clatter or clink as would the keys in ordinary hotels. These seemed to exude a light platinum clangor.

". . . My son, I do not believe that you were listening to Monsieur Cardy. He was asking if these quarters will be satisfactory for you."

Satisfactory? Oh, quite . . . rather pleasant diggings, you know. By the way, might you be able to use a helping hand with the heating system? Sidewalk? Windows?

Silk, plush, lush down, satin, glitter of knobs and faucets, sweep of western Montreal beyond the windows, and Mount Royal towering on the north: an eight-hundred-foot-high bulge of snow and evergreens.

Cardy and the minions vanished, and my father stood looking at his watch.

"Now I must be upon my way, I must get down to the office. I have a very very important appointment, and I fear that I may be a few minutes late, if the gentlemen are on time."

"Dad, when can I see you? How soon can I talk to you or—or whoever else I must talk to—about my job? How soon may I have matters explained, and how soon may I start work?"

The tolerant smile, the all-wise and serene smile which extolled in itself, *Be patient, little mind. Great matters will be explained to you in the end.*

"My son, you have had the misfortune to arrive upon one of my very very busy days. Nothing can be done all at once. But— Say that you come down to the office at four o'clock this afternoon. Then you will have an opportunity to meet a few of my associates. In the meantime, make yourself comfortable. Sign the check for your luncheon."

He always had luncheon. *Lunch* was something carried by a

bricklayer who could not be exalted in rank and price, but was a menial, as were plumbers and carpenters and mechanics. They did things to things. Their unions did not boss the world, any more than did unions of cab drivers and longshoremen.

"The executive offices of the Gold-Copper Trove Mine are on the mezzanine floor of this hotel."

"Oh." Feebly. "I thought this was your home address. I thought you lived here."

He smiled sadly in considering that any oaf might be so mistaken. "No, I live at a different address. Our offices are located here. Sign the luncheon check, sign for anything which you wish. You must be comfortable in your new life in Canada."

Irene had been busy at a suitcase in the corner. If I thought at all I supposed that she was exploring for feminine doodads which she needed in order to set up housekeeping at the dressing table. But she stood before my father now, presenting her last box of candy fetched along from Iowa.

It was a handsome little package. Mrs. Letts, searching for boxes to help out, found one in which some holiday candles had been delivered . . . it was shiny red on the outside. Irene covered the trade embossings with Christmas seals, and we considered the choice assortment to be beautifully presented.

"Dad." There was a strangled note in her utterance as she forced herself to use the intimate term. "We wanted you to have some of our Christmas candy."

"Irene made it herself," I explained.

She whispered, on yielding it into his hand, "We hope you enjoy it. Hope you like homemade chocolates."

He stared down at her, somber and scornful. He didn't even say Thank You. He turned and walked out of the room, and the lock made a melodic click at his departure.

Irene said falteringly, "I guess maybe he doesn't like candy," and ran quickly to the window and stood looking out.

I tried to catch my breath. There was a reddish mist in front of my eyes for a moment. Then it cleared away, and I went to join Irene.

"Well?" Must have said it roughly.

She asked also, "Well?" We joined in a shaky laugh.

"Hon, I explained to you that he's apt to be difficult at first."

"Yes, I can see that. Mack," and she whirled against me, "suppose that there isn't any job? Oh, suppose that there *isn't any job!*"

Dully I told her, "There's got to be a job. Why else would he have sent for me?"

"Yes, I suppose you're right. Well, we're here." She tried to laugh again.

"Yes, we are. No use standing around. Let's get unpacked—hang up our clothes and—"

Soon the telephone rang with a gentility which must have been peculiar to telephones in the Mount Royal Hotel. I went quickly to answer.

Woman's voice. "Oh, hello, Mr. Kantor, welcome to Montreal. This is Edna Kellert, your father's secretary. Mr. Kantor, there is a matter which has come up about the return ticket which you bought in the United States. I wonder if you can bring it to me?"

"Why, what's wrong?"

"We need to have the serial numbers and all that business, to have it properly entered in our expense files."

"I see." I thought rapidly. "We're just unpacking, Miss Kellert. How soon do you need this information? Would an hour from now be all right?"

"Certainly. If you can bring it then."

"I'll come down," I said, and thanked her, and hung up.

Irene was frozen, listening, trying to figure out what was going on. "Who was it?"

"My father's secretary, a Miss Kellert."

"Oh?"

"And she said that she'd need our return ticket to get some figures and— She's not going to get it."

"Why, what do you mean? If she has to have it—"

"She said she had to have the figures—dates and all. I suppose that's what she means: serial numbers of various sections. Well, that's what I'll take to her."

"But if she has to have—"

"She doesn't have to have the ticket. Understand? That's not going out of our possession."

I got it, and sat down with hotel stationery at the desk. I copied information exactly as it was rendered: serial numbers, blanks, amounts indicated, stations indicated, everything. Railroad documents of those days, if one traveled for a distance, were broken into units by divisions and areas. The dates of course were blank. I took down every scrap of information contained on the portions still in my possession, and checked and rechecked them. "There. That's that."

Irene called from another planet, voice weakened by space and distance. "Do you mean that you think he'd take our ticket? Impound it, as it were?"

"I don't know what he'd do. Nobody else knows what he'd do. Maybe *he* doesn't even know what he'd do. But this ticket—or tickets—will remain with us."

I added, "And it won't do him any good to send anyone ransacking around."

After rechecking the information for a third time, I folded the vouchers and put them in an envelope. I got out adhesive tape and scissors which I used in preparing bandages to place over the (then) two open wounds on my leg. I pulled a chair into the clothes closet and found an area above the door, back and at one side, which was not visible to anyone who was not standing on a chair in that same position. Even in a meticulous hostelry like this, the area had not been wiped clean apparently since it was first formed. Dust was there, and cobwebs, and I felt assured to discover them. I taped the envelope flat against woodwork where only an exploring hand could feel it . . . if that exploring hand was owned by a person as tall as I, and who stood upon a chair.

"There. It's put away until we leave this room. You know where it is."

She laughed tremulously. "I'll not forget. If you're murdered somewhere along the way, I can climb up on a stepladder and get it."

I went down to offices of the Gold-Copper Trove on the mezzanine floor. It was a busy suite, stretching along the south side of the hotel, complete with an ominous-looking doorkeeper, and offices and hallways reaching into other offices and hallways beyond. Everyone seemed busy, and there was a great deal of conversation resounding. I told the doorkeeper who I was, and asked for Miss Kellert. He called her on an interphone and soon she came out: a pleasant-looking young woman with heavily marcelled brown hair.

"Yes indeed, Mr. Kantor." She gave me her hand. "I'm glad to make your acquaintance."

"Especially," I said, "since we'll soon be working together, more or less."

"Oh," and her eyes widened. "I didn't know that. Well, did you bring the ticket?"

"I've got the figures. Shall we sit down somewhere?"

She guided me into a small office outside a closed door with my father's name on it, and waved me to a chair beside her desk.

"Now, then. What is it you need to know?"

"Why," she said, "just to have the ticket—or tickets—I guess."

"I understood that you needed data for an expense account or something of that sort—"

"Oh, yes. We have to have all the figures."

"Fine. I've got them here," and I produced my folded sheets of stationery. "Here's everything. There are several serial numbers; maybe you'll want those first. Of course the dates are blank, and this ticket for two persons is only good for a certain period of time, as stamped." I put the notes into her hand. "It's all there. No use of your taking time and energy to copy this stuff down. You'll have everything you need to go on."

She said softly, "Thank you very much," and slipped the

notes beneath the rubber band on her stenographic book. Then
she looked up and smiled. "It's been pleasant meeting you. I
hope your wife loves Montreal the way we do."

"Are you a native?"

"Oh yes." It was obvious that this brief interview was at an
end.

Why he sought to gain possession of those documents I do
not exactly know. Perhaps he planned to rob me of any means
of escape—to make me more utterly dependent upon him and his
weird exertion of whims and fancies. Maybe the request for
serial numbers and such definitions of route was essential to the
charging off of this investment as a business expense, but I
doubt it. Another strange thing is that Miss Kellert, on many
subsequent meetings, never mentioned the matter of tickets or
figures again.

Strangest of all is the fact that my father never mentioned
them either. He had nothing to say about the matter. He may
have been persistent enough to send someone to search our
luggage, but if that feat was attempted we never knew about it
or glimpsed any evidence relating thereto. The return ticket
languished in its hiding place until we carried it away with us
when we went to another address.

As I walked out of Edna Kellert's office, I heard some laughter,
and witnessed scrambling among several girls.

"Oh, no, you've had your share already!" "Well, I want another!"
Such expressions were being cried aloud. Gathered around a
desk stood women who appeared to be secretaries or clerks.
Something familiar there, something of bright red. It was the
candy box in which Irene had packed that portion of her own
homemade trove destined for my father. The box had been put
into these people's hands, or perhaps into Edna Kellert's.

I stood motionless, staring, scarcely believing what I saw, yet
feeling degraded and somehow pilloried, forced to witness my
degradation . . . or Irene's . . . ours . . . hers . . . office girls
laughing and quarreling over her candy.

One broke away from the others, grabbed the box, and fled into Miss Kellert's domain, crying, "Edna, Edna, you're the court of last appeal!" Two or three of the others were laughing as they stood waiting for the treasure to be divided.

I held vision of Irene in her wool socks and overshoes, bundled up with jackets, stamping around that cold kitchen at Mrs. Letts's, manufacturing candy. It was difficult to get my breath for a while, and when I had achieved the feat I found myself in the hotel lobby, not knowing exactly how I'd gotten there. A brochure was in my hand, and I didn't even recall where I'd picked it up. It recited the virtues and beauties of Montreal.

I went back to Irene. She looked at me anxiously. "Did you deliver the information?"

"Certainly. No trouble at all."

"Did you see your father?"

"No, he was in his office. I talked to his secretary and gave her the material—asked her if that would be sufficient for her needs—and she said she guessed so. Now then—" I heard my voice clattering furiously, and it must have hurt Irene's ears. "Get your coat and hat and bag. I have a surprise for you."

"Why, where are we going?"

"We're journeying in a sleigh. Jingle-jingle. We're going to be tucked in with blankets behind some of those fabulous horses, all the way to the top of Mount Royal, and there we'll have a late lunch in the restaurant, and look out at blissful scenery and snow and pines and all and all. Maybe watch the skiers too."

"Darling, we can't possibly afford—"

I commanded, "Don't use that word in my presence again this day. We've got to breathe some fresh air for a change. The air in this hotel seems to have grown suddenly putrid. Come on—no expostulations, no fussing, no nothing. I've got enough money still left to settle the bill for the team and lunch. I *think* I have."

Adding merrily, "If not, we'll see what a local jail feels like. But perhaps Mr. Cardy will be happy to assume the entire bill for us."

6.

Shortly after our return to the hotel that afternoon the telephone rang again.

"Son."

"Yes, Dad."

"I trust that you will allow me to postpone your visit to our offices this afternoon. A number of things have come up which I did not anticipate, and I find my time completely claimed."

"Oh. Thank you for calling. I'm sorry—"

"However, I will see you this evening. We will all see you. It is the urgent desire of the president of our company, Mr. David Ringholt, that you and your wife join us in being guests at dinner at his home. Mrs. Ringholt warmly seconds the invitation. Therefore, if you and Irene will please be in readiness at seven o'clock, and be kind enough to come down to the front entrance at that hour, we will pick you up."

"Dad, may I ask who is *we?*"

"My wife and myself will pick you up."

"Thank you. That'll be fine."

Irene prayed for further details. "He said he and his wife?"

"Yes, ma'am."

"Well— Excuse me, but you hadn't mentioned your father's having a wife at this moment."

"Certainly I hadn't. I didn't know he had one."

"Have you any idea about who she might be?"

"Yes, I do have an idea. I think maybe it's Mrs. Hall."

"Have you told me about Mrs. Hall?"

Mrs. Hall was John Kantor's landlady in Chicago in 1918, and Virginia and I had met her several times. There'd been no pretense of marriage in those days, but they might have been formally married later on. Or not. She was a handsome woman with native sprightliness, and I wondered how she could be content in such constant association with a pompous orator.

Nevertheless she brought out whatever sparks of jollity lay half-curdled in his nature. He called her "Mickey McGuire" in jest, and she had true loveliness in face and figure. (Years later, when Wallis Warfield Simpson came into the international picture, we observed her likeness as reproduced in newsprint and exclaimed about the resemblance.)

Virginia put her nose in the air because of the flagrant and obvious relationship, but I considered Mrs. Hall to be a lively companion. One night she wanted to go to Riverview, a large amusement park on the West Side, and we rode out there in Daddy's chauffeur-driven limousine. Virginia and I sat on the jump seats, the elder people in back, and I was in transports of amusement at Mrs. Hall's running fire of vivacity. How she could bear the companionship of such a stalking monolith is a puzzle I have never solved . . . hell's bells. Sophie Tucker loved him too. So did my mother.

. . . We visited everything that was accessible at the park: in the fun house, on the gondolas, ferris wheel, everywhere. Other people enjoying the festival would call out my father's name in recognition, and wave to him. So would numerous individuals who operated the concessions.

"Dad, who was that man? And that one?"

"My children, these are merely some of the many thousands of people in Chicago who know my face and have listened to my voice."

I told Irene that I hoped Mrs. Hall might be the current bride. Maybe she was still fun, even a decade later.

Irene owned exactly one dress-up costume. Mother had made it: a dark-blue velvet jacket with skirt of paler blue silk. Mother had tried to construct several other gowns for her new daughter without success. She was handicapped in having to use, mainly, old materials which were available. But her ruling inclination was to present Irene in little-girl outfits, and somehow these never suited. Facing the dictate of pregnancy, however, Mother had been triumphant with this jacket and skirt. They were graceful and dignified, and Irene looked particularly charming.

We kept the appointment promptly, and so did my father
and his consort. Yes, it was Ethel. She greeted me like a long-
lost young friend, and I called her Mickey McGuire, and the air
became blithesome . . . momentarily. She was warm in her
welcoming of Irene, and lights of the icy Sherbrook boulevard
applauded. Maybe a fate better than strain was still waiting
ahead.

The Ringholt house stood on Comte Street adjacent to the
city's western limits, and to our eyes seemed a mansion forsooth
and By God. We were not accustomed to households where
brisk lacy French maids took charge of the wraps, and a starchy-
jacketed butler fetched a portable telephone to his employer for
cryptic conversation. Fourteen people sitting down to dinner . . .
yes, we'd seen that happen a time or two at the Laynes', when
relatives arrived unexpectedly from out of town, and extra chairs
were carried in from the bedrooms. I don't think we'd seen place
cards since our last Graeme Players holiday banquet in 1926,
and we held warmer friendship with chocolate soda water than
with Château du Cheval-Blanc and Dom Pérignon. Pontifically
my father turned his glasses down, but I felt no inclination to
follow suit.

Irene whispered, "Hey, baby. Don't get drunk."

"I won't. But I shouldn't wish to offend Mrs. Ringholt."

"Huh."

Postprandial activities began lightheartedly and continued
lengthily with performances by a mother, father and teen-age
daughter. The latter offered a "Titina" chorus medley to her
parent's piano accompaniment and in response to her father's
bellowed request for linguistic changes into French, Italian,
Spanish, Norwegian, German, etc. Gaelic and Urdu may have
been included . . . my recollection grows hazy at this point.
Irene and I sat wrapped in bemused stupefaction. In minor
social activities of our previous existence we had observed
dependence upon a skill at least approaching professional ability
in such renditions. It appeared that we had been deluded.

"Now, then, Mr. Kantor. Please recite something—"

I felt momentary alarm at being influenced to dredge up
"Floyd Collins' Cave" or "Lovely Louise" under such circum-
stances, but rapidly became aware that I was not the Mr.
Kantor to whom reference was made.

"No, Dave, I cannot. It is late, and I am very very tired."

"Yes, John, please do. (Have you heard him recite, Mrs.
Hillsitter? He recites so beautifully.)"

"Please, Mr. Kantor!"

"Not tonight, ladies and gentlemen."

"Aw, go ahead, John."

"Mr. Kantor, tell that one about when that man was drinking
too heavily, and you were a boy, and—"

"Very well."

He had developed a new method of approach in the line of
reminiscence. He would now say, in one form or another, "In
recent years, when my son has had his name appear on various
stories which he has written, I have been asked by many
people, 'Do you, too, write stories?' My answer is invariably the
same. 'I do not write stories. I live them.'

"The incident to which my friend has reference occurred when
I was a little boy, in the streets of Chicago, trying to earn my
share of the family living. We had come not long before from
Sweden to dwell in Chicago, and it was difficult for my father
to find work in his profession because of his inadequacy with
the English language. I am fortunate in having a natural aptitude
for other languages, so I managed to learn a command of
English very rapidly. So rapidly, in fact, that soon I was given
employment as a delivery boy for the telegraph company. I
went here and there, delivering urgent messages.

"One day I was told to deliver a telegram at the home of a
very very famous man, although I did not recognize the name
because I was so newly come to the United States. So with
caution, and somewhat in fear and trembling, I approached this
mansion which stood on Lake Shore Drive."

Sometimes when he told the story during my youthful days, I

had noted that the address was given as Goethe Street or Schiller Street. Sometimes Division Street, sometimes North Avenue.

Now Eugene Field had moved again.

"When I rang the bell of this mansion, a butler opened the door and was about to take the telegram from me, but I told him that I had instructions to deliver it in person, as it was a very very important message. Therefore, when I informed the butler that the telegram must be delivered in person, he guided me into a beautiful beautiful chamber where the man of the house was seated at his desk. There were a number of other gentlemen in the room. Although I did not know it, these men had come to plead with the man of the house. There he sat, with a rather noble expression on his countenance. I remember that he wore glasses and was somewhat baldish, with hair missing above his forehead. He wore a beautiful beautiful velvet jacket, and all in all looked like exactly what he was: the most prominent literary figure in America of that time.

"Although I did not know it—I was just a little telegraph boy, born in Sweden, and with only a cursory knowledge of English, and of American ways and means—here sat many of the greatest editors of that day and age. They had come to plead with Eugene Field. They said that he was killing himself with The Bottle: he was drinking too much, and they came to pray that he would not destroy himself as he was doing. It seemed that when I entered the room they were just concluding their appeal to this great literary man. 'Why do you drink, Eugene? You must end this, you must stop it before it is too late. There must be some reason. Why, why, why do you persist in trying to kill yourself with alcohol?'

"Then, as I stood there—a little boy with my cap in one hand and my telegram for Eugene Field in the other—he turned to the gentlemen, and gestured appealingly. I saw for the first time that, over in a corner of the room behind him, there was a chair drawn up; and on that chair there were two objects: a little toy dog, fleecy and woolly, and a toy tin soldier holding a wooden gun.

"'Why do you drink, Eugene?' the great editors were saying unto this man. 'There must be some reason. Why?' And as I stood there, a little unknown boy listening to these great voices, Eugene Field for the first time spoke his magic words and gave them to the world, and this I was privileged to hear.

"He gestured with his hand, and then said softly, but in a voice which could carry even to my listening ears, over by the doorway— He said:

> The little toy dog is covered with dust,
> But sturdy and stanch he stands;
> And the little toy soldier is red with rust,
> And his musket moulds in his hands.
> Time was when the little toy dog was new,
> And the soldier was passing fair;
> And that was the time when our Little Boy Blue
> Kissed them and put them there.
>
> 'Now, don't you go till I come,' he said,
> 'And don't you make any noise!'
> So, toddling off to his trundle-bed,
> He dreamt of the pretty toys;
> And, as he was dreaming, an angel song
> Awakened our Little Boy Blue . . ."

With muted but gigantic voice he recited the whole thing. People sat with hands shading their eyes . . . a woman was crying . . . the shoulders of our host quaked as he wept.

These were my father's tools, his dupes, his minions, they were the wailing chorus. They would sob and sigh and tell him how overwhelming he was.

"Oh, John, that's a wonderful poem!"

"Mr. Kantor, you recite that in such a masterful manner."

"What an experience for a little boy to have!"

"To think that you were there at the *very moment* when he first uttered those marvelous words!"

His cigar smoke drifted; he sighed heavily, and then said with studied simplicity, "It is not a difficult poem to remember. Especially not in my case. From that moment forth, the words were graven upon my heart."

The weeping and adulation dissolved slowly into murmuring questions.

"John, John, tell us— I've forgotten—or else I never did know. Sure, I've heard about Little Boy Blue and so on, but—"

"Did it do any good?"

"How about that great author, Eugene Field?"

"Did it have any effect, for those men to come and plead with him?"

Massive head shaken gently, the pronouncement coming forth. "No, I am sorry to report that it did no good whatsoever. He stuck to The Bottle. The grief of that lost Little Boy Blue was too much for him to bear, and so he went on drinking. He died of acute alcoholism very shortly thereafter. But even in the supreme tragedy of his passing, the world found itself richer, because of this wonderful wonderful poem. It is recognized internationally as the greatest poem to be written in the past century."

Irene was weary, nodding in her chair, trying to keep her eyes open. We could not leave yet, my father made no move to go. Finally I went to our hostess and asked if Irene might not be allowed to lie down somewhere. That did the trick. There ensued a general scurry . . . we were offered several rides to the Mount Royal. No, no!—my father made a deprecating gesture. He had not realized that it was so late, he and his wife must be going too.

Finally we four rode off together again. On the way, I asked once more the fateful questions. When could I have an appointment? When could I find out about my job . . . ?

"Tomorrow, my son. I will call you tomorrow, and instruct you accordingly."

He didn't call.

7.

My wife slept in surrender to exhaustion, but I tossed and turned for a long time, trying to explore the violence of my own aversion. Only a week or ten days before, when we were still in Iowa, anecdotes had been recited by the elders with profit and charm.

This night my father told a story and I'd loathed every word of the display. Was this because of a basic resentment against the man himself, rather than to a shying away from manufactured detail of the false thing he recorded as fact?

I had uncomfortable premonition that the historian and the novelist would always be at war within me; but trusted that I could muster sufficient audacity to control both inclinations in the end.

The episodes related by Mother, by my grandparents, and Mrs. Letts bore the hallmarks of truth-telling stamped into the very tissues. Mystery and a dainty weirdness had touched their lives; they'd been driven to desperation even when young, had seen and smelled the horrid.

One might never forget that their speculative force preyed after the profound as well as the trivial.

It was as if they affirmed consistently, and in the dignity of age: *This was a strange thing. But it happened.*

Grandma said, "People told me that I must have imagined it, but I was old enough to know the difference. Maybe I was six or eight years old, so that was still in the Eighteen-sixties. Times were stirred up then, just after the War, and there were strange people wandering about, riding in wagons sometimes. Often we didn't know where they were going or why, and maybe they didn't know either. Anyway I was a small girl. I slept with the twins, Willie and Allie. We were in one bed together in the main room of the house, and it must have been chilly weather, 'cause we'd had a big fire in the fireplace that night. Course, we

all went to bed real early, 'cause we had to get up real early, with
so many chores and things to do. I used to wake up sometimes
at night, and lie and watch the fire, and this night I woke up
too—I didn't know what time it was. The fire had burned down a
great deal and nobody had built it up. But there was a little
girl sitting in front of the fireplace. Just a little girl about my
age, all alone. She had pulled up a stool, and there she sat, getting
warm. I could see the firelight on her face and on her hair, and
she had a shawl on. I'll always remember the shawl: it had a
long fringe. She was holding out her little hands to the blaze. I
was scairt to see her like that. She wasn't any of our folks, or
none of the neighbors'. We didn't commonly lock our doors then.
In times of stress there was a bolt—a kind of bar to drop in
slots—but we never bothered with that ordinarily. This child had
crept in quietly, and she was just sitting there. I'd peek at her
up over the top of the covers . . . raise my head a little bit, so
I could see her better across the quilts. She sat and sat, and I
peeked and peeked . . . it seemed so strange to see her there,
and wonder who she was, and why she'd come. Then gradually
. . . well, I just fell asleep again. After a while I woke up, and
the stool was vacant . . . she'd gone. When I told the family
about it next day they all kind of laughed. But I convinced
them pretty soon that this was no imagining. We didn't find any
clues— You know: like a piece of fringe from her shawl or anything. She could have been traveling in a wagon, and saw the
light of fire from our house windows when the wagon stopped
for a while. Maybe they were camping down by Grandpa Bone's
mill; but there were no campers there in the morning—if there'd
been any, they'd gone away."

I said, "Grandma, I'd like to put that in a book."

"Pshaw, honey. It wasn't anything real important. But it
happened."

"I'm going to put that in a novel," and so I did, but not
until Grandma's ashes had been buried for thirty years.

Grandpa said, "Don't talk to me about stepmothers. I don't
want nobody to ever talk about stepmothers. I know all about

em. I had one. She was mean as— Gad, I'd hate to have to describe how mean that woman was! My own mother died when I was just a baby, and my father picked out this one, Lord knows why. He lived to regret it. Pa was away at the time. He was building the railroad west from Dubuque. They were all railroaders then. One of my uncles was station agent in Dubuque, and another was attorney for the railroad. I'll tell you all about Uncle David some day, and the New York Central Railroad, and how rich he became. But anyway that stepmother just raised Ned in the lives of us kids, and there didn't seem to be no way out. I was only ten when the War began, but I tried to enlist as a drummer boy; thought I could run away with the army. Trouble was, I didn't know how to drum, and there wasn't nobody to teach me. Trouble was, too, they said I was too little, and just laughed me out of camp. So I decided I'd go in search of my father. He was working out west on the road towards Epworth, and maybe I could find him, because the construction engines and trains went out there slowly on the new track he was a-building. I sneaked onto a flatcar on the construction train, and set there waiting, and it seemed like it took forever. I had an old tartan wrapped around me—one the folks had brought along from Scotland—and it was kind of like my overcoat in those wintry days. I sat wrapped up in that plaid, and next thing I knew, I looked down and there was a bunch of Irishmen working alongside the grade, and I heard my father's voice. I looked and saw him. Course I didn't want to go no further, because I didn't know where the train would end up, and I might be carried away and never see my father again. So, when I heard his voice I decided to jump off, and the thing was going at a pretty good clip. I just wrapped that heavy wool plaid around me and dove off the car. I landed on a grade, and they said I went over and over, rolling down the hill, and I guess I was knocked out. Last thing I remember hearing was some Irishman yelling to my Pa, 'Mack, Mack, your bhoy is kilt. He's kilt indeed!' But when I woke up my father had me. Trouble was, he took me right back home again and told me to stay there, but I didn't stay long. I found a millwright's family who were coming out here to Hamilton County, so I ran away with them."

Mother told us, "The Indians came by early every autumn, for they wanted to go up into Minnesota for the hunting season. They were Mesquakies from the Tama reservation, and those long fall hunts seemed to be a tradition with them. Grandpa would let them camp—put up their tents and so on—across the river from the mill, and they'd settle down for a while, on their way north; and then stop again when they came back to avoid the Minnesota winter and take up quarters once more on their own reservation, about seventy-five miles southeast of us. My favorite was a young woman called Upta-tupsa, or maybe Upta-tupsee—they seemed to pronounce it both ways. She was quite dainty for an Indian, and she liked me from the start. She used to come and beg at the house. She'd come shyly and sit on the step, and wait for Grandma to give her something. When they returned from the north, we'd let her come into the kitchen where we ate, because sometimes it was too cold for her to sit outside. But, my goodness, she did smell a little, since they had entirely different ideas about hygienic facilities than we! She loved my hair, and used to want to braid it Indian fashion. Your grandmother had a fit, because she thought Upta-tupsa's hands were dirty; but I liked to have my hair braided by her, and so I'd sit patiently and let her do it. She'd smile all the while she was braiding. And one of the men—Grandpa called him Indian Tom—did odd jobs around the mill sometimes . . . carried sacks of meal and grists around, brought in firewood. Grandpa said he was one of the best workers he ever had, for incidentals like that. Upta-tupsa couldn't say my name, Effie— Those Indians could not pronounce the letter F—didn't have it in their language. She always called me Eppie, as in *Silas Marner*. When they came she'd be riding up on a wagonload with all their stuff—blankets and camping equipment—and she'd start waving before they got to the mill. 'Hello, Eppie! Hello!' or as she pronounced it, 'Hayo.' Then when they went away again I'd

come out to wave, and she'd wave at me as long as we could
watch each other, and keep calling, 'Bye, Eppie. Bye.' In another
year or two the Indians appeared, and Upta-tupsa had married
in the meantime, and she had a baby. She looked more wan
and quiet than she had beforehand. When she begged for food,
she'd keep selecting choice bits and put them inside her blanket.
Grandma asked, 'Why are you doing that?' and she would
point down to the camp and indicate that these morsels were
to be taken to her baby. Then the sad thing happened. They
came early next fall, and I heard the grown folks say that the
Indians were coming again, and I ran out expecting to see my
friend. She wasn't there. I went down and stood watching the
preparations for camping, going as close as Grandpa would let
me, and I kept looking and looking for her. Finally Grandpa
went over there and wanted to know where Upta-tupsa was.
Unanimously the Indians all looked somber and turned away.
Indian Tom pointed at the sky . . . I ran home, and cried and
cried."

Mrs. Letts said, "It may be what they call emanation. I was
reading an article in the Des Moines paper the other day about
things emanating. You know, coming out from a good person or
a bad one. Well, this woman was bad enough. She was the
worst I ever had the unhappiness to witness. I used to fairly
cringe away from her, when we met sometimes over there in
Kearns's grocery store. There were three children, all girls, and
you could hear her yelling at those kids a block away. The
youngest one had something the matter with her. You know—
she walked kind of funny, dragging one foot, and she had difficulty in her speech, too, but she fought to overcome that. Everybody admired those girls . . . nobody could bear the mother.
Mrs. Gorringer kind of radiated evil the way a real good person
radiates good: it just crept from her soul. She seemed to have
driven her husband literally out of the house. Years went on, and
nobody could remember much about him because he was seldom home. He'd tried to be a coal miner. They had some little
mines down the Boone River that never amounted to much:

they went in on the slope, and farmers took out soft coal for winter needs. Then he was interested in some kind of bigger coal development over in Webster County. But most of the time when we knew the family he was gone, in Oklahoma 'twas said. Finally he got killed down there. Something blew up and killed several men. I guess they were drilling for oil. Well, Mrs. Gorringer received the income from his small estate, and it was paid in to the Farmers National Bank, and she'd be down there just waiting every quarter when those royalties were due. That was what she lived on—she and the girls—and that was what she took care of em on, if she could have been said to really take care. Luella was the youngest, the one that was handicapped. You'd hear Mrs. Gorringer yelling at her, saying, 'Come here, you fool. You heard me! You're just a plain fool, aren't you?' then there'd be a couple of slaps when the kid got within reach, and poor little Luella, you'd hear her howling. She howled differently from other children, on account of her speech handicap. Sounded kind of like an animal. But, as I say, some teacher helped her in the school, and she did a lot better. And, of all things, she learned to give music lessons. I don't know how she made her hands behave, but she did. That was later on. Well, the girls left home, one after another, just as fast as they got big enough and could go. I remember when the eldest ran away: she was still quite small, and Mrs. Gorringer had her picked up by the marshal in Iowa Falls, and she was fetched home. I don't know why she wanted her home, because the moment the girl could go off, she went again, and this time 'twas said she went to Chicago, and I guess she was safe enough there. Then Dorothy went, and still there was poor little Luella left at home. She'd go to the neighborhood kids' houses and try to give them music lessons too. She only charged twenty-five cents a lesson, and you'd see her hobbling and going. It's the yellow house, right over yonder next to the Curtises'. But it's changed nowadays: has that nice front porch on it, which it didn't have then. And in due time Luella got free from that horrid mother herself. They said the Chicago sister got married, and I guess she had some

little means, enough to send for Luella, so she sent for her. Mrs.
Gorringer was left alone, with nobody to be mean to, except
dogs and cats who didn't have any better sense than to wander
onto her premises. Then we didn't see her around for a while;
'twas hot summer weather, and finally her next door neighbor
said that there was a smell. Yes, a real bad smell. So some of the
men went over there, and the front door was locked solid, but
the back door stood open except for a screen which was hooked.
Hooked in three places, I remember they said. She must have
been afraid somebody would want to get in and steal her, but I
don't know why they would have wanted to. Anyway, they said
the flies were plastered about ten deep, all over that screen,
and that was where the smell was coming from. They called the
authorities, and pulled loose the screen door, and there she was,
inside, lying on the floor. Maybe it was a heart attack; I don't
think they ever did know. The body was in such bad condition
that they had to take it out of there rolled in canvas. We all
stood and watched, but from a distance. Yes, a good substantial
distance, and we had our handkerchiefs to our noses. Men from
the bank talked to the authorities, and then there was a lot of
fussing around, trying to get hold of the girls' addresses. But they
got them finally, and eventually they moved their mother to a
better place. She'd been buried in the potter's field when it happened. Then they came into money—real big money. Word
came from Oklahoma. Some of that land their Pa acquired
turned out to be a real gold mine, or oil mine or whatever you
want to call it. Oil wells were just spouting, all around that
piece, and it was rented out for some big sum. I saw two of the
girls when they came back here one time. I don't know why
they wanted to return to Webster City, but they came. Maybe
it was some business at the bank or something. The eldest sister
Marcia was pushing Luella in a chair, one of these real fancy
invalid chairs. She pushed her down the sidewalk, and I watched
them while I was standing on the front porch fixing my vines.
I was nailing up those vines, and suddenly I said to myself,
'Why, it can't be! But that's Luella over there across the street,

and Marcia is pushing her!' They were both real prettily dressed. Marcia pushed her along the sidewalk, and they stopped in front of the old house, and stood stock still for a while, just looking at it. Then Marcia turned the chair around and pushed Luella back up the street. And before they'd gone two doors away they were laughing about something. Both of them laughing, and talking a blue streak. I heard that Marcia's husband was with them, and they went in the bank and all that, and stayed at the Willson Hotel. Pretty soon they were gone away. So you see that story has a happy ending. But the way the woman died— Flies plastered all over the screen! And it served her right: she was purely evil. But there must have been some good blood back in her husband's family somewhere."

8.

Irene had a case of sniffles. She was in need of immediate medical attendance: she'd traveled a long distance, and the advent of the baby was little more than a month away.

On hearing nothing further from my father, I told Irene that I would beard the lion in his china shop, or the bull in his den, or however we wanted to put it, and go and speak to Dad. He was with one of the company's officers, a man established with his family in the region, who was prompt in advice.

"Get Dr. George J. Strean. He's the best around here."

We were delighted with Strean—brisk and alert, with reddish-tan hair and mustache, and power and simplicity in his nature. He enjoyed a good laugh and contributed to the same enrichment in others . . . an admirable companion as well as a fine obstetrician. He had studied under and assisted the famous Dr. DeLee in Chicago. DeLee and his staff were in the news more than a little, those days. They had been the recourse of Alice Roosevelt Longworth when she gave birth to her first child in her mid-forties.

(How does it come about? So many excellent physicians and

surgeons enrich their lives with other fair ideals. Everything from
archaeologists to orchid growers, top-flight golfers, philatelists
. . . back to music and sculpture. . . . Dr. Strean painted. His
office suite was enlivened with oils which his wife insisted that
he display. It was a good arrangement: his paintings exuded
the same brightness and skill of his medical attainment. They
seemed a kind of built-in insurance for his patients.)

He considered Irene to be O.K. as far as her pregnancy was
concerned, but was disturbed at finding her so pale and tired.
In those days the recommended builder-upper was cod-liver oil,
which prescription she greeted with yowls. There may have
been somehow sometime somewhere a patient who doted on
cod-liver oil, but who in hell ever encountered him? I searched
out cod-liver oil which contained various adjuncts . . . chocolate
or orange . . . they were equally repugnant to the victim. She
swallowed her dosage dutifully, and then screamed and said
yahhh. Dr. Strean declared such reaction to be normal, and
constituted evidence that fundamentally she was in good condition.

Soon she was able to visit his office in the Medical Arts Building. On a glistening day Irene cried that this was the hour for
her examination. She insisted on walking, and we strolled the
several blocks west along Sherbrook.

Strean discovered that we had walked. "No more of that," he
said sharply. "You're a very pregnant little girl, and you're prancing on a layer of solid ice. When you come here again you
must ride, and use the utmost care."

Peel Street, where the hotel was located, was more carefully
cleared, and we ambled there frequently. "I want to stride," she
kept insisting, "right up to the last moment of my pregnancy.
I wish— I wish," she cried in fervor of expanding energy, "that
I could *run*," and then to my concern she'd scamper a few steps.

The crowds on St. Catherine Street knew us during clear
evenings, and sometimes turned their heads and smiled at our
soft singing.

My leg was due for attention, although I had not mentioned

the subject when first urged to come to Montreal. But my general scrawniness came in for remark. Dad learned that the last operation on my leg had been unsuccessful, and said that I should try again. Once more there were consultations, and soon I was talking to a surgeon.

The consulting room of Dr. A. B. Illievitz was located in his home at 1497 Bishop Street. I went there in suspicion and emerged impressed. The man was of miniature size, with sad brown eyes behind his spectacles, and a ragged gray-brown mustache. When Irene met him she spoke of a teddy bear; she was not far wrong in so labeling his appearance. But quickly one became impressed. Once again the man's private passions led in other directions: history, psychology, and above all the musical arts. He performed ably in strings, and found time to join an orchestra favoring the baroque.

Illievitz ordered me off for X rays at the Medical Arts; later, in examining photographs, he pointed out several wandering spicules which in his opinion caused the pain and drainage. Like several other surgeons before and after, he was mistaken in this diagnosis. But that had nothing to do with the charm he exerted, nor with the human respect which I felt for him immediately and continued to hold, even after an unsuccessful operation which left me in exactly the same condition I'd been in before. Indeed he would have been designated as a genius if this manner of exploratory surgery solved anything.

When I began emerging from anesthesia I observed Illievitz standing near, still wearing surgical mask and gown. Light-headedly I addressed him as Bernie, which was his favorite nickname both in the Canadian Army Medical Corps and among civilian fellows. He welcomed this familiarity and cautioned me when I failed to employ it later. A hasty friendship between us was stanchly awarded and stanchly received.

Far as the leg was concerned, I could only shrug. *Well, he tried too.*

Treacherous quality of the streets was demonstrated immediately following this operation. Later that day, when I'd

recovered full consciousness, Illievitz appeared in my room.
Yes, he had removed several sequestra . . . he couldn't proph-
esy anything, he hoped that this might have solved the difficulty.

I demanded, "When can I leave?"

"Why," he said negligently, "there's no reason for your remaining here. Soon as you feel strong enough to dress yourself, you
can go," and then he was called away.

First moment I could get hold of a nurse I asked that she bring
my clothes. She responded in some wonder, but I quoted the
doctor to her. My left thigh was heavily bandaged, but I
managed to slide it into my trousers. I dressed, put on my
overcoat, and away I went. There was still enough daylight to
walk with safety or so I believed. The leg didn't hurt *too* much.

(The leg hurt all the time, year after year. The only way I
could sleep many nights was to hoist it up on a couple of pillows.
I was fearful about the possible effects of sleeping pills, and
refused to take them.)

One can learn to live with pain. If that seems like horrid
discipline, at least it is effective. I had visions of becoming a
groveling monster under influence of drugs. . . . Liquor was
something else. It was fun, it could be indulged in at the end of
a hard day's work if one had the price. A drinker would in
time be compelled to make his own private adjustment against
whatever claim alcohol had put upon his life and professed to be
keeping there. But to me every drug bottle bore its glaring skull
and crossbones.

I started out bold and brash, and within a block ended up
flat on my back. Sympathetic bystanders helped me to my feet;
conveyance was offered, but I was determined to walk. When I
got to my own bathroom and saw the result inscribed in red on
bandages, I didn't feel quite so valiant as before. Fortunately
I was in better condition than my thin body suggested. I wound
a towel around outside the bandage, twisted it to apply more
pressure. Soon this fresh hemorrhage had ceased.

Bernie Illievitz shook his head and stated reprimand at the

first dressing; but there was no more post-operative difficulty. The leg settled down promptly into the same annoying pattern as before: one, two, three open sinuses . . . usually just one.

(That lasted all the way up until 1942, with several other unrewarding operations in between. The eminent George Bennett of Johns Hopkins gave back to me a sound leg in 1942. Promptly I was able to crawl around in a bomber, which was all I wanted to do.)

9.

Dr. Strean spoke his verdict. "Sorry. I can't give you folks permission to go. You can return to the United States the day your baby is six weeks old. Not one moment sooner."

"But—"

"Doctor—"

"Irene and Mack, I've come to regard you as friends in this short length of time. Please believe what I'm saying to you is from the heart as well as prompted by my best application of professional interest. Irene must not attempt that journey to Chicago. The baby might be born on the train, with all sorts of complications. You've simply got to stay here and weather it out."

"I was promised a job, and there is no job. It was all a fabrication."

"You've told me. But it just wouldn't be wise for you to go." He continued, "Now, what do I have to do to make you calm? Shall I offer you some soothing syrup? The moment anything happens, you're provided for. Your father told me to take charge and go ahead, and so I did. You have a room engaged at the Women's General Hospital as soon as circumstances demand, and a nurse will be in attendance."

Irene said falteringly, "If we could only get out of that hotel and be in an apartment or— Somewhere like home."

He laughed. "Home isn't such a safe place. I very nearly

finished up at home when I was an infant. They were going to
have the Jewish ceremony which is considered essential to the
proper launching of small males. Friends and relatives and
neighbors came in; they were going to make a big thing out of it
—a party, in proper studied celebration. Trouble was, I yelled.
I kept yelling my head off. Just bellowing. So some of the wise
neighbors said to my wise parents, 'Give him soothing syrup,'
and a lady went home for a bottle of it. . . . Paregoric? I don't
know what. Soothing syrup of some kind, probably full of mor-
phine. It was considered that a spoonful would be enough, but
my father said, 'Listen to the way this baby is yelling.' I don't
know how much they poured down me, but they got a lot of it
down my gullet by one means or another. Maybe half a bottle
full. And what happened? I went to sleep. I slept through the
party, slept all night, slept all the next day, all the next night.
If they'd given me another spoonful of that stuff I might have
slept forever. So you see—parents aren't capable judges in
these cases. Just go back to the hotel, and be careful of ice on the
way, and we'll see what happens."

It happened in days, almost before we could realize it. Dad
called me to the office. I hurried; I thought it might be about the
job.

"I am told that you are eager to leave the hotel, and therefore
I have arranged for a wonderful wonderful apartment."

"How can we afford an apartment when I haven't any *job?*"

"I fear that you are impatient and inconsiderate, but I am
doing the best I can. I wish you would please give me credit
for that. On Monday you shall move into a beautiful beautiful
apartment on Comte Street. I will provide all the luxuries which
you desire. I am paying the rent, and in addition you will receive
twenty-five dollars each week. This will be in the form of a
drawing account against your future salary."

The beautiful beautiful apartment was bedight with gilt
candlesticks, pink plush chairs, gold-fringed draperies, imitation
Chinese rugs of azure and crimson (we looked in vain for a

jewel-encrusted Nubian slave brandishing a lamp), and a French
maid who answered to the name of Miss Ogilvie. "Long ago zere
ees a Scotsman named Ogilvie who come out to Canada, and he
ees marrying a French girl, and zere son ees marrying a French
girl, and zere son ees marrying a French girl—"

. . . Irene asked, "Do they have sourdoughs in the Province
of Quebec?"

"Dunno. Maybe they're sacred to Alaska and the Yukon."

"But if there were a sourdough in the Province of Quebec,
and in 1898 he bought a funeral home; and then decided to
open a brothel in the funeral home—"

"Shut up, you. You've got your apartment even if I haven't got
a job. I stand pensioned off on twenty-five dollars a week until—"

"Until the baby is six weeks old."

I took Irene to Strean for her weekly check-up, and he appeared mightily innocent. "So you're in an apartment. You
finally *did get* an apartment. Isn't that nice?"

I said, "George. What did you have to do with this?"

"What did I have to do with it? Not a thing. Oh, I may have
advised or— But I didn't *pick out* your apartment," he added
hastily.

"Look, good people, there's so many things you don't understand about the OB business. Sometimes we're called upon to
do the damndest things. I remember once, when I was first working in Chicago, I got called on a case. You know these gypsies?
Well, a gang of them had moved into a vacant store. It was
down on Maxwell Street, if I remember correctly, and they were
occupying that store with wide front windows— Dressed in
native costumes and telling fortunes and all that. A woman was
in trouble: she was about to give birth to a baby. I went in, and
found that matters had progressed too far. She couldn't be
moved, she'd have to have the baby then and there. But it was
an awful thing to deliver a baby with ten thousand bystanders
pressed up against the front windows. So I made the gypsy
women hang some scarves and things . . . they had all sorts of

shawls and other clothing . . . wide flowered skirts and all that.
We covered the front windows while I delivered the baby. Oh,
obstetricians have to do all sorts of things. I remember looking
around and seeing those grinning faces, peering in up above the
scenery. All sorts of things happen in this business!"

10.

It is difficult to re-establish the appearance of Montreal post-
men. Some shreds of memory cast up an illusion of stalwart
beings uniformed in blue piped with red, or red piped with blue,
but I'm not sure.

Our own mailman on Comte Street had fleecy wings. He was
garbed in a dazzling gown, and wore a halo with pride and
honor . . . I think his mailbag was pale blue, the color of the
chilling sky which extended in unabated force above. He wore
silver sandals, and like Mercury he owned wings vibrating from
his heels. Never did he distribute missives of gloom, he had no
truck with letters about death and debacle. Rumor told us that
he had won any number of interstellar awards for the quality
of message which consistently he bore.

Here was Robert Thomas Hardy, an agent in New York City.

Dear Mr. Kantor:
  Glad to inform you that we have sold two of your stories,
"Delivery Not Received" and "A Bad Night for Benny." The
buyer is Edwin Baird, editor of *Real Detective Tales* in
Chicago. I'm happy to enclose our check for the sale of these
properties—

Here was Lida McCord, an agent in New York City.

Dear Mr. Kantor:
  Just tried to call you, but was informed in Montreal that
as yet they had no telephone listed for your new address,
so am writing instead.
  Diversey is sold, dependent on your acceptance of terms

to be prepared. The buyer is the new firm of Coward-McCann, Inc., who are highly enthusiastic about your book.

Do you think it would be possible for you to come down to New York City and talk with Coward personally? This might be better all the way around, as he has some questions concerning the manuscript which he wishes to discuss with you.

If indeed you can come, please inform me as to the date, and I shall try to set up appointments with Coward to meet your mutual convenience.

I think this is especially fortunate because both Coward and McCann were formerly with Bobbs-Merrill and are credited with building that company into a most successful editorial and marketing condition.

Irene had been taking her prescribed nap, wrapped in that veteran batik kimono which I'd loved from the start.

She asked drowsily, "Yes?"

"Honey—"

She sat up.

"I— We've— Sold *Diversey*."

Her eyes grew larger than their wont, her face scrolled . . . tears, the tears.

I sat down beside her on the bed.

VIII. BROKENHEARTED HUSBAND

1.

I dozed in a day coach and finally watched splashes of pink and gold and palest green dabbed above the hills. "Apple colors with the dawn. This must be used in a novel." So it was, but not until *Long Remember*.

New England . . . yonder across the road . . . apple-cobbler colors apparent in its private sunrise, and a few clouds for cream, and a tricorn hat on the head of every Green Mountain Boy.

"Open! In the name of the Great Jehovah and the Continental Congress!" Nonsense.

In time I would come to know two Vans who set down the tale in proper perspective. Carl Van Doren would quote Ethan Allen's own report. "I have the inexpressible satisfaction to acquaint you that at daybreak of the 10th instant, persuant to my directions from sundry leading gentlemen of Massachusetts Bay and Connecticut, I took the fortress of Ticonderoga with about 130 Green Mountain Boys."

Frederick Van de Water sped more sharply to the point. He insisted that Allen yelled to the barricaded British, "Unlock this door, you lobster-backed sons of bitches, afore we bust it down!"

Within hours on this eager day I would be walking the same trails where writers of the past had limped or strode, and be experiencing the same doubts and fears, cherishing the same enthusiasms, admitting to the same dreams.

Here was privilege of profound value. I could consider Washington Irving going to visit his printers, could stand before his house. I had already looked it up . . . Irving Place of course. "If . . . I can by any lucky chance, in these days of evil, rub out one wrinkle from the brow of care, or beguile the heavy heart of one moment of sorrow; if I can now and then penetrate through the gathering film of misanthropy, prompt a benevolent view of human nature, and make my reader more in good humor with his fellow beings and himself . . . I shall not then have written entirely in vain."

Before the train vanished into its tunnel beneath Park Avenue, I had seen enough of a cluttered wintry Harlem to tell me that this might be a keen glimpse of the city, with people's white breath abounding, and the trill of assertion in every traffic signal.

Had I consulted my father about a New York City hotel, he would have said, "My son, I shall make a reservation for you at the Waldorf— Ritz— Biltmore— Vanderbilt— Where you shall be my guest." I hadn't asked him. Instead I asked one of his associates whom I reckoned to be a down-to-earth character and who, when he was poor and young, used to fight in New York under the name of Kid Manz. That was neither his true name nor the one he wore in financial activities, but somehow I trusted the ex-Kid Manz.

"You haven't got much dough."

"No, I haven't."

"You want to be midtown?"

"Yes, I do. Isn't that where publishers and agents and editors have their offices?"

"Try Thirty-ninth Street [Thirty-seventh Street?] and Seventh Avenue, the northeast corner. You can get a good clean room for only a few bucks."

It hadn't seemed any distance at all in looking at a map. I kept lugging my small suitcase, and my leg was growing weary, and it protested . . . had it been an artificial leg it would have squeaked. . . . This was Forty-second Street, so Thirty-ninth

Street [Thirty-seventh Street?] could not be too far away. I
came to another intersection, with yelp of police whistles on
high and the boiling of mid-forenoon traffic . . . the sign didn't
say *Seventh Avenue,* it said *Times Square.* A street pierced to
the north and there was another which seemed slanting into
the northwest, and both were going away in different directions
at the south. If any tangle had been contrived for the purpose
of bewildering rubes, this was it.

I gathered a few shreds of courage and approached the
nearest policeman. He was eight feet tall, four feet wide, and
had a neck like a tire bulging out above the collar of his uniform.
"Please. Can you tell me where Seventh Avenue is?"

They didn't call policemen pigs in those days—nor were
dissidents pigs either—but he glared as if truly he had discovered one. He bellowed, "Dis is Sevent Evenue!" and then
swung round to corrode the traffic again. Those were the first
words ever addressed to me in New York City. If anyone had
prophesied accurately that twenty-odd years hence I would be
doing a patrolman's job with the New York City Police Department, and initially in that same area (Sixteenth Precinct), I
would have passed out on the sidewalk.

At the as-yet-un-face-lifted hotel I was toted aloft in an
elevator wherein the operator handled cables with his *hands.*
He gave them a jerk or a twist, and the elevator shot up. When
you came down, the descent also was abetted by hands grasping
the ropes or cables. This maneuver was not calculated to build
confidence in the heart of a greenhorn. Still, since I was on the
fourth floor, I didn't have too far to fall when the elevator
crashed, and might even survive.

Away with such appraisal. I was a fresh-grown author whose
novel had been accepted, and I was in New York to see my
publishers, and to talk with agents and editors, and observe and
taste and feel and shake hands with all that comprised the con-
temporary literary world.

In addition to such beguiling activities, I might even see the
Statue of Liberty before the day was done.

2.

Lida McCord turned out to be an alert gray woman, strictly tailored as to costume and attitude. She congratulated me heartily on the interest shown by Coward-McCann.

"They're going to have a distinguished list, and you're fortunate to be on it. It may be, too, that they're fortunate to have you. Who can tell about the future?"

(Who could tell that Coward-McCann and I would do fifteen books together? No one could have told it, any more than one might make substantial prophecy at this moment or next week or in a century to come. The only solid fact about the present is that it is the Present for that infinitesimal fraction of a second when it is recognized as the Present, and promptly it becomes the Past. And the Future comes sweeping against inked type of the Present in that same instant eternally, and then becomes part of the printed Past.)

"I suppose you know how it is in this business. There are many little companies starting up from time to time, then dying down. In contrast a firm like Coward-McCann should be approached with strict reverence."

Lida McCord lowered her voice and whispered with awe, "Eleven million dollars. That's what folks say."

I asked feebly, "If he's got eleven million dollars, why does he want to go into the publishing business?"

"Why, Coward wants to *accomplish* something in the world. Something more than he's already accomplished in athletics. You know—he's an international star in tennis and squash—holds all sorts of championships. I've met him only once. A wonderful young man!"

. . . All the way down Park and then along Fourth, I tried to reiterate that I was going to my publisher's offices for our first conference—but it seemed untrue. As if I were deluding

myself, and had no claim on the Future, and perhaps no true
claim on the Present.

. . . A mixed-up muddle of elevators, hallways, outer offices,
people sitting at many desks, inner offices beyond. I began to
have the weak notion that I was a fake. I wasn't as big as they
thought me to be. The book wasn't as good as I had believed.

As for publishers, neophytes thought of them as grave gray
scholars. This man's name was Thomas, but commonly he was
called Tim. Only in squash circles and public prints attending
them was he almost invariably referred to as "the great Tom
Coward"; otherwise he was Tim or Timmy to friends and relatives, and there were enthusiastic choruses of both. Thirty-one
years old, handsome, brown hair bearing sandy and reddish
lights, blue eyes sharp as stars . . . he had a ringing laugh and
incredible jauntiness. (Some years afterward I took a writer,
Thomas W. Duncan, to him for the first time; and recall how
Duncan spoke of Coward's "effortless magnetism.") He exuded
his crackling power like a dynamo . . . quick to speak, quick to
think and, in those days, quick to consider. He underwent his
own changes in time, as all must do; but I would have named
him the beau ideal of young publishers at our first meeting.

There was considerable of the born actor about him. It was
not astonishing to learn later that his father was Edward
Fales Coward, drama critic and amateur actor, who stood in vast
repute throughout the theatrical profession. Groton, Yale, overseas in the World War, U. S. State Department in Washington:
these experiences were already cemented in Tim Coward's
background . . . his rough nasal voice vibrated with energy.

A peculiarity of his conduct was an extreme ability to make
any individual sitting opposite him feel that Coward had been
waiting eagerly just to talk to that person, just to seek his
opinions, just to hear what he had to say . . . this meeting would
clarify future activity, and result in profit and honor for all concerned. His native cordiality swept diffidence before it.

I wondered if rumors about eleven million dollars had anything to do with my immediate yielding collapse on Coward's

doorstep. But no, no. Had I heard instead that he'd put a young lifetime's scant savings into this perilous venture, along with the unknown Mr. McCann's doing the same, I would have been fully as smitten.

"First thing to solve is the question of lunch. Your agent told me that she expected you'd be here this morning, so deliberately I saved a luncheon date. Are you free?"

"Yes, sir, of course."

"Fine. I've got the manuscript here." He indicated a cardboard box. He leaned back and yelled at the top of his lungs, "Dobbs!" Next instant a plump little girl with a kitten face appeared at the door. "Dobbs, please take all calls, and notify me only if you think I'd wish to be interruped. We're going into conference. Please close the door."

He got rid of an emaciated relic of a cigar butt which he had been gnawing, opened a humidor, and passed it to me. These were La Vencadoras: tiny at one end, swollen at the other—gigantic cigars of a type I'd never seen before.

"Do please have a cigar, and we can chew this matter over together while we chew our cigars. Now then— I've got a few notes here. First off, about the legal situation—"

I didn't know what was meant by that.

"Well, you've drawn some very piercing portraits, and I want to know how many of them are real. You know?—real people who might be easily recognized. I take it that your J.R.P. is actually Richard Henry Little. Correct?"

I nodded.

"I've never met Mr. Little. I've seen him at a distance in a club or a hotel, somewhere in Chicago; but I don't often go to Chicago—used to sometimes when I was with Bobbs-Merrill. It rains cats-and-dogs invariably whenever I visit the damn town. How do you think Richard Henry Little's going to feel about this?"

I told him haltingly that I'd supposed Dick would love the portrait.

"Frankly I'm not so certain. Of course it would contribute to the book's success, wouldn't it?"

Al Bromley the humorist had sold his self-illustrated self-published *Bed Time Storries* . . . five thousand copies on the first day of its issue in Chicago. "Snowshoe was running around in a taxi, carrying consignments of books from the Weinthrop printers to shops and department stores, hour after hour," I explained. "And that was due to his popularity in Dick's column."

"Did Little sustain his contributor loyally?"

"He certainly did. First of all he wrote the introduction. He'd been calling attention to the appearance of Snowshoe Al's book for several days—or rather, in several issues of the *Tribune*, just before the date. The morning of publication Dick had a long paragraph about it."

"Do you feel confident that Little would respond in the same way to *Diversey?*"

"I'd always supposed so." I spoke a bit squeamishly, beginning to have doubts for the first time. I'd never really considered Dick's evincing any attitude but that of excitement and pleasure.

"Well, I hope he responds in the way you suggest; but one can't be too sure about these things. Still, that's beside the point. We respect *Diversey*. We're impressed with your skill in writing a sharp and quick-moving story of this nature, showing us what modern Chicago is like. Is this your first novel? What shall I call you—Mack? Most people call me Tim or Timmy."

I told him about —*And Angels* and how it had been withdrawn from circulation on my writing of *Diversey*.

"Good. Then you've already served a sort of apprenticeship, and I think it shows in this book. Now, I'd better inquire about other people. What about Gold, or Wise, as you call him in the novel? Steve Gold, or Abe Wise?"

"Utterly fictitious."

"What about this man Spence Sailor?"

"Mr. Coward," I began, and he corrected me into Tim. "Tim, I'll tell you something that I've never even told my wife Irene. When I was in Chicago last fall, hoping to have Swanson

publish the book as a serial in *College Humor,* I gave it to
Spence Sailor to read. His name is actually Cliff Palmer, and
we were fellow inmates of that same rooming house. I took it to
him in the afternoon, and he read it during that afternoon and
most of the night following. He was delighted—didn't have a
resentment in the world. He's by no means a primitive individual.
I'd call him rather complex as to personality," and I wondered
afterward why Coward smiled gently as I spoke. "But he's a good
deal like some other people I've met, who've been concerned in
activity on the wrong side of the law. He makes a hero out of
himself *to* himself. All publicity, or imagined publicity, becomes
a delight."

Coward nodded. "Anybody else?"

"The landlord. I call him David Henderson in the book.
His name is Albert H. Norris, and the novel is dedicated to him."

In those days Tim could never sit immobile for long. He was
up and strolling about the office, looking out of the window,
coming back, nodding as I talked.

"I think," he said, "that Richard Henry Little and possibly
his wife—he has one, hasn't he?—might be the stumbling
block. Don't get your heart set too much on his evincing a benevolent attitude toward the whole thing. He's had enormous
publicity in the past—a great deal of it self-created perhaps.
But some of these rough-hewn grouchy individuals don't like to
see themselves portrayed as such. I know that from experience—
not as a writer, but as an editor. Let me assure you that we'll
have our own publicity campaign, and it will be as well handled
as seems justified at the time. I take it that you're Marry
Javlyn?"

"Well, in some respects—"

"Oh, let it go at that," he said gruffly. "You're too young a
novelist—I'm sure you wouldn't be able to get that far away from
yourself to begin with. What about the girl Josephine?"

"Fictitious. Odds and ends of other girls in her makeup. One
girl in particular—the way she talks, with that run-together
manner of speech—"

He told me that that was another thing. He wasn't at all certain when he began reading the book that those slurring run-together words were effective. Later he decided that it didn't matter.

"Obviously you were striving for authenticity in the manner and mode of speech, and I don't think most readers will object too strenuously. Maybe some of the critics—" He shrugged. "Hell, one can never decide about the critics anyway. Except"—turning to me suddenly—"in one respect. What about all those passages of exotic prose with which the book is larded?"

I was miserable on the instant. Irene had wondered about those same interludes, and so had I—secretly.

I said with stubbornness, "I put those in because they seemed to belong."

"Well, you're trying to mirror the struggles of a young writer, and that's as it should be. But you've got that long sequence about the poem—the poem which appears in the paper, just at the time your precious gangster is killed. What is it: 'Funeral. Chopin for a Gangster'? Isn't that enough in there by itself? You've described the writing of it—the struggle, the orgiastic quality of the conception—and it plays its part in the tale. You can almost feel it being written. But isn't that enough? Couldn't some at least of those others come out—be omitted completely? Can't you make your point without them?"

He continued, "I have here our readers' reports. Two are from readers associated with our own organization. One is an outsider. Friend of mine: Beatrice Kaufman."

I didn't respond.

"George Kaufman's wife?"

Again I shook my head.

"Oh, for God's sake, my boy!" he cried with petulance. "I'm talking about George Kaufman, the playwright. *Beggar on Horseback*. He and his wife came to dinner one night when we had some people at the house, just at the time I was reading *Diversey*, and I asked her if she'd care to try it. Now, here are the reports. I've got to go to the can. You sit here and read these three opinions while I'm gone."

Both of the regular publisher's readers criticized my novel vigorously when it came to the ornate prose . . . one was almost violent on the subject. In the case of Beatrice Kaufman, criticism was much more reserved. She spoke about this interlarding at some length. It was pleasant to learn that she enjoyed some of the passages as poetry at least, but was doubtful about the necessity for their inclusion. All these years afterward, and long after I met and knew Beatrice, I can still remember the icy thrill as I read her summing up in the closing paragraph.

"I don't know," she had written. "I'm not one hundred per cent certain. In criticizing these passages and doubting the necessity for their inclusion, I may be just as stubbornly having the nerve to pass judgment upon a work of true genius."

When Coward returned I was the one who was standing, looking out of the window.

He chuckled when he closed the door. "Not planning to jump, are you?"

"Can't jump," I said, "even if I should want to. My wife's going to have a baby in another week or so."

"You don't say?" and he was beaming and gleeful. "Marion and I just had our first child a few months ago. We have a little girl."

I congratulated him, and he chuckled and said, "No, don't jump. I didn't tell you, but we've included in the proposed contract an option on your next two novels. Those are two more good reasons for not jumping."

I reminded him that Mrs. Kaufman in particular had expressed reluctance at having to dispute my moonbeams.

Coward said, Yes, but she had indeed queried them, and the other readers were hard-boiled about the matter.

"There's never any telling which way the critics are going to leap. Any publisher who lies awake nights worrying about it, is giving himself a damn hard time for no good reason whatso-

ever. But suppose we go over the script, and you indicate a few
poetic interludes which might come out painlessly. We'll play
along with you if you feel that some must be preserved."

. . . Five of the fluffy-word things were retained, the rest
abandoned. Neither of us felt entirely suited by the outcome.
Naturally I wanted more of them and Coward wanted fewer.
After I'd agreed to the deletion of a couple of doubtful ones,
he promised to keep the five selected as most urgent.

He looked at his watch. "Let's go to lunch. Anywhere you
want to go especially?"

"Thank you. You're observing a fledgling author on his first
day in the big city."

"What about a speak-easy?"

I owned only a Chicago-born notion of speak-easies. There
the term referred to dirty dives on streets fringing the Loop
where you could buy a couple of needled beers along with a
bad bologna sandwich. My indifferent response cut me out of
Leon and Eddie's or any such bountiful cafes until more years had
passed.

"Would you like to go the Yale Club? Yes? Good."

Thomas Ridgway Coward would go down in local history as
president of the Yale Club three terms, 1939–42, and he lived to
be inordinately vain about it.

(This was the first day of an acquaintance which would ripen
into a deep and complex and finally embittered relationship
through years to come.)

Checkroom at the northwest corner of the lobby, the dozen
people who called to Coward or whom he saluted on our way
to the elevator. "Hello, Casey! . . . Why, Mr. Wyndham Lewis,
how do you do? Last time we met was in London." Quick
exchange of conversation in affectionate regard with the man
called Casey.

Coward told me after we got off at the taproom, "Cass
Canfield, you know. Casey's his old nickname. Harper's. Quite
likely he'll be the next president there."

Greetings from the staff, table by the window . . . a warming

hour, the window was open a trifle, pigeons came on tinted feet
to peck at scraps of cocktail crackers.

. . . Somebody pinch me. Irene, truly this is how it feels to be
sitting, ready for lunch with your publisher in New York City.
I thought it would happen, we both dreamed it would happen,
we weren't sure it would happen, we were positive that it
would happen. But— But—this is how it feels. I hadn't thought
it would be like this, it's difficult to describe. And what would
my publisher say if he could see me sitting in the old chair, and
you coming in to put music on the machine when I wanted it
played, or thought I needed it played? *Marche Slav*, the *Scotch
Symphony* . . . who would have thought that Tchaikovsky and
Mendelssohn would be helping on my meager novel? I've sold
it: we'll be signing a contract tomorrow. I had to take out a lot
of those ornate passages, but maybe the book will be the better
for it . . . I don't know . . . I tried not to be unduly stubborn.
But doesn't an author have to stick up for what he thinks is
right? If I hadn't thought the embellished paragraphs were
desirable I wouldn't have put them in, in the first place. I
don't know, I don't know: it's quite confusing. . . . I know who
Mr. Wyndham Lewis is, yet don't know for sure, I've heard the
name . . . Cass Canfield of Harper's. . . . New York is so massive
that the sensitive should be terrified by it; yet one must not
lope away yelling, if this is to become an enhancement of his
life. And I feel confident that in time we will be New York's and
New York will be ours. But it isn't Chicago, no it isn't Chicago.
Not by a dang sight.

3.

I was very tired now, and hoped to take a nap. Returned to
the hotel, I lay down but found myself too tense to sleep. There
was another agent to see. Robert Thomas Hardy, who'd sold my
stories to *Real Detective Tales*. I called his office, and he invited
me to visit him next day. (Again I was gaudily lunched. This

time at Longchamps. I thought I was in Paris, France, for sure,
by gum.)

Weather had turned gloomy, with clouds, but not very cold.
After various fumblings I found my way down to the Battery, by
subway train and by walking. The Statue of Liberty stood riveted
to her torch in threatening attitude, and there were boats traveling over there. I'd supposed that she stood on the island where
immigrants landed. Not so; Bedloe's was a quite different place.
I went over on the regular ferry run with some holidaying
Italian families, and we crept to the top of the statue, and
peeked out at the scenery. Manhattan menaced as if it too held a
cold strong arm on high . . . at night there'd be lights, I
imagined them winking on the buildings. I recognized the Singer
building. Long ago there was a postcard with that picture on
it, and Herbert and I used to show it in a postcard projector.

Gulls flipped back and forth, and some of them begged after
a passing steamer, and their echoing grievance made me feel
puny and unwanted. Maybe that was the way gulls were intended to make men feel. A few whistles tooted as mournfully,
and I was glad to clamber down the stairways and sail back to
Manhattan along with those singing Italian celebrants whose
children skipped wild and prettily. The adults plied themselves
and me with delicious homemade wine they'd brought in picnic
baskets. One had a concertina, and I tried to sing merrily along
with them, but about the only words I knew were "Funiculi,
Funicula" and "O Sole Mio." Nevertheless it fetched back notion
of Tartini and the Mandel Brothers days with a rush, and I
got a lump in my throat.

Desperately I wanted to call Irene that evening by telephone,
but felt that I shouldn't spend the money. All knowledge and
impulse dictated that we get out of Montreal as soon as possible.
The doctor's statement, "You should not leave until the baby is
six weeks old," haunted verily. I had absolutely no notion of
trying to lay down a financial law to Coward, and tell him that
I must have a cash advance on the book . . . paid by the day
the baby was six weeks old? That would only annoy him or any

other publisher, and weaken my position editorially as well as
practically. Better leave everything in his hands and in the
agent's.

At the hotel an overpowering weariness descended. I lay down
and was asleep in minutes. I slept long and hard. Once I woke
up feeling a little hungry, had a drink of water . . . next thing it
was late evening, and streets roared with taxicabs bearing
patrons away from the shows.

I found a dairy lunch and dined, then shoved myself amid
throngs strolling on Times Square: herds of people, many in
evening dress, laughing and marching en masse. They didn't seem
at all real, not in phalanx. Somebody had made them up,
and was cranking a crank.

A crowd thickened around a large open car parked in front
of a theater. Pushing, staring, grinning, all trying to get a little
closer; I shoved along with them, wondering what the center of
attention might be. In the car sat a beautiful woman in witching
fur cape, a woman with jewels at her neck and in her hair;
she was laughing, chatting with two brilliantly clad men who
accompanied her, and with another who emerged from the
theater and forced his way through the crowd. Voices whispering
all around. "Mae Murray . . . Mae Murray." O fair and lustrous
whimsy which she was. . . . A day would come when we'd read
about her departure from reality . . . wan old woman crouched
alone in a St. Louis railroad station, not knowing how she'd
gotten there or why, and with no one knowing who she was. And
worse than that, at first—no one caring.

4.

On Saturday the fourth of February my father gave himself a
nice party for me. Those present included officers and directors
of the Gold-Copper Trove—maybe they had trustees as well—
along with miscellaneous wives, daughters, nieces, secretaries
and such.

This revel took place in a private dining room at the Mount Royal, and supposedly was arranged to compliment a freshly contracted author who had attained the ripe age of twenty-four that very day. In fact Mr. John Kantor was already informing the populace that he himself, and only he, had arranged my contract with Coward-McCann. To the best of my knowledge he was still insisting that he did not write stories—he lived them instead—but there were signs of his weakening in that direction as well.

A commercial photographer was summoned to record this event for posterity, and if it was his dedicated intention to present a collection of the most congealed countenances in the Dominion then he succeeded in manner and manor most kingly. I still possess a copy of this perpetration, and have just mooned over it tenderly. Only the Duke of Argyle's gracious cousin has his jaws apart, and probably he was sneezing.

5.

Dad was in a foul mood when our baby was born, and intentionally or no I contributed to his displeasure.

Early in the morning of Thursday the 9th, Irene began to have pains. I took her over to the Women's General hospital. It was just across the street from Montreal, in a suburb called Westmount . . . only a few steps beyond the city line, and several blocks from our apartment.

A room had been ordered by Dr. Strean. I relinquished Irene into the care of one Miss Francis, an elderly nurse who hobbled on lame legs but was charged with vitality and confidence. "Madam must have her tea," she declared—hourly, it seemed— and she'd bring a huge cup of the best, dosing it with cream and sugar which her patient did not fancy. . . . When Strean came to examine, he beamed and winked, and whispered that Miss Francis was one of the best in the region.

Doctor, nurse, room: they exuded antiseptic coziness. I was

overcome with a sense of obligation to my father. Whatever false promises he'd given about a job, at least Irene was comfortably installed and in the best of hands.

What could I do to show appropriate gratitude? When Irene rested at noontime, I hiked for the Mount Royal Hotel and found my father at his office. I said—somewhat bashfully, since after all he was advancing the wherewithal—"I'd like to take you to lunch."

He looked at me ponderously and shook his head. "My son, I must have luncheon with Mr. Katz and Mr. Smith and Mr. Gresham. However, you may join us."

The five of us went down together. I had the nagging notion that he might request me to tell Mr. Katz and Mr. Smith and Mr. Gresham about the drowning of Charley Morean, and instruct me to form a fist according to his pattern.

Charitably those days were vanished. My error came in making intimate revelation while the others were still with us at table.

"You tell me that you took Irene to the hospital early this morning. I am now aware that I have not asked you about the baby's name. What are you going to name the baby, when it is born?"

"We decided that long ago. If it's a girl, we'll call her Carol Layne; but probably we'll use the name Layne commonly instead of Carol."

"And if the baby is a boy?"

I explained, "Irene's favorite brother was Kenny. He died suddenly only a few weeks after Irene and I met. So— I guess I might be excused for using my own name for a middle one— If it is a boy, he'll be Kenneth MacKinlay."

The other men smiled in friendly fashion (I don't see what else they could have done). My father sat with his full lips apart, his eyes slowly concealing themselves under lowered lids.

"Did I understand you correctly? Did you say you will name the child, if it is a boy, Kenneth MacKinlay?"

"That's right."

He sat in embittered silence, and barely heeded the others when they thanked him for the lunch. Then he glared at me with contempt and got up slowly. "There will be another John Kantor in this world, if I have to go out and make one myself," and he strolled away with the rest.

The waiter presented me with the check for the entire group. I didn't have anything like enough money to pay it, so I signed as I had done when we occupied a room at the hotel. When he saw the name he said, "Ah yes. Gold-Copper Trove." In some bitterness I made bold to write on the tip as well. I had sense enough not to follow my sire to his office, but went back to the hospital.

A very-much-annoyed Irene wanted to go home, but Miss Francis said Tut-tut, and fetched Madam some more tea.

I worked very late that night. The story concerned gangsters, with a memory going back to days of the World War. An incident which occurred during a battle in France had its culmination in a Chicago apartment ten years later. . . . It meant toil and toil and more toil, but so did most stories, and I kept hacking away.

Then I ran dry and could only stare stupidly at the typewriter. Finally I reached for a sheet of copy paper and began to scrawl a lyric. The title was on it before the poem was written, and the title was "Lady Layne."

> O, Lady Layne was spinning
> And her garden grew with pink—
> Her eyes were watching not her skein
> But for an armored link
>
> A-shafting up the harbor
> Where the sea men go
> With poniards in their belting,
> And hair as gold as tow.
>
> O, Lady Layne was singing
> Like a thin thrilled lyre—

And never songs for psalters
But singing for her squire;

And by the russet turret
When moon was icing pane—
A blithe brown Saxon
Kissed Lady Layne.

Happened to look at my watch . . . eleven-forty p.m.

(I hold the copy now: a carbon of torn and crumpled manuscript paper with its clipping from the "Line O' Type" column attached. This was the one which I sent to my mother, inscribed, "For Mother to read to Layne some day. Written twelve hours before Layne was born.")

I went back to work on the story.

Thus I lay sound asleep when they called from the hospital in mid-forenoon, and told me that I'd better come over to Westmount. This was a generation before the days of that British doctor and his husband-sharing-wife's-childbirth plan. Irene had insisted all along that she wanted me with her in the delivery room. I wasn't very keen on the idea, but—if she wanted it—

She only thought she wanted it.

When I got to the hospital on this chill bright Friday, her room seemed a center of activity. Miss Francis was there, and a million other nurses were standing by. Irene, racked with pain, was sitting up in bed— I thought she was dying. She seemed gasping for breath, and her hair was wet and tousled.

Dr. Illievitz had dropped by for a friendly call while making his own rounds, and had just preceded me in at the door. Irene glanced up, and if I ever heard a pettish voice it was hers.

She snarled, "Oh, go away." I wasn't even insulted: I fled.

Illievitz whispered to her, "I'll take charge of him. Don't worry, he'll live." He escorted me downstairs to a sitting room, and insisted on halting for a chat.

"Look, Bernie. I ought to go back upstairs."

"She doesn't want you."

"Well, I ought— At least I should wait outside. Shouldn't I?"

"Let me tell you an adventure story. I had a very interesting case yesterday. It was a ski accident—" He related the complete details, which I didn't consider particularly amusing or necessary. He merely wanted to keep me out of trouble, but I couldn't recognize his motive.

Finally he said, "I must leave the Women's General, and get over to McGill." I hurried back upstairs to find Irene gone and the bed all rumpled. There was nothing for me to do except to pace in the traditional urgent attitude of disturbed fathers. I paced and paced and paced. I was at the far end of the corridor when a door opened across the hall from the nursery, and Miss Francis emerged, carrying something wrapped in a pink blanket. She saw me and turned in my direction as I raced forward. She opened up the blanket to reveal the baby's face. Nor was the baby all nasty and red and wrinkled as one might fear she'd be. Her hair was blond and she had her lips set with rigidity, and the lower lip rolled out as if she had taken a vow not to speak even if spoken to.

"Yours," said Miss Francis. "A girl. Now please excuse me." She went limping into the nursery.

Someone had made up Irene's room all nicely fresh . . . only then was I aware that I'd seen the scurryings going on. In a few minutes more Irene arrived via stretcher, and I waited until she was settled in her bed. She was barely conscious, but smiling . . . waves of anesthetic smell rose on high. I went in and kissed her, and they told me I could stay for a moment.

She said, "Do you know? It's a girl," and then drifted off again. Later she had no recollection of my having been there.

Oh, veritable mountain ranges amid wintry clouds! It was all over . . . beautiful baby delivered . . . my wife was fine . . . they'd told me so. "Now," they said, "let Mrs. Kantor sleep, and you come back later in the day."

Next thing I knew I was at the Mount Royal, with no recollection of how I got there. Oh yes, I did remember vaguely stopping at the apartment to get our passports. They might be necessary for what I had in mind.

I visited the suite on the mezzanine floor, walked past everybody and opened the door of my father's office where as always he was in conference. "Dad, it's a girl. Irene and the baby are doing fine," and then I closed the door and went to Number Two on my list.

That was the United States Consulate. I had cased this joint previously—knew exactly where to go, where to turn, what steps to take. Carol Layne could make a decision, according to laws in force, when she became twenty-one years old. She could be either a Canadian or a citizen of the United States. Canadian, because she was born in Canada under the British flag; a United States citizen, because she was born of United States citizens sojourning abroad. That was the term used in connection with the matter, although *sojourning* scarcely described our situation.

The hour of the baby's birth must be set forth, so I gave the exact information: eleven-forty a.m. The clerk looked at his watch. "Well—" He laughed. "You didn't waste much time in getting here, did you?"

Stepping pridefully with the first precious certificate folded in my pocket, I realized that I had eaten nothing since dinner the night before. Couldn't even remember where I'd eaten or what I'd eaten. I was famished, and sought the nearest cafeteria. During that lovely meal I would take out the certificate again and again, and sit looking at it.

After lunch I sent essential telegrams home to the United States. *Six pounds, fourteen ounces* . . . that was what the baby weighed.

Returned to the hospital, I found the door of Irene's room closed. I tapped lightly. No answer, no Miss Francis on hand. I opened the door and stared to see Irene lying there with shaking shoulders, sobbing hysterically.

"Oh," she gasped, "why didn't you come sooner?"

I said, "Irene. Is the baby—?"

"She's fine."

"I know. I saw her. I saw you too."

"No you didn't. *He* was here. He came first."

I said, "I was here in this room. I spoke to you and kissed you, but you don't remember it now."

"*He* was here," she wailed.

"God Almighty. Who was here?"

"Your father." Words barely whispered. . . .

"He was here? In this room? When?"

"While ago. He—he said you were broken-hearted—"

"He said what?"

She'd been asleep, he'd come while she was sleeping. When she awakened he was standing opposite the foot of the bed, looking out the window. She greeted him weakly, and he turned and took an unlighted cigar out of his mouth.

"So you have a baby girl. I know that, I was informed. Your husband is broken-hearted."

I couldn't speak for a moment. "Broken-hearted? Why, Irene," I quavered, "I saw the baby just after she was born. Miss Francis was carrying her to the nursery. She's wonderful—"

"Oh, darling, are you broken-hearted? He said you were broken-hearted because it was a girl."

I said, "I stopped by the office, poked my head in the door, told him it was a girl, and that you were both fine. Then I left."

The prattling little record still playing feebly. "He said you were heartbroken because it was a girl."

I told Irene, "This is a wonderful day. Friday, February 10th. It shall go down in history. Also six weeks from this day you and I will be on a train headed for Chicago." I sat down on the edge of the bed, put my arms around Irene, and finally she stopped crying. I didn't leave when Miss Francis came with tea—just shook my head and she took the tray away. After Irene had gone back to sleep I left. My father had given me many vile moments, but this was the first time I'd ever actually thought of killing him.

What else he would do to us or try to do to us I did not know, but there came one more ugly scene. It occurred when I went to his office, bristling, demanding to know why we had been sent for in the first place. I asked to see him alone, but there were some firm members present. Nevertheless he told me to proceed with what I had on my mind, and I did.

In the middle of what might be called my discourse, he turned to the other men and said, "I could wish that my son had my own voice, which has been compared to that of the great actor Boris Tomashefsky. But instead he talks more shrilly, like his grandfather McKinlay."

I exploded. "My grandfather McKinlay is a poor old man, weak and crippled. All he has left to him are his pioneer memories and his reputation for unclarified honesty. I have in my possession—elsewhere—some letters which he received in 1901 and 1902 and 1903. There are receipts as well, for monies which he paid out in bail, or in making good on bad checks signed by another man."

He sat leering, his face scrolled and contorted. He imitated a few of my words in an enervated tone.

I said, "My grandfather McKinlay, at whose name you jeer, and in whose house I was born because you didn't provide other quarters for my mother— I'll tell you what the local banker said about him. Julius M. Jones was one time a major and paymaster in the Federal Army; he became a successful banker later on. He said, 'I would lend Adam McKinlay any amount of money, any time, without one scrap of paper. Only on his given word that he would pay it back.'"

He made pretense of imitating me again with that dreary warble. "'Only on his given word that he would pay it back.'"

This was my last scene with him then, nearly the last that I ever had. I turned to leave. At a cry from my father I looked back to see him bursting into glee. Again his face was demoniacal and he beat his fist on the desk. "By God," he cried, "how I love to burn him up!"

I did not know that the day would come when he would write a check drawn on the Royal Bank of Canada, and sign my name to it. But it would.

I did not know that he would steal two hundred and ninety thousand dollars from his friend and partner, David Ringholt. But he would, he would.

IX. *"THE DIVERSIONS OF DIVERSEY"*

1.

Sun-spattered, solid ice was melting, conduits were chiseled through congealed armor on the sidewalks, a coating left from winter's accumulation. People who walked St. Catherine Street had been marching high in the air, but now ditches were carved at intervals across sidewalks, and melting poured out through the canals.

We sat in a Crescent cab with Layne between us in her basket, and I kept grasp on that basket all the way to the station.

Irene meditated. "It doesn't seem like six weeks since she was born."

"Six weeks to the day. This is the day George Strean said we could leave."

"It seems like six months."

"Maybe six years?"

As the taxi turned in at Windsor Station, Irene demanded, "What are you looking so artless about?"

"Surprise."

"What surprise?"

"Wait and see. When we get aboard the train."

. . . A drawing room, into which I led my saucer-eyed companion.

"Yes, yes, yes, lady! We can't possibly afford it, I know we can't, but we've got it."

Fervently I outlined the situation. "So we couldn't take our infant—basket and all—into a lower berth, and try to expand space there. Suppose we purchased two berths, what would that entail? Certainly all travel is expensive, and we can't afford to travel; but in this case we can't afford *not* to travel."

Such explanation was not very reasonable from the economic point of view, but it was impressive. I even lied a little, giving the effect that Doctor Strean himself had ordered this commitment. He had done no such thing, but he might have hinted. When I asked him, "Will it be all right if we travel to Chicago in a drawing room?" his quick acquiescence was gratifying.

"But what will we do in Chicago? We won't have any money and—"

"I'll sell another story to *Real Detective Tales*. Your folks are expecting us—we've written to them—and I sent a wire last night, telling them that we'd arrive on Saturday. We can camp down in your old room for a few days, until I sell this other story and collect the money for it. Then we'll find a place of our own."

. . . Our porter cooed over the baby and threatened her with his dark finger; the uniformed men from Customs and Immigration poked their own fingers. Official formalities were at a decisive low. The men merely wanted to know whether we were fetching any liquor into the United States.

Confession came promptly. "They have some candy up here in Canada which consists of chocolates fashioned into the shape of tiny liquor bottles. The contain champagne, brandy, cordials— We've got a box of that, and here it is, and that's all the liquor we've got with us."

"I heard you," Customs said. "Box of candy. Candy's permitted. Didn't you say they were chocolate creams?" and he put his thumbs to his ears and waggled fingers at Carol Layne.

Our lives had been demeaned and repressed with treachery. Now we were free. It was as if we could look at our wrists and ankles. Scars would be there, for long, but shackles were gone.

. . . Bundles of snowy napkins, each to be soiled and put aside in its own time. Thermos bottle of formula to have its doses measured out and warmed for the bottles— Standard routine of parents traveling with an infant: this we observed fervently. It seemed constituting no drudgery, it was a brave portion of flight and release.

Irene was positive that the quality of her breast milk had improved on the instant.

"If I keep on like this, I'll have more milk than one child can take. I'll need to go into the business."

"You can be a wet nurse, and earn money on the side." I even remembered the name of a wet nurse from Latin days in high school. *Nutricia.*

The baby wore in turn the kimonos, almost the only articles of clothing Irene had been able to prepare for her in the Mrs. Letts days. They were of flannel, and tied in the back with tiny tapes. . . .

My fear pervading was that Irene might collapse, now that tautness of a foul experience was released. Our doctors had warned about that very possibility. "It's been a bit rough on you both. But, Mack, you're much more extroverted than she, and you've been able to brazen it off to some extent. Watch Irene carefully and see that she doesn't become overstrained. It'll take her a while to escape from this experience."

I sang to her when she did not need to be sleeping . . . had always loved to draw cartoons, and drew a series of them. Principally they concerned our daughter through various stages of an advancing career, clad always in those flannel dressing gowns. She grew tall and demanding. Disregarding her physical resemblance to Irene, so apparent even at birth, I had her graduate into a gawky string-bean of my own physical type, complete with spectacles and pipe and even a mustache. These delineations were reviewed by a somewhat hysterical mother, but at least she was laughing.

We'd had no appetite for food before. Instantly we developed ravenings, raptly we studied the menu . . . tried to select the cheapest items available, though nothing seemed very cheap. Soups and eggs and sandwiches were our stand-bys, but I took mine in the dining car and insisted that Irene be served in the drawing room: we couldn't leave the baby unattended.

We were barely conscious of the receding flow of Canadian countryside and villages beyond our windows. *You're out of jail,* wheels kept ticking from beneath. *Out-of-jail, out-of-jail, out-of-jail* in reassuring rhythmic lullaby which caused us to sleep as deeply as the baby slept, if as fitfully.

It was on this trip that I confessed for the first time about the incident in Toronto when we were outward bound . . . my perilous scramble up onto the observation platform.

"Oh, don't get off the train now! What if I landed in Chicago, baby and all, without you?"

I told her, "Guess it would have been worse in Montreal," and she agreed with fervor.

I comforted myself also with awareness that the unused portion of our ticket, which had been drawn complete in its return to Iowa, would bring a little cash. We were traveling only a shade above the disaster level.

In Chicago, putting aside necessary money for tips and taxi to the Layne apartment, I saw that we possessed a balance of about thirty dollars. I had two thirds of this in my pocket, and Irene owned a Canadian ten-dollar bill and some change in her purse.

"Mack. That's not very much."

"How many families do you think have hit Chicago with less than this? Plenty. And there's now an editor in town who likes my stories."

Calamity came promptly after we landed. We had taken all our possessions into that drawing room on the train. Now ensued the tortuous experience of getting this stuff into a taxicab. . . . It was done: bags piled in the front seat and jammed into the taxi's trunk. We hustled grandly with the baby in her basket on Irene's lap, and the typewriter between my feet on the floor. Bright gay ride up through the North Side . . . wisely we pointed out evidences of spring apparent in Lincoln Park which could not be glimpsed amid ice still clinging in Montreal.

At 2200 Wilson our driver displayed himself as a horrid man.

I made the first journey upstairs, lugging things, and Irene's stepmother would not be delayed. She wanted to see Layne, and came hastening down while the driver deposited our effects on the sidewalk with scant ceremony. I paid him, tipped him in what seemed a lavish gesture, but no reasonable gratuity would have sufficed. The next moment he was gone . . . of course we had no registration number, no license number, nothing. The taxi had departed with Irene's purse still lying on the back seat, crammed with her feminine gauds and necessities, and the ten-dollar bill.

Vague resulting calls to the Yellow Cab offices were received with resentment. The purse was never turned in.

"Hello, Chicago!" we said, with nineteen dollars and fifty-some cents in hand.

2.

On Monday morning I took the unused portion of our return passage to railroad offices and was told that it might be weeks before the small refund was paid. Whenever it came, it would be welcome. I begged that they'd hurry it up as speedily as possible, which a kindly clerk promised to do.

Then I went seeking Edwin Baird, editor of *Real Detective Tales*. He was vice-president of his company, just as H. N. Swanson was an officer of its twin, the Collegiate World Publishing Company. A moneyed man named J. M. Lansinger was president of both.

The offices were located in a small building back in a court at 1050 North LaSalle Street, but on separate floors. A trifle fearful of the ominous experience of initial encounter with Baird, I told a receptionist first that I should like to see Swanson. But he was busy—had someone with him. I wondered if it might not be James Montgomery Flagg again. On a previous classic occasion the noted illustrator visited Swanson, and also during the same errand had visited the men's room a few doors away. There, in sketching mood, Mr. Flagg took crayon in hand and devised a fine picture on the wall of that chamber, depicting himself in the act of doing what he was doing. This called for considerable comment. But I hold distinct recollection that President Lansinger ordered this original offering to be painted out.

I gathered shreds of courage, and requested that, since Swanson was occupied, I might be admitted to the presence of Edwin Baird.

He sat behind his desk, hammering madly. "Hello! I'm just writing an editorial. Let me finish this paragraph," and he typed away. He was an alert individual seeming quite elderly—away up in his forties, no doubt. Baird had bright blue eyes, a vigorous smile, and an old-fashioned newspaper city room manner. He wore a felt hat to cover the bald dome which was his head.

When he'd concluded the paragraph he stood up and offered his hand. "I remember the name. Haven't I bought something of yours recently?" He gestured to a single chair beyond the desk where several illustrations or attempts at illustrations were roosting. "Just take em off," and I did. "And sit down," and I did. "Let's see. What were the things I bought from you?"

"All in all, you've bought three stories of mine. Two through Robert Thomas Hardy, and one which I sent you myself."

"Sure! That one about the surveyor. I like your stories, they move fast, they have things happening in them, and that's what my readers like too."

"I've brought another. Here it is."

He looked at the title. "'This Guy Baum.' Not bad—makes you wonder who he is. What did I pay you?"

"One cent per word. Still paying it?"

"Certainly. I have different rates for different writers, depending on their success with my public. Whether people write in, say they like this stuff— You know: audience reaction. Sometimes I pay considerably more than one cent a word. Just you keep trying. What are you doing in Chicago?"

"I was in Canada, waiting for a job which had been promised to me. The job never came through, so now we're back in the States, and Chicago's our former home. Mr. Baird, how long would it take you to read 'This Guy Baum'?"

He glanced at the thin manuscript. "I'll try to read it tonight. Usually take home a lot of stuff to read. In a big hurry?"

"I've got a wife and baby girl, and we just came to town Saturday."

He repeated, chuckling, "Wife and baby girl, and you just came to Chicago on Saturday. Guess you need that one cent per word. If your story's any good, I'll buy it."

I said haltingly, "It does concern—the World War—in part—"

"That wouldn't be out for me. But I wouldn't want a solid war story."

"This isn't."

"O.K., I'll read it tonight. Give me a ring tomorrow."

"What if I call, in person?"

"I see. You want your check. Very well, if I like the story I'll write you an order to Mrs. May. She deals out the checks here, and maybe you can persuade her to give you one immediately. That's *if* I like the story. Now let me finish my editorial. See you tomorrow."

I went as far as Swanson's office and took another peek. His door was open and I could see him at his desk, going over mail. I stuck my head in. "Hey."

He smiled, and beckoned. "How did Montreal work out?"

"I didn't get the job I was promised."

"So now you're back in the United States again. Did you bring me a bottle of booze?"

"Certainly not. Couldn't afford it. We did bring a box of those tiny chocolates with liqueurs inside them."

"Thanks, I'll take my booze straight. Got any manuscripts to show me?"

I shook my head. "Been talking with Baird."

"Going to write some detective stories?"

"He's bought some stuff of mine. I wish you'd buy some."

"I still don't think that you can write—at least readily—
the kind of prose I need for *College Humor.*"

"You ought to have bought *Diversey.*"

He shrugged. "Maybe so. Time will tell. Have you sold it
yet?"

I shook hands with myself.

"Who to?"

"Brand-new publishing house: Coward-McCann. They expect
to start in the fall, and *Diversey* may be their first book."

"Brand-new publishing house." Swanson repeated the words
slowly. "Yes, but they're a little different from most. Both Coward and McCann used to be with Bobbs-Merrill, and really
built that firm into something. Congratulations. I think you're
with a good house."

"In the meantime, what can I do for you?"

He closed his eyes, and considered. "Little sketch. Nostalgic.
You know— What about 'The Wheaten Dance' which you
wrote last year? And wasn't there another one about old-fashioned Christmas or something? Some of those with purple words
in. Go ahead and try a brief sketch like that. Pay you twenty-
five bucks if it matches up."

I went back to Wilson Avenue feeling slightly un-bruised.

3.

We were not the only relatives momentarily accepting shelter
at the Laynes'. Irene's next elder brother Harold was out of a
job, and had come back to the city from Wisconsin with his
wife, seeking employment. They were ensconced in a bedroom
directly across the hall from Irene's old room where we were
installed. I offered lugubrious apologies to Irene's father and
stepmother for our own pauperish descent upon them, but they
only beamed and praised the baby. (They have been in Heaven
for the past few decades, occupying especially comfortable

situation demanded with fervor by those who knew them on
Earth.)

Harold's wife lifted her voice in song.

As a general rule humankind should welcome in others the
act of resorting to melodic enterprise. Critters destined to be
people gave forth sounds, it must be presumed, when they were
still running on all fours. Chantings and carolings of varied
nature have enriched religious and social activities through the
millennia, or perhaps have detracted from their virtue. Those
who heard and saw Miss Irene Closz singing in the Baptist
Church choir circa 1914 can never forget, and will never be
quite the same again; although most of us are gone now. We
judge the earliest ballad singers to have been soloists, and must
pray that the Lay of the First Minstrel was a pleasant one.

I do not declare, forty-odd years after Harold's wife's melodic
utterance struck our ears, that her effort was of the worst. She
was divorced from Harold not too long after this encounter, and
for all I know may still be extant, buxom if a bit whimsical, but
persistently alert with song. It is even possible that her repertoire has extended to include numbers other than the two—
and two alone—to which she gave voice in that late March of
1928. They were "Just a Cottage Small (by the Waterfall)" and
"Muddy Water." We observed poetic concern with unabated
moisture in these plaints, which pealed perhaps half a dozen
times each hour. Whether the cottage was ever actually drowned
in mud, we never did learn. There are times when even the
raptures of a fabled Jenny Lind might prove inappropriate at
a distance of say twelve feet, and filtered through, say, two
thin walls. Such occasions include the scheduled and demanded
nursing of infants, and the bumbling attempts of a hag-driven
writer to concoct a marketable short story.

If malcontent gods dwelt amid ghostly wild onions or ashes
of the Chicago fire, they'd glowered with the disappearance of
Irene's bag and among moist arias from the next room.

They were willing to smile again Tuesday.

Any sort of composition was impossible in the borrowed

chamber. I took paper and pencil and went over to one of our old favorite courting spots beside the lake. There I managed to contrive a sketch of the sort suggested by Swanson, and would be twenty-five dollars richer by the time he put the order through . . . just a little sketch.

I bearded Edwin Baird in his den later that same day—(would *Bairded* be better?)—and found him enthusiastic about the story I'd left with him.

"'This Guy Baum' has enormous suspense. Glad to buy it." He looked me over briefly, speculatively. "Like me to make out an order for Mrs. May? Maybe she'll give you a check on the spot."

Thirty dollars. Things were looking up. We had to get away from that Waterfall and the Muddy Water beneath it. Irene was a demon nursing mother, she couldn't go apartment hunting. I went, unwilling to spend much time at the task, but aware of necessity . . . the place was on Dover Street just north of Wilson. Allegedly a whorehouse district, but there were gangs of kids around. You walked up two flights and found a squeezed little den which didn't seem too dirty. There was a hole-in-the-wall kitchenette and a toilet; only one miniature basin. I was doubtful about facilities for washing baby clothes, but couldn't spend days in search. Cautiously I rented the joint for the standard fifteen dollars per week, and moved Irene and Layne to this haven the next morning. It turned out to be a jolly little hell-hole. Strain of journeying and general circumstance were telling upon mother and child, and in the case of a breast-fed infant this gave rise to protracted coughing howls of starvation which ruptured the atmosphere.

A herd of buffalo dwelt on the top floor and were forever trampling and rumbling. A general bathroom where I had thought the baby's things might be laundered was also on the floor above. I went up in advance of Irene and laboriously scrubbed out the bathtub. Irene prepared to perform the first washing but returned in disgust.

"Not in that place! I refuse to wash her clothes in a bathroom

where other people come to take baths— I don't care how
well you cleaned the tub. They'll have to be washed right here
in this tiny lavatory."

"The people?"

"No, stupid. The God-damn baby clothes!"

It seemed that I had written under difficulties on previous
occasions, but this was the first time I'd ever tried to compose
beneath a bower of diapers. We rigged lines across the room,
and I had to push diapers aside in order to claw my way to the
typewriter. Then they dripped down the back of my neck. It
did not seem inappropriate to concoct a story entitled "The Ten
Thousand Dollar Bag." Ten thousand dollars represented the
quintessence of delight. If I could not actually lay hands on
those packets of neatly wrapped currency which figured in the
tale, I could at least do so in imagination.

Jessie Layne hastened over to call and see how we were
fixed. She arrived to find damp laundry, typewriter clacking
away, baby howling—if six-and-a-half-week-old infants can be
said to howl—and a young mother torn between rage and collapse.

Mrs. Layne settled herself in a chair after Irene cleared some
junk away. "Well, at least you now have a place of your own.
You have this darling little baby—"

"Darling little baby?" yelled Irene, glaring at the basket.
"Sometimes I think I'd like to throw her out the window!"
An assertion cut short by the scream of genuine terror which
issued from her stepmother.

Recently I had notion to include a paragraph or two from
"The Ten Thousand Dollar Bag" in this epistle. I dug the
crumbling magazine out of a file cabinet, and took one long
look at the story. Why Baird bought it I'll never know, but buy
it he did. He was not a father, so could have had no knowledge
of writing under a canopy of diapers; but perhaps the urgency
of our situation filtered through to him somehow. Strangely
enough when the story appeared in print there ensued fan mail
praising this perpetration. *Real Detective Tales* became a crutch

in lame and needful moments, but some of the material therein was published with audacity.

The check for the *College Humor* sketch arrived promptly in the mail. Our budget was not as skinny as before, but a thousand necessities stared us in the face. Mighty among them loomed the shape of a baby carriage.

"I've been thinking," I informed Irene.

"In what terms?"

"In terms of 2829 Cambridge."

"But you said that you didn't think we ought to go back there. You didn't think it would be wise for you to be in that neighborhood when *Diversey* was published."

"I'd still be reluctant. I might be the target for— Well, I might be some sort of target. I have no desire to be any sort of target. But the book won't be published until August. I haven't even got the proofs yet, though there was a letter saying that they'd be coming soon. What are we waiting for? Everything's clean there, and if we could get an apartment like Mother and I used to have— There's a fine big sink—"

"Oh, God, yes!" cried Irene. "Yes, yes, yes!—I'm all excited about it. Just pray that the Norrises have room."

"I'm praying for more than that. I snuck over to Sears, Roebuck yesterday—the big place up on Lawrence—and I saw a baby cab— It's really beautiful. Nice big one. Got a top that moves back and forth, and everything. You've been worrying about getting the baby out of doors—"

"But we can't afford—"

"Course we can't afford it. Can't afford nothing. I'll get down there to Cambridge tomorrow and see what the situation is."

The situation was that they wanted most awfully to welcome the baby. Even the ordinarily cross-grained Mrs. Norris was voluble in excitement. "We feel that she kind of belongs to us, one way or another—"

Pop said, "Maybe she does. Maybe she got started, right here in this building."

"No she didn't," I explained. "She got started later than that, but we don't know just where—"

Mrs. Norris said, with rare and affectionate dispassion, "Now you two boys behave," and Pop smiled agreeably at being called a boy.

"You know what? The couple that's had your old apartment—the one you used to have with your mother, second floor south at the rear— Well, he got transferred to Milwaukee, and they're going out Sunday."

I asked, "Can you afford to let it sit idle for two days? Our week's up Wednesday, on Dover Street, but it isn't just that. Fact is, I've got a story I must finish for *Real Detective Tales* before I move anywhere. I'm positive I can get it done in time to move on Wednesday."

I did get it done, and carried it to Edwin Baird, and he read it while I was sitting in Swanson's office talking about the possibility of a short story there.

Baird said, "What's it about?" and I said, "Modern Chicago," and he said, "Is it gripping?" and I said, "No, but very funny," and he said, "I need to read something funny. I'll read it right now," and he did.

When I came back from the Swanson office Baird had come to the last page, and I sat and felt delight at watching his reaction.

He put the manuscript down. "Well, you kind of telegraphed the ending—at least you did to anyone like this old guy— I was a police reporter for years, you know. Anyway, you're right: it *is* a funny story. I'll buy it right now. How long is it?"

I'd counted the words, really counted them. "Thirty-two hundred and fifty words, Mr. Baird."

"Ed is what they call me in this business. Nobody but my wife calls me Edwin. Guess you're Mack, aren't you?' Let's get it on that basis, it'll be pleasanter. . . . What did you say—thirty-two hundred and fifty?"

He typed out an order for Mrs. May to draw a check in the amount of thirty-two dollars and fifty cents. I went away feeling good. Daringly I'd already bought the baby cab, and a rapt Irene was trundling Layne around a neighborhood where off-spring were alleged to be washed down the toilets rather than welcomed. It was a nice carriage: fifteen dollars and eighty cents. I was proud every time I looked at it. Wicker shone in the sun, color of honey . . . I envisioned a brawnier Layne able to sit up and appreciate the scenery. But this would do wonderfully for now, and she could sleep in it any time she wanted to.

Two years to the week since Irene and I met at the Graeme Players. . . .

Wednesday was the big day and a fair one. We packed the carriage to the top with diapers, bottles, blankets, and Layne's entire wardrobe, which actually didn't take up too much space since it consisted at the moment mainly of the kimonos Irene had stitched, a few dresses—perfunctory gifts from people in my father's firm at Montreal—and a splendid bonnet, the gift of T. R. Coward. That bore the magic name of Best's on the box, and Irene exclaimed, "Just imagine! Our daughter having a bonnet from *Fifth Avenue!*" My typewriter, paper, etc. were in the carriage at the bottom, and this cargo I wheeled from the Dover address to 2829 Cambridge. Pushing loaded prams is good for young fathers, but that seemed like a rather lengthy shove.

Then the trip back north by Broadway streetcar—the dash to the given-up apartment, suitcases lugged downstairs, precious baby basket, precious baby (she wasn't howling, she looked big-eyed, she liked this hullabaloo) . . . taxicab driver telling us about his own child; the sweeping up to the curb in front of Norrises'; Mrs. Norris and her friend and lodger Mrs. Davis hovering; Pop hastening downstairs to peer and poke and make the kindly animal sounds which most people believe are essential to the welcoming of infants . . . those two good magic words *Welcome Home* sounding again, and our loving this sort of music.

4.

Thirty-two-dollar-and-fifty-cent stories were all very well in their way, but I needed to learn rapidly that that was no compensating manner in which to function in the one-cent-a-word department. Baird mentioned novelettes constantly. I didn't know quite what a novelette was, never having encountered one of those creatures dancing ahead of me. The very name sounded skittish and French, suggesting something deer-like which might have waltzed away from a zoo and was bent on joining a carnival.

"That guy Musselman, who was just leaving the office when you came in— He's one of my best boys. Just finished a fine novelette for me. So has Vincent Starrett. Why don't you do a novelette?"

"On what subject?"

"Figure that out for yourself. You're a writer, aren't you? You've got to understand that those weentsie short stories you've been doing are just so much filler. The main substance of the magazine is novelettes. It's a length which readers can really appreciate—you know, get their teeth in. Plenty of opportunities for a build-up of character and dramatic sequence and so on."

A painter named Andrew Benson did most of the covers for *Real Detective Tales*. These appeared in lurid hues: policemen shooting it out with bandits, private detectives shooting it out with Treasury agents, etc.

"Take a look at this fine cover Benson left here!"

It was somewhat less than ethereal and no mistake. A girl in a mink coat stood up in a red car and held a pistol directed against Humanity in general, and the armed gentlemen accompanying her didn't look very succulent either. An officer and a young fellow carrying a payroll bag were cringing away from this contingent, and golly you couldn't blame them.

"Well," I said, "it's certainly vivid enough."

"Fine cover!"

"What in particular does it illustrate?"

Baird laughed loudly. "I don't know. He just made the painting, and said that he thought it would be a good cover, and I think so too."

"You mean—" Dumbfounded Mack Dept. "You mean an artist came in here, and brought you a painting to be used on the cover of your magazine, and you want to use it, and you haven't got any story to go with it?"

He grinned. "That's the situation."

"And you want to buy the cover?"

"I've already bought it."

"Well, how's about my doing the novelette to go with it?"

"Think you could?"

"Course I could," I said with confidence, not betraying the squeamishness which squealed inside.

"Needs a good title. Let me see—" and he went title hunting. "*The Chicago Racket.* That ought to hustle the customers in. Half my subscribers seem to be old housewives or crippled-up ex-night-watchmen who live out in the suburbs or in country towns, and just dote on what they think is the real inside about Chicago gangsters and hoodlums and bank holdups."

"Something of that sort?"

"Make it robbers. We'll call it *The Chicago Racket.*"

I blinked, and asked how long the story should be.

"Oh, novelette length." It turned out that he considered anything above seventy-five hundred words to be a novelette. "Say eight or nine thousand words, but certainly not more than fifteen thousand. Study that picture there and see what you can do with it."

I wrote *The Chicago Racket* in the next two days, and Baird made out a magnificent voucher, and Mrs. May drew the check.

But I yielded to alarm. "Look." To my editor. "Maybe you're filling up the magazine too fast with my stuff."

"Don't worry about that. You keep coming up with good stories, and we'll want em anyway."

"But you won't want two or three in the same issue by the same author?"

"We'll just put pseudonyms on. Fact is, I'm scheduling *The Chicago Racket* for the same issue in which I'm running another story of yours. So we'll just put a fake name on it. Let's see. I used to know a guy on a paper named Joe Feeney. Guess he's dead now, but it doesn't matter. *The Chicago Racket* by Joe Feeney. O.K.?"

I'd heard of hack writers, and had never set out to be one, and now I was one. On the streetcar, going home, I kept awarding myself the designation. "You're a *hack writer*." At first it had a mausoleum sound to it; but I considered the certified milk for Layne's formula . . . thirty cents a quart, when ordinary milk cost maybe ten cents. . . .

Irene needed some new dresses most pitifully.

Well—

5.

We had been offered a vapid reception at the Littles'. Bursting with desire to exhibit our offspring on the first sunny Sunday which followed our move back to the Diversey section, Irene arrayed Layne in her best dress and jacket, and with fatuous pride we wheeled her all the way down to Chicago Avenue. It turned out that neither Dick nor Shelby fancied children, especially tiny ones. Dick threatened the baby with his mighty fist and uttered a few savage growls which only caused our daughter to sniffle and wail. Shelby stood, cigarette holder poised, and said, "Ugh. What a perfectly *ador*able infant!" and that was about the end of it. Fellow "Line" contributors who were present couldn't have cared less either. R.H.L.'s diggings constituted no baby gallery worth mentioning.

Uncomfortably I recalled a previous incident when a relative of Dick's and her husband appeared from Washington with their own progeny, and camped down at the Littles'. R.H.L. turned sullen, stamped out of the apartment, refused to return until late in the evening.

"First thing in the morning," he growled to me, "what do I hear? 'I want *oatmeal.*' That's what I hear. What a thing to wake up to! 'I want *oatmeal!*' Well, God damn it, *I* didn't want any oatmeal and—and— First off in the morning. Jesus Christ. 'I want *oatmeal!*'"

Should have known better than to lug Layne down there in the first place.

We fared little better in an exhibition tour to the Graeme Players. Miss Graeme's interest had waned completely, once we were no longer available as actors for her purpose. Even the fact that our romance had begun and prospered under her auspices found her unenthusiastic. Several members whose company we had enjoyed still remained our friends, and we hosted small confabs at our kitchenette apartment as soon as we were able to supply refreshments. But experience taught us a common verity: that a man's or a family's social activities are generally tailored to immediate demands of his profession and the associations included therein.

It turned out that Edwin Baird promulgated a Saturday night salon attended by writers who furnished the material with which his magazine was stuffed, and a few others active in the newspaper realm. The Bairds dwelt in a new cooperative apartment building on Lake Shore Drive which seemed to us the acme of Chicago perfection.

Mrs. Baird was a jolly soul, vastly fat, and wearing a bright auburn wig. She greeted Irene cordially. "Good evening, my dear. So glad that you could come. I hear that you have a darling little baby girl. What did you do with her? Did you leave her with her nurse?"

As one-cent-per-word people we were not exactly up to our ears in nurses attending our young; but this fact seemed unrecognized by our hostess, then and in the future. She spoke

often of the baby and her nurse. She might not realize that we
knew a sad-faced but reliable fellow lodger who was glad to
add two dollars to her slender income by baby-sitting.

The Bairds boasted a lodger: a young lawyer named Bailey
Samelow at the time, who later changed his name to Stanton.
He wanted a Lake Shore Drive address for his home, and could
not yet afford an apartment of that variety; hence he took room
and bath with the Bairds. He was a handsome man on the
smallish side, grave and dignified as to manner, and no one
could have sensed the tragedy which lay before him. In years
to come, as a moneyed politician, he would enter into disastrous
marriage which ended in murder and attempted suicide. Attempted is the word . . . it made a monster out of him . . . he
had to be wheeled to trial, and wheeled to the penitentiary.

No scourge of the future obtruded here. People liked to go
to the Bairds', even many who were far beyond them in intellect and accomplishment. There shone the intelligence, easy
deportment, and gentility of Vincent Starrett. For all his literary erudition, Starrett favored a nice check as well as any other
writer younger or older than himself. Already admired internationally, he was the traditional ungowned professor who
encouraged the young to stand forth and speak their minds and
their hearts.

Fred Babcock of the Chicago *Tribune* staff was another
regular in attendance. So were two effervescent gentlemen who
worked together on a medical journal, dwelt together in a small
apartment not far away and—to the amazement of those of our
years and background who were observant but not yet very
cognizant—traveled together and seemed to do *everything* together. Whatever their attachment, they were vivid company.

Saturday evenings sparkled with hilarity. Ed Baird might in
time reveal himself as acquisitive to an unhappy degree, but
he liked to laugh and sing. Some of the guests who appeared
frequently were not the most profound in the world, but
neither were they the most constrained. This was not a bad

scheme to be caught up in. Nor is any other such situation which generates an honest and hearty cheer.

In Lake County near Libertyville, Fred Babcock spent warm weather months in a log cabin on the estate of his sister and her husband. One Sunday the whole troop of us were invited up there to spend the day. Layne suffered from some infant megrim— It was on the mild side, but Irene couldn't leave her. She insisted that I stood in extreme need of anti-typewriter therapy, however, and shipped me off with the rest.

I came home goggle-eyed that night.

"They served a wonderful lunch in the middle of the afternoon. But guess what we had for our first course. Fresh tomato juice!"

"Fresh tomatoes—?"

"No, no. Just the juice. Squeezed out, and then— I guess it was kind of strained. Not raw tomatoes, you see. Or tomatoes put up in jars or cans. Just—pure—juice. His sister fixed it, and she and a maid brought it over to Fred's cabin in great big pitchers."

"Goodness, I never heard of such a thing. How did it taste?"

"Wonderful. Put a little salt and pepper in it and— Great. And you know what? Vincent Starrett said he saw some in a delicatessen the other day, in cans. That's right. Just plain canned tomato juice. What do you know about that?"

Irene said, "It might even replace orange juice," and we went into hearty laughter at the audacity of the idea.

Ah. 1928. Great year for the tomatoes.

. . . A man of lesser soul than Vincent Starrett might have remained pompous and aloof, and reluctant to attend on such commonness. He was born to share and charm. Irene said that she would remember him forever as he was then: lounging in gray tweeds, and wearing immaculate white shirts and wide silky black neckties, with that vaunted wave of shiny silver hair falling over his forehead.

"Just think," we said, "he treats us as equals. And, you know, he's *forty-one years old!*"

6.

Another man with silver hair called on us one day. I came home
to find Irene entertaining him with tea, and the baby entertaining him with grins as he bent above her and made sweeping
motions with his worn delicate fingers. *Baybee, baybee* he
whispered; and then, in shaking hands, explained with pride,
"From Foster Avenue I walk all the way here. Walking is
good." He was my other grandfather, Joseph Kantor, father of
John.

I held few memories of him, we had never been close, the
antics of my father precluded any intimate or understanding
association with relatives on that side. My mother had spoken of
him with gentle affection. I might look at such regard in terse
annoyance. What did that count for? Mother still existed in
spiritual slavery to the lunatic posturings of John.

This day the elder came as if sent by magnetic effort, to
speak with his persistent Swedish accent so difficult for untrained
ears to accept; yet to discourse capably on the brutal subject
which needed his calm interpretation.

He said, "Come. You walk too," and he was eighty-four, and
when he'd made farewell to Irene and his great-granddaughter
we went along the northbound streets. He stepped rigidly,
almost daintily in precision. . . . His life before he met Tobia
Margolis in Copenhagen seemed shut and locked. I have strong
belief that he experienced military service with its attendant
perils, uncertainties, benefits. He was slim, precise in bearing,
owning a native courtliness which bore no relation to John
Kantor's pomposity and made John seem doughy and stuffed
in comparison.

. . . So. You say you hate your father, you hate Yan.

. . . That is too bad. It is sad, but no one should blame you.

. . . He was always so.

. . . Sometimes I think it was my wife. She spoiled him,

everything must wait for him. Yan is great, he does nothing
wrong, everything is for him. But also he is that way when he
is small.

. . . A little boy, so high. And—what you know?— When he
is young, his hair it is not black. No. Brown, light color, pale.
But oh— So very— Like this always. What you call it. Fake? *Ja.*

. . . He is a lying little boy. Lies, all lies. Always.

. . . When we are in Karlskrona it is lies. My wife, she cry.
Oh where is Yan? He is gone. The nursemaid— No, no Yan.
The servants run to look. No. He is gone.

. . . My wife is crying. All the maids look everywhere. They
call me and I go to look. I meet some boys. They tell me:
by the pier, where are the ships. A little boy down there.

. . . I go. And it is Yan.

. . . And he is very small. So high. And all the other boys,
big boys, around. They stand around like this. And he is in the
middle, telling lies.

. . . They stand around him. They laugh and say, Listen to
him talk. The little *Yehuda.* They call him that. What stories
he is telling! The little Jew, they call him that. *Yehuda.*

. . . It is lies. He come from here, he come from there. Is
living in a— What you call it? House so big. A palace. That is
where he lives.

. . . I take him home. And he is crying, does not want to
go. My wife, she scream and yell. Oh, it is Yan. The darling
Yan! He is not dead! Dear Yan!

. . . I want to beat him. Give him spank, because he talk
so bad, and telling lies. No, no. His mother never let me put
my hand on him. Never, never spank dear Yan.

. . . And so. Like that. His whole life. Lying always.

I walked with Grandpa Kantor up to Foster Avenue. He
took me into his tiny apartment and displayed some patents
from the Swedish chamberlain empowering him, Joseph Kantor,
to sell clothing and other goods to the royal household. "See.
My name. On there. But all these paper is in Swedish. So—
You cannot read it. But it is there."

Again he donned his threadbare dark blue topcoat—brushed, brushed, neat and brushed until the seams stood out—and walked me to the corner. Something reoccurred—I spoke once more about my father, but Grandpa Kantor by that time was musing in abstraction. I spoke the name a second time.

"Who? Yan?" He spat. *"Bah!"*

He stood there on the corner. We shook hands, parted, then I walked a bit. I looked back—he was standing on that corner still, and watching me. I waved. He lifted up his slender cane in a salute . . . that silver-headed cane, I wish I owned it now.

It was a visit and a walk to be remembered. He died the same month when bound copies of *Diversey* first appeared.

7.

Galley proofs came, and I read them toilsomely. It would be wonderful to have a book in which there were no typographical errors, and I hoped against hope that this would be possible in the case of *Diversey*. For several evenings, late into several nights, I worked on the galley proofs and prided myself that they were sent back in perfect condition. But here arrived an inquiring letter signed by one of the Miss Forenbachs.

Coward-McCann was oozing with Miss Forenbachs. I had seen two or three of them in the office in January, and wondered how many more there were . . . maybe three or four? Harriet Ashbrook, publicity director, said that when Mr. McCann emerged from his private office and cried, "Miss Forenbach!" half the women in the place stood up. One was at the switchboard; one handled correspondence and calls relating to manufacturing; another was Jim McCann's own secretary— Can't recollect whether the name was spelled in this fashion or whether it was Fouhrenbach or Fourenback. However they spelled themselves, there they were.

(Similar to Cagneys. Years later James Cagney and I formed a friendship, and he used to tell about a job he had in Yorkville when they were scraping the bottom of the barrel, and he was very young. He got a job as waiter in a restaurant. . . . The proprietor complained to him, "My dishwasher's quitting Saturday night. Know anyone I could get for a good dishwasher?" "Sure," said Jim, and sent one of his brothers to take the job. Later there was need for a nighttime waiter. "Sure," said Jim, and sent another brother. Then the cashier had to move out of town. "Where will I get another cashier?" "I know just the gal," Jim cried, and promptly a pleasant middle-aged woman arrived to take over the realm of the cash register. "My God," the proprietor exploded. "Is her name Cagney too?" She was the boys' mother.)

Perhaps the Miss Forenbachs came to Coward-McCann in the same manner or perhaps they didn't. But anyhow here was the letter, and I knit my brows over it.

"I'm writing to discover whether you want to see page proofs. Mr. McCann's out of town and I appealed to Mr. Coward. He said that he doubted that it was essential for you to see them, but thought I'd better write and ask. Let me know immediately if you want to see the pages, and I'll send them on. The examination must be done quickly because we'll soon be manufacturing."

This was something of a poser. Page proofs? I didn't wish to appear among the unearthly ignorant; perish the thought. But I'd never heard of such things. Certainly I read proof for our newspaper in Iowa. So did Mother, so did Miss Ella Stickney, the bookkeeper. But I sought perfection in proofreading, and if one wanted perfection, there was but a single way to achieve it. Better see the page proofs.

On they came, and for a time I sat entranced, cuddling them. Here they were, complete with the dedication. "To Albert H. Norris, Who Collected Rent From Forty Hurried Humans, Or Sometimes Didn't." And a quotation which I insisted must follow the title page: ". . . All the little devil-folk are ankle-deep in tears." Then the sheet for contents, and finally the text of the first chapter, beginning on page 11.

Every now and then I began to discover ominous words. MAKE LINE. Yes, that was it. Like an order from headquarters. MAKE LINE.

What the hell were those people doing? Why couldn't they leave me alone? This was a fine time to tell me to make lines. I'd do it, of course—they were the publishers, they knew what it was all about, but this seemed a silly business.

I did a little cussing to Irene.

"Look at this. Do you suppose it's typical of New York publishers?"

"What do they want you to do?"

"They say MAKE LINE. They want me to add enough words to make another line."

"They should have asked you sooner. Shouldn't they?"

"Guess they didn't know how it would look until it was set up and—" I hesitated over the word. "Paged. That's what they call it. It's now *paged*, but they need another line here."

"Surely you're ingenious enough to give them one."

I growled about it and studied the proof again.

He risked his way across the boulevard from the Wrigley building and read the bronze tablet erected in memory of a Negro who built the first house in Chicago, before he moved creepily toward the Tower.

O.K. I thought, I'm resourceful enough for that, and I inserted the word "entrance" to go after Tower.

But it was an annoying business, and I was still resentful, and would be for some time.

. . . Forty yards back. A black figure, strangely flat, with claw hands crushed among the weeds, and polished shoes protruding into the highway. "H'lo," Wenceslaus muttered, "H'lo, you!" The figure did not move. Then as his match flame wavered higher, Pete saw a long pool widened out from the figure.

There it was again: that ominous and demanding MAKE LINE.

Oh well. I inserted three words, "toward the ditch," and went on with my work. There weren't too many of the MAKE LINE adjurations . . . there were enough to build contempt for all book publishers.

But that was only a story. Probably Gold did have something to do with it. If he was going to get his, anyway, there wasn't any sense in turning down a good opportunity. Especially when nobody expected him to do the job or know anything about it.

They had the nerve to demand it again! MAKE LINE.

All right, all right, all right. I changed it to "Or know anything about what happened," and hoped they'd be satisfied.

Jim McCann came to Chicago, and was entertaining me at lunch when I approached him on the subject.

"I think it's something that ought to be done editorially before the thing is set in type. This MAKE LINE business. I don't see why you demand it at the last minute."

"What are you talking about, Mack?"

"On those page proofs. Every now and then the editors tell me to make a line."

"Tell you to make a line? I don't understand what you mean."

"Yes, they do. I wish I had some of the original page proofs here to show you. Well, I did it, but it was a God damn nuisance."

"You mean—" He paused, and then spoke the words slowly and considerately. "You mean there was a line every now and then at the bottom or top of the page, the way it was set up, where it said in capital letters MAKE LINE?"

"That's exactly what I mean. A little late in the game for that. As I said, you people seemed to want it, so I did it."

Jim was not a big man, but he roared so loudly that people in the hotel restaurant turned to look at him. He took off his glasses, tried to wipe them, flung them aside, put his head down on the table in cradled arms, and came as close to going into hysteria as a sober man can in any public place.

"Oh, God! You kill me! That wasn't any direction to *you*, that was to the compositors! An extra line was needed on the page, and they'd simply have to space it differently. Don't you see? It was for the *compositors* to make a line, not the author. Oh, God!"

For a long time after that—I think up until the year of his death—Jim would regard me astutely whenever we were together, and suddenly break out with, "Mack, will you please make a line?"

This joke spread throughout the organization. For years afterward I received odd looks from members of the staff whenever I went into the office. They'd go further, they'd say, "What's your line?" or "Don't feed me a line," or "How's the thin red line?"

It was one way of learning details of book manufacturing. Unrecommended.

8.

I wrote assiduously for Edwin Baird and appeared in every issue of his magazine under one name or another. Now I started exploring outside those bullet-punctured portals with fair result. The *Rotarian* Magazine, *Flying Stories* . . . I sold a new tale to *McClure's*. They were going out of business after less than a year of experiment, and the story ended up in another of their subsidiaries. But it brought two hundred dollars.

We still thought it wise to be away from the Diversey neighborhood, so had gone to Rogers Park. That was far north, up toward suburban Evanston. Sheridan Road stretched only half a block away, and we were in a man-sized building which actually had unfurnished apartments for rent. Ours was furnished; you had to climb two flights of stairs, but the baby cab could be parked below in a safe alcove. And we owned a kitchen, a tiny dining room, a big living room, a bath . . . the in-a-door bed could be whirled out of sight into a dressing room. We were proud of what we had accomplished in only a few months, and already I held dream of a new coat for Irene.

A *fur* coat. Before the ginger of winter came stinging off the lake.

If in the midst of striving we had managed to exert any benefit to our cosmos at large, we were promptly and amply repaid. In the new abode we shared an inside back porch with our next-door neighbor—a plump woman perhaps a decade beyond us in age. Her name was Olga Wootten. Separated from her husband, childless, she was in the ramification of getting a divorce.

She came out on the porch to talk to Irene the day we moved in . . . invited us into her home . . . was at the door with goodies for mother and baby within hours. Here was a dame with eager affection and gentility. Promptly we hoped that Olga would endure forever, and said as much to each other (trying to still that mysterious disquietude which crept to make itself known: that she would be around only a couple of years longer).

At odd hours she'd scratch at the rear door like a good-natured hen; but if we didn't answer promptly—which meant that we were out or otherwise engaged—she'd go away quietly. Other times she'd pop in to worship the baby. Layne loved her from the start, and her big eyes brightened when she saw Olga coming. The woman had never owned a child, but in some manner she recognized the strains and perils of baby-tending and rearing, and was always ready with advice and encouragement.

Or with whatever other intimate aid she could offer.

"Take a tip from me, Mack."

"Tip?"

"Don't get behind in your rent."

"Olga, what do you mean? It won't be due for—"

"The landlord's wife was on the back stairs, and she saw the milkman delivering that certified milk you get."

"Well?"

"She uttered the opinion that her own daughter wished that *she* could afford certified milk for *her* baby, but *she* couldn't manage anything so expensive. 'I'm glad to have tenants,' Mrs. Whoozit told me, 'who can afford to buy certified milk for their kids. That means, of course, that they'll never get behind in the rent. Not if they can afford *that.*'"

This little tip was of the Gee-Thanks school for certain. I took it as warning and rule. Never did get behind with the rent while we were there, except for one fateful week when Mrs. May was gone out of town: no checks were being drawn for *Real Detective Tales* authors. The 1341 Estes Avenue air was chilly until we got squared around again. It meant owing the milkman briefly as well, and that wasn't any fun either.

Commentary on 1928 prices.

Olga: "That old woman on the porch over yonder has been fighting with her daughter again, complaining about what she spends at the grocery."

Irene: "Well, one can't blame her much if the girl is extravagant."

Olga: "I don't think she's extravagant. It's just that everything costs so much these days."

Mack: "Indeed that's true. You know something? Now, we get our milk from the dairy, and Mother insists that she should buy butter and eggs out in Iowa and send them to us because she thinks they're better for us. But aside from that, I go down to the grocery store to get stuff for one day, and maybe part of the next, and do you know I can't get out of that grocery store without spending at least a dollar!"

Olga, Irene and Mack, in chorus: "Isn't it *awful?*"

9.

We held the book and passed it back and forth. It was sacred and beautiful and ugly and flaunting all at once. Red binding stamped in black type . . . the jacket red-white-and-black. It bore a menacing man with a gun pointed at you on the backbone. Front of the jacket was a jumbled mess of printing press, a car, a machine gun, newspaper type, bars of music, and an ominous figure smoking— Guess what? A wicked cigarette.

Irene made feeble comment. "Maybe it's a little garish. Or do you agree?"

"The publishers must know what they're doing. They know the sort of jacket which might appeal. Maybe this will—appeal."

We could not forget the aspiration bound inside. Whatever of stark necessity or human tenderness I could manage to inscribe the year before, was contained therein. Filmy anecdote, the imagining and sex of the hard-driven young; and over all a striving for attainment which forever must haunt the eager and ambitious.

"Did you—go and buy the *Tribune* yet?"

"You must have roused when I got up before daylight. I found papers on a newsstand."

"You didn't say anything. Did— Did Dick—?"

"There's not one line in his column."

"I can't believe it."

"Take a look."

The "Line O' Type" column held its ordinary collection of verse, paragraphs by R.H.L., communications true or alleged. It bore not one word about *Diversey*, first or middle or last.

"What was it you told me about Tim Coward, and what he said?"

"He said, 'I think that Little, and possibly his wife, might be the stumbling block. Don't get your heart set too much on his evincing a benevolent attitude toward the whole thing. Some of these rough-hewn grouchy individuals don't like to see themselves portrayed as such.'"

"But you portrayed Dick as a kindly and generous man. A kind of symbol to young aspirants."

"That's what *we* thought. Obviously he doesn't think so." I told her, "We didn't know it at the time, couldn't realize it, couldn't even guess. We were gambling on the approval of a very whimsical man."

"And Shelby—?"

"I think without doubt that she's influenced him in his attitude."

"Not just disapproval. Enmity."

"Whatever you want to call it. Should you like to see any other local reviews? I've got the *Herald-Examiner* here."

"Who wrote the review in the *Examiner?*"

"That fellow James Weber Linn has a whole column on it. It's called 'The Diversions of *Diversey.*'"

"James Weber Linn? Isn't he a minister or something?"

"May be. He's associated with the University of Chicago."

If I may speak seriously about a book which deals with life in so youthful a fashion, I shall call the kind of existence and the kind of characters it presents nauseating. Not because there are not many existences and characters of the sort, but because of the apparent completeness of Mr. Kantor's ignorance of any other sort. It is as if he were studying cockroaches under the impression that they were butterflies. . . . Of all literary conceptions of Chicago I have seen, this is beyond competition the cheapest and the most prosaic.

Irene burst into tears. "Don't— Don't read any more—"

"Oh yes I will."

No life, no characters . . . could be simpler, cruder or more obvious than the life of violence and animality which Mr. Kantor . . . concerns his talent with; or Miss Maureen Orcutt; or Mr. Charles MacArthur. . . . Their ideal situation, apparently, is the shooting of a greasy bootlegger by an illiterate epileptic in a house of ill-fame.

She wept. "I can't stand it. Please—don't read any more."

. . . So this was what the literary life was like. This was the author's portion . . . take the bitter along with the sweet. We'd thought we had something worthy of commendation, but according to folks like this it was the sum and quintessence of rot.

"There are no epileptics in your book, no houses of ill-fame! You've got some young lovers sleeping together, that's all. This man is not only being vicious and cruel! He's lying at the same moment."

Dimly I was beginning to arrive at an evolving truth. The moment you set something down on paper and allowed it to be put before the public in type, you were no longer master of any opinion except your own.

It was not enough for you to tell yourself that the wise and discerning might see values in your work which others did not see. You stood at the mercy of the inexperienced and inept as well as the capable. You were introduced by people with profound sympathy and understanding, as well as The Jealous who were writing about you only to expose their loathing of any idea or ideal which they did not share.

In writing a book you had a wound which you were baring. Some might choose to treat and bandage that wound—praise it, count it eventually as a scar acquired bravely. Others might choose to ignore it; and still others wish to infect it with any venom they could bring.

You had revealed and offered yourself. You and only you had made yourself vulnerable.

10.

Unhappily I was correct in my assumption that the Littles' withdrawal was occasioned by fury and nothing else. Friends insisted that I should visit the *Tribune* in person, go to Dick's desk, see him, ask him what the trouble was. I didn't think it would do any good, but I went. All he did was to scream vituperation, and go stamping off across the room.

Fanny Butcher, the *Tribune*'s honored book reviewer, was appalled at Richard Henry Little's attitude. So were many others, either on that newspaper or writing for the "Line O' Type" column. They called or wrote to express sympathy, though I was too sore to accept such commiseration readily.

Miss Butcher stated in her column that J.R.P. of *Diversey* was

unmistakably R.H.L. of the "Line O' Type" . . . it was obvious
that I regarded him with affection if not worship, and that it was
a splendid portrait of a complex man.

(We didn't set eyes on the Littles for years. Then, one time
after success with a book club choice, we were living in the East,
and visited Chicago briefly. We went into a lower North Side
drug store late in the evening. Dick and Shelby were there.
They separated, Shelby coming to stand beside me, Dick coming to stand beside Irene. They cleared their throats, indulged in
their little laughter . . . finally embraced us. Their apartment
was nearby . . . would we come up? We went, and spent a tire-
some and uncomfortable hour. The wound was too deep and too
lasting, and no good might come from their airily disregarding the
close association of the past, and making up for it now by a
few highballs and a brief display of adulation. We never saw
either one of them again.)

Edwin Baird said, "I've got a review for you. Somebody sent
it in. Here it is."

There was nothing attached to show the source, and I didn't
recognize the type style of any particular newspaper, and neither
did he. He gave a wry smile. "Well, read it at your leisure. It
isn't very good."

Not very good? It condemned me to seven hells. It was written
by someone named Catherine Munson, but I didn't know where
she hailed from and still don't know. She spoke about "a book nobody should want to read, written by a man nobody ever heard
of."

However, Mr. Kantor, before you slip back into the
scheme of things undesired and unwanted, there is just
one thing. Your book is prefaced by a charming line, "All
the little devil-folk are ankle-deep in tears." Before you
vanish into the oblivion that is so justly yours, won't you
please tell us where you got that charming little line?

Olga Wootten asked, "Well, where in hell did you get it?"
"Wrote it myself."

Also hurtful was the comment made by a reviewer whom I had met briefly, and who was writing for a newspaper rival of the *Tribune*. His name is not appended because he may still be alive, and I should not wish to embarrass him.

It is unfortunate that Mr. Kantor selected the region adjacent to Diversey Parkway, Broadway and North Clark Street as the scene of his enterprise. It is a quiet neighborhood, not known to be ruled by hoodlums. Why didn't he select some place on the southwest side? Blue Island Avenue, for instance. It would then be more believable. Gang activities are nil in the region which he selected. Probably he chose that because he lived in the neighborhood.

When my extenuation came it came with a roar heard throughout the nation. It came on the 14th of February, 1929, and still occupies an oozing spot amid atrocities. The address was 2122 North Clark Street, and seven men lay on a garage floor or were draped over shattered chairs with their blood and brains and torn clothing spewed together. It was called the St. Valentine's Day Massacre.

Telephone call from Cliff Palmer that afternoon.

"Mack, you heard what happened today?"

"Yes, who hasn't?"

"There's some guys coming over to my apartment tonight. I live in a new place; it's on North Clark Street too. Here, I'll give you the address and telephone number— They're going to be talking some things over. Maybe you'd like to know more about what happened."

"I'll be there."

I had no notion that my wife was even within earshot.

That evening, after a cheering Valentine drink and a cheering Valentine supper, I said, "Honey, I'm going out for a while," and went to get my hat and coat. I came back to find a calm Irene ensconced against the outer door with her arms folded.

"What's the trouble?"

"No trouble," she said.

I laughed, and came over to kiss her and draw her aside. She said, "If you go, I'll go."

"But— You *can't*."

"Where were you going?"

"Well, I was just going over to Cliff Palmer's apartment for a while. He's living at a new address."

"Yes, you took it down when you were talking with him on the telephone. Well, my dear, you're not going. Just call him up and tell him you can't come. Or—if you don't want to bother with that—don't call. Just let it go."

Actually I didn't feel rage at her attitude. I tried to feign rage and wasn't successful.

"Baby, you don't understand. You can't get that old notion out of your head. I'm—not—any—gangster."

She shrugged. "Neither was that doctor who was killed on Clark Street today—the dentist, or whatever he was. He just liked to hang around with hoodlums. So, I regret to say, do you. I'm adamant about this. Just as I was adamant before about the wine orders, and the precinct captaincy."

POST-MASSACRE MEETING
NOT ATTENDED BY AUTHOR

11.

But that would occur six months in the future, and this was August, with *Diversey* newly published.

I felt nervous and insubstantial, bruised by local attitude.

Our devoted Olga came into the kitchen. "I am a noble volunteer."

"What you mean—volunteer?"

"Volunteer Layne-sitter. You've both been trying to restrain nervous frenzy, and I want you to go out. You take Irene somewhere and— And buy her a drink. If you're broke it'll be on me."

We said we didn't need a drink but— Did she mean it? Would she sit with Layne?

"Certainly. She hasn't eaten any more tufted yarn off that day bed, has she?"

"Not that we know of. She seems placid enough now."

"Has she eaten any more papers of matches?"

"We haven't found any more red stuff on her lips or any more half-dissolved matches. But," Irene said, "she'll probably come down with phosphorus poisoning. Her new little teeth will fall out as fast as they come in."

"That won't be this evening. What about broom straws? Swallowed any more?"

"No, just that one. We fed her mashed potatoes, according to doctor's instructions."

I explained, "I had to dig around with a spoon in the contents of— Well, in the contents— Finally I found the straw, and it was long and sharp. I'm going to put her in a dime museum. Right This Way to See Six-Months-Old Baby With Vulcanized Insides."

"Go on," said Olga, "get out of here," and we got.

There was an untenanted house on the lake shore of our neighborhood. Grass grew long there, windows were blank, and no one else seemed ever to come near. We had picnics in the afternoon sometimes, and Layne could roll on her blanket. At night it was eerie but—

In minutes we were listening to the few talkative waves, and counting lights of water-cribs offshore.

"Do you suppose that any of the reviews elsewhere will be better?"

I said that we could only pray. We strolled along the shore for a while, and then went back into the noise of early evening traffic. We put our noses against a widely lighted window where new cars were on display, and shook our heads and said that we didn't want a car . . . doubted that we'd ever wish to own one even if we could afford to.

(Hell's bells. The next spring saw us the proud possessors of a secondhand Chevrolet—one of those stalwart and numerous coaches with green body and yellow wheels—the first moment I could get fifty bucks together for a down payment.)

We went on to treat ourselves to sodas, and Irene picked out a bar of forbidden candy as an award for Olga. Then we headed back for the apartment, feeling battered by experience but still agreeably toughened, and ready to kick any derogator in the jaw.

We walked in classic ignorance of the future, preening ourselves on how fortunate we were each to have the other. As yet we could struggle only under the whipping of ambition, and with desire to establish ourselves as competent Author and Wife in our own eyes and the eyes of beholders.

Of the strains which dissolve most early marriages among creative folk, we held no awareness, no indication that such exertion would come snapping into our lives. Neither of us had ever looked at another individual of the opposite sex with desire since the moment we met. In ignorance we assumed calmly that we never would. We had not one inkling of those complex passions which baffle the mature of our kind, and which would goad us to the brink of divorce again and again. Smugly we dwelt, docile and untried.

Mounting suspicion, the rivalry—the contempt and resentment hurled back and forth by those same sinners who would love in identical fashion of the hordes who came before them, and of the herds to follow— There was not even the imagination of such peril within our tiny affectionate scope. We were a Girl Scout and a Boy Scout who had not yet entered the army or been to a war.

12.

Olga put down her book when we came in, and rolled her eyes at accepting proscribed candy. "Layne hasn't stirred. She's still sound asleep, and never moved once. The telephone hasn't rung.

However there's a telegram over there on the table. A boy delivered it at the door."

I tore it open.

From Harriet Ashbrook at Coward-McCann.

Heartiest congratulations from Tim Coward, Jim McCann and all of us here at Tim-Jim Inc. New York reviews in total perfectly splendid and just wait till you see next Sunday's *Times*. Am sending whatever clippings available. Just ordered another printing this afternoon. Tim says tell Mack we hope he's already started on that next novel. Affections from all.

Irene came over and put her arms around me and closed her eyes. She didn't say a word, but every now and then I'd feel her shiver slightly.